Pre-Algebra

A Reference Guide and Problem Sets

Book Staff and Contributors

Paul Thomas   *Senior Content Specialist*
Suzanne Montazer   *Senior Art Director*
Stephanie Shaw   *Cover Designer*
Christopher Yates   *Designer*
Lee Horton   *Illustrations Editor*
Mary Beck Desmond   *Text Editor*
Joseph Rincione   *Project Manager*
Christopher Frescholtz   *Senior Project Manager*

Bror Saxberg   *Chief Learning Officer*
John Holdren   *Senior Vice President for Content and Curriculum*
Maria Szalay   *Senior Vice President for Product Development*
Tom DiGiovanni   *Senior Director, Product Development*
Kim Barcas   *Creative Director*
Sally Russell   *Senior Manager, Media*
Jeff Burridge   *Managing Editor*
Corey Maender   *Program Manager, High School*

Lisa Dimaio Iekel   *Production Manager*
John G. Agnone   *Director of Publications*

About K12 Inc.

Founded in 1999, K12 Inc. is an elementary and secondary school service combining rich academic content with powerful technology. K12 serves students in a variety of education settings, both public and private, including school classrooms, virtual charter schools, home schools, and tutoring centers. K12 currently provides comprehensive curricular offerings in the following subjects: Language Arts/English, History, Math, Science, Visual Arts, and Music. The K12 curriculum blends high-quality offline materials with innovative online resources, including interactive lessons, teacher guides, and tools for planning and assessment. For more information, call 1-888-YOUR K12 or visit www.K12.com.

ISBN 1-60153-027-7

Printed by RR Donnelley, Roanoke, VA, USA, June 2011, Lot 062011

Pre-Algebra

A Reference Guide and Problem Sets

Contents

How to Use This Book

Welcome to *Pre-Algebra: A Reference Guide and Problem Sets*

This reference guide was developed to accompany the online portion of K12 Inc.'s High School Pre-Algebra program and also serves as a reference for any student of pre-algebra. Each section of the book presents an overview of a topic area. You can use this book to familiarize yourself with aspects of pre-algebra, or to review materials you are studying in other books or online sources.

How This Book Is Organized

Units of Study

The following units of study are included in this reference guide.

- The Basics
- Addition and Subtraction
- Multiplication and Division
- Fractions
- Combined Operations
- Number Properties
- Geometry Basics

- Ratio, Proportion, and Percent
- Analytic Geometry
- Perimeter and Area
- Square Roots and Right Triangles
- Solid Figures
- Counting and Probability
- Statistics

Pronunciation Guide

See page 520 for a key to the pronunciations in the Glossary.

Glossary

See page 521 for a Glossary with brief definitions of some key terms.

Symbols

See page 526 for a list of mathematical symbols.

Properties

See page 527 for a list of number properties.

Formulary

See page 530 for a list of formulas with illustrations.

Sample Graphs

See page 534 for some sample graphs.

Selected Answers

See pages 536–548 for answers to selected problem-set questions.

Navigating a Topic

Topic Each section explores a topic in pre-algebra.

Introduction Start here. Important concepts and skills you will learn about this topic are identified at the beginning of each section.

Examples Study the examples and their solutions that illustrate the topics and concepts covered in each section and unit of this reference guide.

Definitions Words introduced with this topic will be **boldface** when they are explained in the text.

Helpful Information Reminders about things you've learned and other helpful tips are highlighted in the page margins in this way.

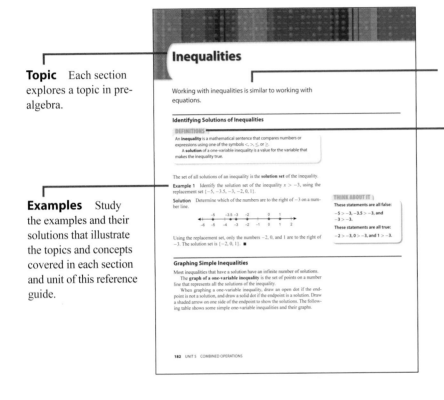

Inequalities

Working with inequalities is similar to working with equations.

Identifying Solutions of Inequalities

DEFINITIONS

An **inequality** is a mathematical sentence that compares numbers or expressions using one of the symbols $<$, $>$, $\leq$, or $\geq$.
A **solution** of a one-variable inequality is a value for the variable that makes the inequality true.

The set of all solutions of an inequality is the **solution set** of the inequality.

Example 1 Identify the solution set of the inequality $x > -3$, using the replacement set $\{-5, -3.5, -3, -2, 0, 1\}$.

Solution Determine which of the numbers are to the right of -3 on a number line.

Using the replacement set, only the numbers -2, 0, and 1 are to the right of -3. The solution set is $\{-2, 0, 1\}$. ∎

THINK ABOUT IT

These statements are all false:
$-5 > -3$, $-3.5 > -3$, and $-3 > -3$.

These statements are all true:
$-2 > -3$, $0 > -3$, and $1 > -3$.

Graphing Simple Inequalities

Most inequalities that have a solution have an infinite number of solutions.
The **graph of a one-variable inequality** is the set of points on a number line that represents all the solutions of the inequality.
When graphing a one-variable inequality, draw an open dot if the endpoint is not a solution, and draw a solid dot if the endpoint is a solution. Draw a shaded arrow on one side of the endpoint to show the solutions. The following table shows some simple one-variable inequalities and their graphs.

182   UNIT 5   COMBINED OPERATIONS

REMEMBER

A fraction bar represents division. It is also a grouping symbol.

Formulas Instructions and formulas are introduced prominently on the page.

CIRCUMFERENCE OF A CIRCLE

The circumference of a circle with diameter d and radius r is

$$C = \pi d \quad \text{or} \quad C = 2\pi r.$$

Selected Answers See how you did with the problem set by checking the selected answers in the back of the book.

Problem Set The end of each section is where you will do the math so you can learn the math.

Problem Set

Solve and check.

1. $2x - 12 = 14$
2. $5x + 16 = 56$
3. $12.5 + 3x = 20$
4. $18 - 6.3x = 49.5$

5. $-1 + 12x = 29$
6. $10 - 1.4x = 10.8$
7. $-12x + 14 = -3$
8. $-24x - 15 = -2$

Solve.

9. $6 + \dfrac{x}{3} = 1$
10. $-4 + \dfrac{a}{5} = 8$
11. $-1 = \dfrac{x}{9} - 2$
12. $-3 = \dfrac{3}{4}r + 2$
13. $\dfrac{2}{9}x - 7 = 9$

14. $6 = \dfrac{9}{10}a - 1$
15. $\dfrac{x+3}{5} = -1$
16. $44 = \dfrac{n-6}{2}$
17. $-1 = -\dfrac{x+1}{5}$
*18. **Challenge** $\dfrac{3-x}{9}$

Pages 171–172

1. $x = 13$ 3. $x = 2.5$ 5. $x = 2.5$ 7. $x = 4$ 9. $x = -15$
11. $x = 9$ 13. $x = 72$ 15. $x = -8$ 17. $x = 4$ 19. $x = -4$
21. $-\dfrac{4}{3}$ or $-1\dfrac{1}{3}$ 23. $x = 11$ 25. $a = 22.1$ 27. $b = 3$
29. $x = -23$ 31. $s = -8.2$ 33. **A.** Let $n =$ the number.
$3n + 5 = 38$; The number is 11.   **B.** Let $n =$ the number.
$\dfrac{1}{3}n - 7 = 5$; The number is 36.   **C.** Let $n =$ the number.
$5n = 2n + 18$; The number is 6.   **35.** Let $x =$ the price of
the sweater. $x + 0.4x = 46.28$; The price was $44.50.   **37.** Let
$x =$ the amount earned by each laborer. $x + (x + 0.50x) +$
$(x + 0.50x) + (x + 0.80x) = 4205$; The laborer earned $725,
each carpenter earned $1087.50, and the supervisor earned
$1305.

Introduction

Pre-Algebra is a funny name for this book. Though much of it is about getting ready for Algebra, much of it is about other topics as well. First, you need to solidify your arithmetic skills. Once you know how to add, subtract, multiply, and divide positive and negative numbers (including decimals and fractions), you will have the basic skills needed to start tackling basic algebraic concepts. In addition to arithmetic and algebra, this book also covers geometry, probability, and statistics—important topics that provide opportunities to apply your solidifying arithmetic and developing algebra skills.

Math is learned at the tip of a pencil. As you work through the topics in this book, you will see several worked examples that show you how to solve some problems, but the most important part of each topic is the problem set at the end. Reading problem solutions can help you find good strategies and best practices for solving problems, but you really learn math only when you solve problems yourself. Do the math to learn the math.

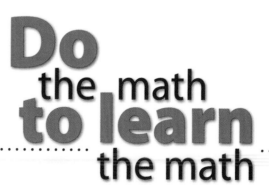

UNIT 1   The Basics

You won't get far if you don't know basic grammar and vocabulary.

Let's start at the very beginning; it's a very good place to start. Just as you need to know basic grammar and vocabulary as you begin to learn any language, you need to know some basic building blocks as you begin to learn algebra.

Big Ideas

▶ Expressions, equations, and inequalities express relationships between different entities.

▶ If you can create a mathematical model for a situation, you can use the model to solve other problems that you might not be able to solve otherwise. Algebraic equations can capture key relationships among quantities in the world.

Unit Topics

▶ Order of Operations

▶ Variable Expressions

▶ Translating Words into Expressions

▶ Comparing Expressions

▶ Replacement Sets

▶ Related Equations

▶ Translating Words into Equations

▶ Solving Problems

Order of Operations

Addition, subtraction, multiplication, and division are *operations*.

When an expression has more than one operation, you must use the **order of operations** to simplify it. To **simplify a numerical expression** means to find its value.

ORDER OF OPERATIONS

Step 1 Multiply and divide from left to right.
Step 2 Add and subtract from left to right.

Simplifying Expressions Without Grouping Symbols

Example 1 Simplify.

A $1 + 2 \cdot 5$

Solution

$$1 + 2 \cdot 5 = 1 + 10 \qquad \text{Multiply.}$$
$$= 11 \qquad \text{Add.} \quad \blacksquare$$

B $6 \div 2 \cdot 3$

Solution

$$6 \div 2 \cdot 3 = 3 \cdot 3 \qquad \text{Divide.}$$
$$= 9 \qquad \text{Multiply.} \quad \blacksquare$$

C $5 \cdot 2 - 6 \div 2$

Solution

$$5 \cdot 2 - 6 \div 2 = 10 - 6 \div 2 \qquad \text{Multiply.}$$
$$= 10 - 3 \qquad \text{Divide.}$$
$$= 7 \qquad \text{Subtract.} \quad \blacksquare$$

D $12 + 55 \div 5 - 2 \cdot 10 + 9$

Solution

$$
\begin{aligned}
12 + 55 \div 5 - 2 \cdot 10 + 9 &= 12 + 11 - 2 \cdot 10 + 9 && \text{Divide.} \\
&= 12 + 11 - 20 + 9 && \text{Multiply.} \\
&= 23 - 20 + 9 && \text{Add.} \\
&= 3 + 9 && \text{Subtract.} \\
&= 12 && \text{Add. } \blacksquare
\end{aligned}
$$

Simplifying Expressions with Grouping Symbols

Grouping symbols are symbols such as parentheses ( ), brackets [ ], and braces { }. Perform all operations inside grouping symbols first. If there is more than one set of grouping symbols in an expression, perform the operations in the innermost set of grouping symbols first.

ORDER OF OPERATIONS WITH GROUPING

Step 1 Perform operations within grouping symbols.
Step 2 Multiply and divide from left to right.
Step 3 Add and subtract from left to right.

Example 2 Simplify.

A $5 \cdot (2 + 7)$

Solution

$$
\begin{aligned}
5 \cdot (2 + 7) &= 5 \cdot 9 && \text{Add inside the grouping symbols.} \\
&= 45 && \text{Multiply. } \blacksquare
\end{aligned}
$$

B $20 \div (10 \times 2)$

Solution

$$
\begin{aligned}
20 \div (10 \times 2) &= 20 \div 20 && \text{Multiply inside the grouping symbols.} \\
&= 1 && \text{Divide. } \blacksquare
\end{aligned}
$$

C $24 - [4 \cdot (6 - 5) + 5]$

Solution The parentheses are inside the brackets. Use the order of operations to simplify $6 - 5$ first.

$$
\begin{aligned}
24 - [4 \cdot (6 - 5) + 5] &= 24 - [4 \cdot 1 + 5] && \text{Subtract inside the} \\
& && \text{parentheses.} \\
&= 24 - [4 + 5] && \text{Multiply inside the brackets.} \\
&= 24 - 9 && \text{Add inside the brackets.} \\
&= 15 && \text{Subtract. } \blacksquare
\end{aligned}
$$

THINK ABOUT IT

If the expressions in Example 2 did not have grouping symbols, the values would be different.

2A
$$
\begin{aligned}
5 \cdot 2 + 7 &= 10 + 7 \\
&= 17
\end{aligned}
$$

2B
$$
\begin{aligned}
20 \div 10 \times 2 &= 2 \times 2 \\
&= 4
\end{aligned}
$$

2C
$$
\begin{aligned}
24 - 4 \cdot (6 - 5) + 5 &= 20 + 5 \\
&= 25
\end{aligned}
$$

Placing Grouping Symbols to Get a Specified Value

You can get different values for an expression by changing the placement of grouping symbols.

Example 3 Place grouping symbols in the expression $90 - 10 \div 2 + 3$ to get expressions that have the values 16 and 82.

Solution

Get the value 16:

$$(90 - 10) \div (2 + 3) = 80 \div 5$$
$$= 16$$

Get the value 82:

$$90 - (10 \div 2 + 3) = 90 - (5 + 3)$$
$$= 90 - 8$$
$$= 82 \ \blacksquare$$

TIP

Solve Example 3 by trial and error. Experiment by including different parts of the expression in parentheses.

Simplifying Expressions with a Fraction Bar

The fraction bar represents division. It can be used as a grouping symbol.

Example 4 Simplify.

 A $\dfrac{60 \div 3}{2 + 2}$

Solution

$$\dfrac{60 \div 3}{2 + 2} = \dfrac{20}{4}$$ Simplify the numerator and denominator separately.

$$= 5$$ Divide the numerator by the denominator. $\blacksquare$

B $\dfrac{3 \cdot (17 - 5)}{4 + 9 - 1}$

Solution Use the order of operations to simplify the numerator and denominator.

$$\dfrac{3 \cdot (17 - 5)}{4 + 9 - 1} = \dfrac{3 \cdot 12}{4 + 9 - 1}$$ In the numerator, subtract inside the parentheses.

$$= \dfrac{36}{12}$$ In the numerator, multiply. In the denominator, add and subtract from left to right.

$$= 3$$ Divide. $\blacksquare$

THINK ABOUT IT

You can write the expression $\dfrac{60 \div 3}{2 + 2}$ as $(60 \div 3) \div (2 + 2)$.

Application: Business

Example 5   A plumber charges $25 to make a visit plus $65 per hour. Suppose the plumber works on a project for a total of 3 hours. Write and simplify an expression to find how much the plumber will charge for the project.

Solution

$$\boxed{\text{total charge}} = \boxed{\text{\$25 for the visit}} + \boxed{\text{3 hours at \$65 per hour}}$$

$$= \quad\quad 25 \quad\quad + \quad\quad 3 \cdot 65 \quad\quad \text{Write an expression.}$$

$$= 25 + 195 \quad\quad\quad\quad\quad\quad \text{Multiply.}$$

$$= 220 \quad\quad\quad\quad\quad\quad\quad\quad \text{Add.}$$

The plumber will charge $220 for the project. ∎

Problem Set

Simplify.

1. **A.** $8 \div 4 + 4$

    B. $8 \div (4 + 4)$

2. **A.** $3 + 10 \div 10 + 3$

    B. $(3 + 10) \div (10 + 3)$

3. **A.** $(15 - 2) \cdot 3 \cdot 2$

    B. $15 - 2 \cdot 3 \cdot 2$

4. $21 + 17 \cdot 2 - 15 + 1$

5. $5 + 18 \div 3$

6. $24 \div 4 \div 3 + 1$

7. $25 \cdot 5 \div 5 - 20$

8. $35 - 5 \cdot 2 + 16 \div 4$

9. $21 \div 7 \cdot 3 - 4 \cdot 2$

10. $24 \div (3 + 5)$

11. $(4 + 16) \cdot 8 - 2$

12. $47 + [3 \cdot 8 \div (3 + 1)]$

13. $36 \div (3 \cdot 2) - 1$

14. $9 \cdot [2 + (35 - 5 \cdot 3)] + 7$

15. $29 + (5 \cdot 2) \div (10 - 8)$

16. $[16 \cdot (4 + 1)] \div 10$

17. $\dfrac{28}{4 + 3}$

18. $\dfrac{10 \cdot (2 + 4)}{14 + (7 - 1)}$

19. $\dfrac{(8 + 4 \div 2) \cdot 2}{10 \div (1 + 1)}$

20. $21 + \dfrac{15 \cdot 2}{9 \div 3}$

Place grouping symbols in the expression to get an expression that has the given value.

21. Get the value 35: $23 + 3 \cdot 5 - 1$

22. Get the value 67: $5 \div 5 + 6 \cdot 2 + 9$

23. Get the value 10: $9 + 3 \cdot 5 \div 2 + 4$

24. Get the value 14: $3 \cdot 5 + 9 \div 3$

25. Get the value 3: $17 - 5 \div 1 + 3$

Solve each problem.

26. Apples cost $2 per pound and grapes cost $3 per pound. Brad bought 6 pounds of apples and 5 pounds of grapes. Write and simplify an expression to find how much money Brad spent.

27. Li planted a flower that was 6 inches tall. It then grew 2 inches per week for 4 weeks. Write and simplify an expression to find the new height of the flower.

28. The temperature of a liquid starts out at 65°F. The liquid is cooled and its temperature falls 6 degrees per hour for 4 hours. The temperature of the liquid is then increased by 10 degrees. Write and simplify an expression to find the final temperature of the liquid.

29. A tank holds 400 gallons of water. A crack forms and 20 gallons of water leak out every hour. Write and simplify an expression to find how much water is in the tank after 12 hours.

30. At the swim meet, a swim team had 2 swimmers finish their race in first place, 3 swimmers finish in third place, and 2 swimmers finish in fourth place. The chart shows the points earned for each place finished. Write and simplify an expression for the total number of points the swim team received.

Place Finished	Points Earned
Fifth	1
Fourth	3
Third	5
Second	8
First	10

31. Ann read 3 pages per day every day for 9 days. Jamal read 2 pages per day every day for 14 days. Write and simplify an expression to find how many more pages Jamal read than Ann.

*32. **Challenge** Part of the floor shown below is covered by tiles. Each tile is 1 foot wide and 2 feet long. There are 265 tiles. Write and simplify an expression to find how much of the floor, in square feet, is *not* tiled.

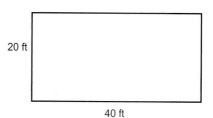

20 ft

40 ft

Variable Expressions

An **expression** is a group of mathematical symbols.

Expressions can contain numbers, variables, and operation symbols. A **numerical expression** consists of numbers and one or more operations.

A **variable** is a symbol that represents a value. In most cases, variables are letters, such as x, y, a, and n. Most variables in this book will be lowercase and italicized.

A **variable expression** consists of one or more variables and one or more operations; it may also contain numbers.

Numerical expressions do not contain variables. Variable expressions do.

Numerical Expressions	Variable Expressions
$8 - 6 \cdot (3 + 1)$	$8 - 6 \cdot (a + b)$
$\dfrac{25}{8 - 3}$	$\dfrac{x}{y - z}$

A numerical expression has only one value. But a variable expression can have different values, depending on the values that are **substituted** for its variables.

Evaluating Expressions

To **evaluate a variable expression**, replace all the variables in the expression with numbers and simplify. Remember to use the order of operations when simplifying.

When working with variable expressions, there are a few ways to show multiplication. You may be used to using the multiplication $\times$, but in algebra, you will most often see a raised dot. Also, you can show multiplication by putting a number right next to a variable. For instance, $6a$ is the same as $6 \cdot a$ and $6 \times a$.

> **REMEMBER**
>
> Multiplication can be shown in different ways. All of the following mean *six times the quantity three plus one.*
>
> $6(3 + 1)$
>
> $6 \cdot (3 + 1)$
>
> $6 \times (3 + 1)$

Example 1

A Evaluate $7n + 5$ when $n = 8$.

Solution

$$7n + 5 = 7 \cdot 8 + 5 \qquad \text{Substitute 8 for } n.$$
$$= 56 + 5 \qquad \text{Multiply.}$$
$$= 61 \qquad \text{Add.} \quad \blacksquare$$

B Evaluate $x - y + 2$ when $x = 11$ and $y = 3$.

Solution

$$x - y + 2 = 11 - 3 + 2 \qquad \text{Substitute 11 for } x \text{ and 3 for } y.$$
$$= 8 + 2 \qquad \text{Subtract.}$$
$$= 10 \qquad \text{Add.} \quad \blacksquare$$

C Evaluate $\dfrac{c - 5d}{10 \cdot (2d + 1)}$ when $c = 200$ and $d = 4$.

Solution

$$\frac{c - 5d}{10 \cdot (2d + 1)} = \frac{200 - 5 \cdot 4}{10 \cdot (2 \cdot 4 + 1)} \qquad \text{Substitute 200 for } c \text{ and 4 for } d.$$
$$= \frac{200 - 20}{10 \cdot (9)} \qquad \text{Simplify the numerator and denominator separately.}$$
$$= \frac{180}{90}$$
$$= 2 \qquad \text{Divide.} \quad \blacksquare$$

THINK ABOUT IT

Vary means *change*. Thus, when a variable changes its value, the value of the expression changes too.

Application: Temperature

Example 2 To approximate the temperature in degrees Celsius after an increase in altitude of f feet, you can use the expression $b - 2 \cdot \dfrac{f}{1000}$, where b is the beginning temperature. A hiker climbs 4000 feet to a summit from a parking lot, where it is 35°C. Approximate the temperature at the summit.

Solution

$$b - 2 \cdot \frac{f}{1000} = 35 - 2 \cdot \frac{4000}{1000} \qquad \text{Substitute 35 for } b \text{ and 4000 for } f.$$
$$= 35 - 2 \cdot 4 \qquad \text{Divide.}$$
$$= 35 - 8 \qquad \text{Multiply.}$$
$$= 27 \qquad \text{Subtract.}$$

The temperature at the summit is about 27°C. $\blacksquare$

Application: Sports

Example 3 The distance around a rectangle is its *perimeter* and is given by the expression $2l + 2w$, where l represents length and w represents width. Find the perimeter of a soccer field that is 100 yards long and 60 yards wide.

Solution

$$2l + 2w = 2 \cdot 100 + 2 \cdot 60 \qquad \text{Substitute 100 for } l \text{ and 60 for } w.$$
$$= 200 + 120 \qquad \text{Multiply.}$$
$$= 320 \qquad \text{Add.}$$

The perimeter of the soccer field is 320 yards. ∎

Problem Set

Evaluate each expression for the given value(s).

1. $7 + 10y$ when $y = 6$

2. $30b$ when $b = 0$

3. $\dfrac{35}{n - 1}$ when $n = 6$

4. $x + 2x$ when $x = 4$

5. $\dfrac{4 \cdot (8 - b)}{b}$ when $b = 2$

6. $12 + g \cdot (9 \div g)$ when $g = 3$

7. $16 + a \cdot a$ when $a = 3$

8. $5x + 18x$ when $x = 6$

9. $3z + 4 + z$ when $z = 5$

10. $(8 + 3a) \cdot a$ when $a = 2$

11. $k + k \div 2$ when $k = 20$

12. $\dfrac{25 - n}{n}$ when $n = 5$

13. $\dfrac{df}{e}$ when $d = 2, f = 9,$ and $e = 3$

14. $m + \dfrac{n}{m} \cdot 9$ when $m = 4$ and $n = 36$

15. $k + m \div 2$ when $k = 40$ and $m = 10$

16. $\dfrac{a}{c} + \dfrac{b}{c}$ when $a = 24, b = 12,$ and $c = 4$

17. $\dfrac{a}{b - 2c}$ when $a = 27, b = 15,$ and $c = 3$

18. $[2 \cdot 3q + 1] \div p$ when $q = 4$ and $p = 25$

19. $9 \cdot (x - 7) - y$ when $x = 11$ and $y = 19$

20. $7c - 4 + d \div 3$ when $c = 10$ and $d = 33$

21. $\dfrac{v - 2w + 12}{w + 5}$ when $v = 68$ and $w = 4$

*22. **Challenge** $\dfrac{r - \dfrac{15}{s}}{12 - 2s} \cdot \dfrac{3 \cdot \left(\dfrac{r + s}{2}\right)}{\dfrac{r - 3}{2} + s}$

when $r = 23$ and $s = 3$

Solve each problem.

23. The area of a parallelogram is given by the expression bh, where b represents the length of the base and h represents the height. Find the area of a parallelogram whose base is 16 inches and whose height is 9 inches.

24. To find the length of an object in inches when you know its length in feet f, you can use the expression $12f$. How many inches long is an 8-foot long sofa?

25. Doctors use the expression $\frac{c}{h}$, where c represents total cholesterol and h represents HDL (good) cholesterol to find a patient's cholesterol risk ratio. Doctors are concerned when the ratio is greater than 4.

   A. Find the risk ratio for a patient whose total cholesterol value is 141 and good cholesterol is 47.

   B. Find the risk ratio for a patient whose total cholesterol value is 108 and good cholesterol is 36.

   C. Should the risk ratio for either patient give the doctor reason for concern?

26. The expression $\frac{c}{4} + 37$ can be used to approximate the current temperature in °F where c is the number of times a cricket chirps in one minute. What is the approximate temperature if a cricket chirps 60 times in one minute?

27. The volume of a cone is given by $\frac{Bh}{3}$, where B is the area of the base of the cone and h is the height of the cone. Find the volume of a cone whose base is 153 square inches and whose height is 11 inches. (Hint: Your answer should be in cubic inches.)

28. To find the average of three bowling scores, a bowler uses the expression $\frac{g_1 + g_2 + g_3}{3}$, where $g_1, g_2,$ and g_3 are the scores for each of the three games.

   A. Find the bowler's average when his scores are 147, 165, and 150.

   B. Find the bowler's average when his scores are 210, 265, and 190.

   *C. A bowler's average for three games is 150. Two of his scores were 150 and 155. What was his other score?

*29. Challenge The volume of a sphere is given by $\frac{4\pi r^3}{3}$, where r is the radius of the sphere. Estimate the volume of a sphere whose radius is 8 centimeters by using 3 for π. (Hint: $r^3 = r \cdot r \cdot r$.)

Translating Words into Expressions

To solve problems, you sometimes need to translate word phrases into variable expressions.

You can use the following table to help determine what operation is indicated by a particular word phrase.

MATCHING WORDS AND PHRASES TO OPERATIONS

Addition	Subtraction	Multiplication	Division
plus	minus	times	quotient
more than	less than	product	separate
increased by	decreased by	of	into equal
sum	difference	combine	groups
total	shorter	equal groups	
longer	younger		
older			

Think carefully when you translate. The phrases in the table do not automatically indicate particular operations. For example, *two is less than six* is written $2 < 6$; there is no subtraction involved.

Translating Word Phrases into Variable Expressions

Example 1   Translate each word phrase into a variable expression.

Ⓐ the sum of 16 and a number

Solution   Possible variable expression:

$16 + n$ The word *sum* indicates addition. Use any letter for the variable. ■

Ⓑ 6 less than twice a number

Solution   Possible variable expression:

$2x - 6$ To represent 6 *less than* a quantity, you need to subtract 6 *from* that quantity. In this case, the quantity is twice a number, or 2 times a number. ■

C 20 students separated into equal groups

Solution   Possible variable expression:

$\frac{20}{n}$ or $20 \div n$ You do not know how many equal groups, so use a variable for the number of equal groups. Use division to separate into equal groups. ■

D the number of seconds in m minutes

Solution   Variable expression:

$60m$ You need to combine m "groups" with 60 seconds in each group. Use multiplication to combine equal groups. ■

TIP

Order matters in subtraction and division. In Example 1B, $6 - 2x$ is *incorrect*. In Example 1C, $\frac{n}{20}$ and $n \div 20$ are *incorrect*.

THINK ABOUT IT

In parts A, B, and C, the answers are given as *possible* expressions because they could contain different variables.

Translating Variable Expressions into Word Phrases

You can write a word phrase for a variable expression in more than one way.

Example 2   Translate each variable expression into a word phrase.

A $m - 8$

Solution   Possible answers include:

the difference of m and 8
8 less than m
m minus 8 ■

B $bc + 2$

Solution   Possible answers include:

the product of b and c, increased by 2
2 more than the product of b and c ■

C $b \cdot (c + 2)$

Solution   Possible answers include:

the product of b and the sum of c and 2
b times 2 more than c
b times the quantity c plus 2 ■

THINK ABOUT IT

Notice that the parentheses in Example 2C form an expression whose meaning is different from the expression in Example 2B.

Application: Age

Example 3

A Sam's mom is 2 years older than 5 times Sam's age. Write a variable expression to represent the age of Sam's mom.

Solution   Variable expression:

$5s + 2$ Let s represent Sam's age. To represent 2 years older, add 2. The word *times* indicates multiplication. ■

REMEMBER

Expressions show relationships between different entities.

(continued)

B The ages of three sisters are consecutive odd whole numbers. Write a variable expression to represent the age of the oldest sister if the age of the youngest sister is y.

Solution Consecutive whole numbers, such as 5 and 6, have no whole numbers between them. Consecutive odd whole numbers, such as 5 and 7, have no odd whole numbers between them.

Notice that to get from an odd whole number to the next consecutive odd whole number, you add 2. Therefore, the ages of the sisters are y, $y + 2$, and $y + 4$.

The variable expression for the age of the oldest sister is $y + 4$. ■

Problem Sets

Translate each word phrase into a variable expression.

1. 15 less than a number

2. the product of 18 and a number

3. the quotient of a number and 7

4. a number increased by 1

5. 25 decreased by the sum of 6 and a number

6. 10 more than 3 times a number

7. combine 6 groups of n items

8. the difference of twice a number and 3

9. the difference of 3 and twice a number

10. the sum of 16 and 4 times a number

11. the quotient of the sum of 3 and a number and the number

12. n items separated into m equal groups

13. x inches shorter than 22 inches

14. the total of 14 and the difference of a number and 2

*15. **Challenge** 5 times the product of 2 and one less than a number

Translate each variable expression into a word phrase.

16. $g + 24$

17. $2 \cdot (3 - x)$

18. $k \div 2j$

19. $3mn$

20. $3 + m + n$

21. $\dfrac{2}{n + 3}$

22. $\dfrac{500}{n} + 1$

23. $(a + b) - (2c + d)$

Solve each problem.

24. Cassie is 4 centimeters shorter than Maria. Write a variable expression to represent Cassie's height.

25. Write a variable expression to represent the sum of four consecutive numbers if the least number is p.

26. There are 100 flowers on a truck bed. f flowers are removed from the truck bed and the remaining flowers are divided into 3 equal groups. Write a variable expression to represent the number of flowers in each group.

27. Isaiah is 3 years younger than twice Jack's age. Kaleb is 4 times Isaiah's age. Write a variable expression to represent Isaiah's age and then another to represent Kaleb's age.

28. The heights of three boys, in inches, are consecutive even whole numbers. Write a variable expression to represent the height of the shortest boy if the height of the tallest boy is n inches.

29. Dario recycled b bottles and c cans and received $0.05 for each. Write a variable expression for the amount of money Dario earned by recycling the bottles and cans.

30. Mahal bought p pounds of grapes at $2.99 per pound. She paid for the grapes with a $20 bill. Write a variable expression for the amount of change Mahal received.

*31. **Challenge** The sales tax on an item is 5% of the item's value. Write a variable expression for the sales tax of the item. Then write a variable expression for the total cost of the item.

*32. **Challenge** The width of a rectangle is 2 inches more than half its length. Write a variable expression to represent the length of the rectangle. Then write a variable expression to represent the perimeter of the rectangle.

Comparing Expressions

The symbols for comparing expressions are $=$, $\neq$, $<$, $>$, $\leq$, and $\geq$.

You can use a *number sentence* to compare expressions.

DEFINITIONS

An **equation** is a number sentence indicating that two expressions have the same value. An equation is formed by placing an equals sign ($=$) between two expressions. For example, the equation $4 + 6 = 10$ indicates that $4 + 6$ and 10 have the same value.

An **inequality** is a number sentence formed by placing an inequality symbol ($\neq$, $<$, $>$, $\leq$, $\geq$) between two expressions.

Examples: $5 \neq 8$, $6 > 1 + 3$, $6 - 5 < 2$

Comparing Expressions

Example 1 Compare the expressions by using $<$, $=$, or $>$.

Ⓐ $5 \cdot 2 + 7 \;\blacksquare\; 5 \cdot (2 + 7)$

Solution Simplify each expression. Then insert the correct symbol.

$5 \cdot 2 + 7 \;\blacksquare\; 5 \cdot (2 + 7)$

$\quad 10 + 7 \;\blacksquare\; 5 \cdot 9$

$\qquad 17 < 45 \;\blacksquare$

Ⓑ $\dfrac{10 - 6 + 14}{6} \;\blacksquare\; 5 \cdot 6 \div 10$

Solution Simplify each expression. Then insert the correct symbol.

$\dfrac{10 - 6 + 14}{6} \;\blacksquare\; 5 \cdot 6 \div 10$

$\qquad \dfrac{18}{6} \;\blacksquare\; 30 \div 10$

$\qquad\quad 3 = 3 \;\blacksquare$

Open Sentences and Solutions

An **open sentence** is an equation or inequality that contains one or more variables. Examples: $x + 3 = 5$, $x - 1 > 4$, $F = 1.8C + 32$

An open sentence can be either true or false, depending on what values are substituted for the variables. A **solution** of an open sentence with one variable is a value that makes the sentence true. The solution of the equation $x + 3 = 5$ is 2. One solution of the inequality $x - 1 > 4$ is 6, and there are many more solutions.

You will see two more inequality symbols in open sentences. The less than or equal to symbol ($\leq$) indicates that one quantity is no more than the other. The greater than or equal to symbol ($\geq$) indicates that one quantity is no less than the other.

Example 2 Determine whether the given value is a solution of the open sentence.

A $5x - 4 = 2$; $x = 2$

Solution Substitute 2 for x and simplify. Then decide if the sentence is true.

$$5x - 4 = 2$$
$$5 \cdot 2 - 4 \overset{?}{=} 2 \qquad \text{Substitute 2 for } x.$$
$$10 - 4 \overset{?}{=} 2 \qquad \text{Multiply.}$$
$$6 \neq 2 \qquad \text{Subtract.}$$

The sentence is not true when $x = 2$, so 2 is not a solution. ∎

B $36 = a \cdot (a + 5)$; $a = 4$

Solution Substitute 4 for a and simplify. Then decide if the sentence is true.

$$36 = a \cdot (a + 5)$$
$$36 \overset{?}{=} 4 \cdot (4 + 5) \qquad \text{Substitute 4 for } a.$$
$$36 \overset{?}{=} 4 \cdot 9 \qquad \text{Add inside the parentheses.}$$
$$36 = 36 \checkmark \qquad \text{Multiply.}$$

The sentence is true when $a = 4$, so 4 is a solution. ∎

C $y \leq 2x + 5$; $x = 3$ and $y = 11$

Solution Substitute 3 for x and 11 for y and simplify. Then decide if the sentence is true.

$$y \leq 2x + 5$$
$$11 \overset{?}{\leq} 2 \cdot 3 + 5 \qquad \text{Substitute 3 for } x \text{ and 11 for } y.$$
$$11 \overset{?}{\leq} 6 + 5 \qquad \text{Multiply.}$$
$$11 \leq 11 \checkmark \qquad \text{Add.}$$

The sentence is true when $x = 3$ and $y = 11$. ∎

Using Formulas to Compare Expressions

To compare expressions using formulas, substitute given values into the formulas and evaluate the expressions.

Example 3   Compare the area of a rectangle with length 4 feet and width 3 feet to the area of a rectangle with length 6 feet and width 2 feet.

Solution   Substitute the given values into to the formula for the area of a rectangle with length l and width w, $A = lw$.

First Rectangle   Second Rectangle

First Rectangle	Second Rectangle	
$A = lw$	$A = lw$	Formula for area of a rectangle
$= 4 \cdot 3$	$= 6 \cdot 2$	Substitute given values.
$= 12$	$= 12$	Multiply.
	$12 = 12$	Compare.

The areas of the two rectangles are equal.

Example 4   Jane traveled for 3 hours at a constant speed of 50 miles per hour. John traveled for 2 hours at a constant speed of 60 miles per hour. Who traveled the most distance?

Solution   Substitute the given values into the formula for distance, $d = rt$, where r is the rate of speed and t is the time traveled.

Jane	John	
$d = rt$	$d = rt$	Formula for distance.
$= 50 \cdot 3$	$= 60 \cdot 2$	Substitute given values.
$= 150$	$= 120$	Multiply.
	$150 > 120$	Compare.

Jane traveled the most distance.

Problem Set

Compare the expressions by using $<$, $=$, or $>$.

1. $2 \cdot 2 + 9 \quad\rule{1em}{1em}\quad 9 + 6 \div 3$

2. $16 - 5 \cdot 3 \quad\rule{1em}{1em}\quad 5 \cdot 3 - 2 \cdot (5 + 2)$

3. $(17 - 5) \div 2 \quad\rule{1em}{1em}\quad 2 \cdot 3 \cdot 4 \div (2 \cdot 3)$

4. $9 + 2 \cdot 8 \quad\rule{1em}{1em}\quad (9 + 2) \cdot 8$

5. $(12 + 6) \div 3 \quad\rule{1em}{1em}\quad 2 + 5 \cdot 8 \div (2 \cdot 5)$

6. $(3 + 5) - 2 \quad\rule{1em}{1em}\quad 2 + 3 - 1 \cdot 3$

7. $(19 - 4) \div (2 + 1) \quad\rule{1em}{1em}\quad 4 + (2 + 3 \cdot 2)$

8. $(20 \div 2) \div 2 \quad\rule{1em}{1em}\quad 4 \cdot 3 \div 2$

9. $7 \cdot 8 \div 4 \cdot 3 \quad\rule{1em}{1em}\quad 16 \div 2 \cdot 4 + 10$

10. $3 \cdot [5 \cdot (6 + 1)] \quad\rule{1em}{1em}\quad 10 \cdot (4 + 6) - 5 \cdot 3$

11. $26 - 10 \div 2 \div 5 \quad\rule{1em}{1em}\quad 42 \div 7 + 5 \cdot 6$

12. $\dfrac{7 \cdot 9 \div (2 + 1)}{7} \quad\rule{1em}{1em}\quad \dfrac{50 \div 10 \cdot 3}{10 - 7}$

13. $\dfrac{2 \cdot (3 + 15)}{4 + 5} \quad\rule{1em}{1em}\quad \dfrac{5 \cdot (21 - 5)}{3 \cdot 9 - 7}$

14. $5 \cdot [(1 + 3) \cdot 2] - 6 \cdot 2 \quad\rule{1em}{1em}\quad 2 \cdot [64 \div (2 + 2)] - 2 \cdot 3$

Determine whether the given value is a solution of the open sentence.

15. $3x = 6; x = 3$

16. $14 = b + 9; b = 5$

17. $4 + 7g = 81; g = 11$

18. $28 = 3 \cdot (y + 3); y = 4$

19. $\dfrac{d + 15}{d + 4} = d - 5; d = 7$

20. $2w - 5 = w + 10; w = 16$

21. $\dfrac{4m + 2}{7} = \dfrac{42 - 3m}{m - 8}; m = 10$

22. $5 \cdot (h + 4h) = 3 \cdot (7h + 4); h = 3$

23. $y \geq 3x - 2; x = 2$ and $y = 4$

24. $y < x^2 - 2; x = +3$ and $y = 7$

25. $p + 2q < 16; p = 5, q = +5$

26. $4 \cdot (f + 3) \leq 5g; f = 7, g = 8$

*27. **Challenge** $u^2 + v^2 > 313; u = 13, v = 12$

*28. **Challenge** $\dfrac{-6}{(2 + s)} \geq 5r; r = -1, s = 1$

Solve each problem.

29. Hae Sung bicycled for 3 hours at a rate of 19 miles per hour. Clarence bicycled for 4 hours at a rate of 14 miles per hour. Evaluate the expression rt, where r represents rate and t represents number of hours, to find who traveled the greatest distance.

30. The expression lwh gives the volume of a rectangular prism with length l, width w, and height h. Is the volume of a rectangular prism with $l = 5$ cm, $w = 6$ cm, and $h = 4$ cm greater than, less than, or equal to the volume of a rectangular prism with $l = 5$ cm, $w = 5$ cm, and $h = 5$ cm?

31. Shaelun has 12 dimes and 14 nickels. Kirby has 14 dimes and 10 nickels. Write expressions for the amount of money each has. Is the amount of money that Shaelun has greater than, less than, or equal to the amount of money Kirby has?

32. Friendly Fitness Gym has a startup fee of $50 and a monthly fee of $10. Wonderful Workout Gym has a startup fee of $100 and a monthly fee of $5. At the end of the first year, is the cost of membership at Friendly Fitness Gym greater than, less than, or equal to the cost of membership at Wonderful Workout Gym?

33. The expression $\dfrac{4 \cdot (220 - y)}{5}$ estimates the value equal to 80% of a person's maximum heart rate when they are y years old. A personal trainer wants to get his client's heart rates above this value for 30 consecutive minutes. Use $\dfrac{4 \cdot (220 - y)}{5} \geq 140$ to determine which of the trainer's clients shown below should get their heart rates up to at least 140 for 30 consecutive minutes.

Name	Age
Ms. Fields	35
Mr. Reese	20
Mrs. Diaz	55
Mr. Shuang	50
Ms. Silva	40

Replacement Sets

A replacement set for an open sentence is a set of values that are possible solutions. That is, the values in a replacement set are tested to see if they are solutions.

A **solution** of an open sentence with one variable is a value of the variable that makes the sentence a true statement.

A **set** is a collection of objects. Each member of a set is an **element** of the set. The elements of a set are enclosed in braces, so the set containing the elements 9, 12, and 15 is written as {9, 12, 15}. The symbol $\in$ is used to show that a value is an element of a set.

> **TIP**
>
> The symbol $\in$ means *is an element of.* For example,
> $3 \in \{1, 3, 5, 7\}$.

> **DEFINITION**
>
> A **replacement set** for an open sentence is a set of values that are allowable as solutions of the open sentence.
>
> A **solution set** for an open sentence is a set of values that are solutions of the open sentence with the given replacement set.

A solution set can have any number of values. An open sentence can have zero, one, or many solutions, depending on the type of open sentence.

Finding Solutions of Open Sentences from a Replacement Set

Example 1   Identify the solution set of the open sentence using the given replacement set.

A $2x + 1 = 5$; replacement set {0, 1, 2}

Solution   Substitute each replacement set value for x.

$2x + 1 = 5 \qquad\qquad 2x + 1 = 5 \qquad\qquad 2x + 1 = 5$

$2 \cdot 0 + 1 \overset{?}{=} 5 \qquad 2 \cdot 1 + 1 \overset{?}{=} 5 \qquad 2 \cdot 2 + 1 \overset{?}{=} 5$

$0 + 1 \overset{?}{=} 5 \qquad\quad 2 + 1 \overset{?}{=} 5 \qquad\quad 4 + 1 \overset{?}{=} 5$

$1 \neq 5 \qquad\qquad\quad 3 \neq 5 \qquad\qquad\quad 5 = 5 \checkmark$

The only solution is 2. The solution set is {2}. ∎

B $x + 3 < 10$; replacement set $\{5, 6, 7, 8\}$

Solution   Substitute each replacement set value for x.

$x + 3 < 10$	$x + 3 < 10$	$x + 3 < 10$	$x + 3 < 10$
$5 + 3 \overset{?}{<} 10$	$6 + 3 \overset{?}{<} 10$	$7 + 3 \overset{?}{<} 10$	$8 + 3 \overset{?}{<} 10$
$8 \overset{?}{<} 10$	$9 \overset{?}{<} 10$	$10 \overset{?}{<} 10$	$11 \overset{?}{<} 10$
$8 < 10$ ✓	$9 < 10$ ✓	$10 \not< 10$	$11 \not< 10$

Using the given replacement set, the solutions are 5 and 6. The solution set is $\{5, 6\}$. ∎

Finding Solutions of an Equation with the Variable on Both Sides

If the variable occurs more than once in an equation, remember to substitute a possible solution for each occurrence of the variable.

Example 2   Identify the solution set, if any, using the given replacement set.

A $x + 6 = 14 - x$; replacement set $\{4, 8, 10\}$

Solution   Substitute each replacement set value for x.

$x + 6 = 14 - x$	$x + 6 = 14 - x$	$x + 6 = 14 - x$
$4 + 6 \overset{?}{=} 14 - 4$	$8 + 6 \overset{?}{=} 14 - 8$	$10 + 6 \overset{?}{=} 14 - 10$
$10 \overset{?}{=} 10$	$14 \overset{?}{=} 6$	$16 \overset{?}{=} 4$
$10 = 10$ ✓	$14 \neq 6$	$16 \neq 4$

The only solution is 4. The solution set is $\{4\}$. ∎

B $x + 11 = 15 + x$; replacement set $\{4, 6, 26\}$

Solution   Substitute each replacement set value for x.

$x + 11 = 15 + x$	$x + 11 = 15 + x$	$x + 11 = 15 + x$
$4 + 11 \overset{?}{=} 15 + 4$	$6 + 11 \overset{?}{=} 15 + 6$	$26 + 11 \overset{?}{=} 15 + 26$
$15 \overset{?}{=} 19$	$17 \overset{?}{=} 21$	$37 \overset{?}{=} 41$
$15 \neq 19$	$17 \neq 21$	$37 \neq 41$

No member of the replacement set is a solution. No member of the replacement set makes the open sentence true. The solution set is a set with no members, called the **empty set** (written as $\varnothing$). ∎

THINK ABOUT IT

The equation in Example 2B has no solution, even using the set of all numbers as the replacement set.

NOTATION

$\{\ \}$ or $\varnothing$ null or empty set

Application: Temperature

Example 3 The formula $F = 1.8C + 32$ is used to convert degrees Celsius (°C) to degrees Fahrenheit (°F). For 41°F, the equation is $41 = 1.8C + 32$. Find the temperature in °C that corresponds to 41°F by using the replacement set $\{3, 4, 5\}$ for C.

Solution Substitute each replacement set value for C.

$41 = 1.8C + 32$ $41 = 1.8C + 32$ $41 = 1.8C + 32$

$41 \stackrel{?}{=} 1.8 \cdot 3 + 32$ $41 \stackrel{?}{=} 1.8 \cdot 4 + 32$ $41 \stackrel{?}{=} 1.8 \cdot 5 + 32$

$41 \stackrel{?}{=} 5.4 + 32$ $41 \stackrel{?}{=} 7.2 + 32$ $41 \stackrel{?}{=} 9.0 + 32$

$41 \stackrel{?}{=} 37.4$ $41 \stackrel{?}{=} 39.2$ $41 \stackrel{?}{=} 41$

$41 \neq 37.4$ $41 \neq 39.2$ $41 = 41 \checkmark$

5°C corresponds to 41°F. ∎

> **REMEMBER**
>
> Algebraic equations can capture key relationships among quantities in the world.

Problem Set

Identify the solution set of each equation or inequality using the given replacement set.

1. $6x = 18$; $\{1, 3, 9\}$

2. $24 = x - 9$; $\{8, 15, 33\}$

3. $4 + 7z = 46$; $\{0, 6, 42\}$

4. $3 \cdot (a + 3) = 42$; $\{11, 12, 13\}$

5. $\dfrac{x + 31}{x + 1} = x + 1$; $\{1, 5, 6\}$

6. $2x + 8 = x + 16$; $\{2, 8, 20\}$

7. $\dfrac{2c - 8}{c - 8} = \dfrac{4c + 2}{7}$; $\{10, 11, 12\}$

8. $5 \cdot (x + 3x) = 5 \cdot (2x + 4)$; $\{0, 2, 3\}$

9. $2x + 4 = 16$; $\{2, 4, 6\}$

10. $5 = 9 - x$; $\{4, 6, 8\}$

11. $\dfrac{3x}{4} = \dfrac{36}{3x}$; $\{3, 4, 8\}$

12. $x^2 + 6x + 9 = 64$; $\{5, 7, 9\}$

13. $4 - 2z < 6$; $\{0, 1, 2\}$

14. $\dfrac{a}{3} > 4$; $\{3, 4, 12\}$

15. $3r < 6$; $\{0, 1, 2\}$

16. $2x + 4 > x - 2$; $\{3, 4, 5\}$

17. $2 \leq x \leq 4$; $\{1, 2, 3, 4\}$

18. $28 = 7a$; $\{4, 21, 35, 196\}$

19. $n - 16 > 20$; $\{34, 35, 36, 37\}$

20. $3m + 9 = 24$; $\{3, 4, 5\}$

21. $x - 3 = \dfrac{2x - 1}{3}$; $\{5, 8, 11, 14\}$

22. $1 + 4m < 3m - 5$; $\{5, 6, 7\}$

23. $\dfrac{48}{q + 2} \leq 8$; $\{4, 35, 196\}$

*24. Challenge $4 \leq x < 7$; $\{1, 2, 3, 4, 5, 6, 7, 8, 9, 10\}$

*25. Challenge $3 < \dfrac{x}{2} \leq 8$; $\{2, 4, 6, 8, 10, 12, 14, 16\}$

Solve each problem.

26. The formula $V = lwh$ gives the volume V of a rectangular prism with length l, width w, and height h. A box whose length is 18 inches and whose width is 8 inches has a volume of 720 cubic inches. Use $720 = 18 \cdot 8 \cdot h$ and the replacement set $\{3, 4, 5, 6\}$ to find the height of the box.

27. The formula $C = \dfrac{5(F - 32)}{9}$ is used to convert degrees Fahrenheit (°F) to degrees Celsius (°C). For 15°C, the equation is $15 = \dfrac{5(F - 32)}{9}$. Find the temperature in °F that corresponds to 15°C by using the replacement set $\{50, 59, 68\}$ for F.

28. Sandy has $14 to buy a pizza for her family. A medium pizza costs $11.50 plus $0.75 per topping. Use the inequality $11.5 + 0.75t \le 14$, where t is the number of toppings and $\{1, 2, 3, 4\}$ is the replacement set, to determine how many toppings she can put on the pizza.

29. Tabitha has test scores of 80 and 78 in her mathematics class. To receive a B grade, she must obtain an average greater than or equal to 80 but less than 90. Use the replacement set $\{80, 81, 82, 83\}$ to determine which test scores on the last remaining test will enable Tabitha to get a B for the course.

Related Equations

You can use *related equations* to solve equations.

If you start with 5 and add 2, the result is 7. If you subtract 2 from 7, the result is the number you started with: 5. A set of **related equations** all communicate the same relationship between three values, but in different ways. Any time you have an addition equation, you could write two subtraction equations that describe the same relationship between the values.

RELATED EQUATIONS FOR ADDITION AND SUBTRACTION

For any *a*, *b*, and *c*:

$a + b = c$
$a = c - b$ } All three of these are related equations.
$b = c - a$

Example

$5 + 2 = 7$
$5 = 7 - 2$ } All three of these are related equations.
$2 = 7 - 5$

Writing Related Equations for Addition and Subtraction

A good strategy for writing a set of related equations for addition and subtraction is to identify the sum and write the addition equation first. Then, to write the subtraction equations, subtract each different addend from the sum.

Example 1 Write a complete set of related equations for the given equation.

A $8 + x = 14$

Solution The sum is 14. Subtract 8 from 14 in one subtraction equation, and subtract x from 14 in the other subtraction equation.

$8 + x = 14$

$x = 14 - 8$

$8 = 14 - x$ ∎

B $35 - p = 21$

Solution Because p is subtracted from 35, the sum in the addition equation is 35. Subtract 21 from 35 in the other subtraction equation.

$p + 21 = 35$

$21 = 35 - p$

$p = 35 - 21$ ∎

> **TIP**
>
> The equation $14 - 8 = x$ is equivalent to $x = 14 - 8$. The equation $14 - x = 8$ is equivalent to $8 = 14 - x$.

Writing Related Equations for Multiplication and Division

Multiplication and division are also inverse operations, so you can write related equations using those operations.

RELATED EQUATIONS FOR MULTIPLICATION AND DIVISION

For any nonzero *a*, *b*, and *c*:

$$ab = c$$
$$a = \frac{c}{b}$$
$$b = \frac{c}{a}$$

All three of these are related equations.

Example

$$5 \cdot 2 = 10$$
$$5 = \frac{10}{2}$$
$$2 = \frac{10}{5}$$

All three of these are related equations.

A good strategy for writing a set of related equations for multiplication and division is to identify the product and write the multiplication equation first. Then, to write the division equations, divide the product by each different factor.

Example 2 Write a complete set of related equations for the given equation.

Ⓐ $4y = 24$

Solution The product is 24. Divide 24 by 4 in one division equation and divide 24 by y in the other division equation.

$$4y = 24$$

$$y = \frac{24}{4}$$

$$4 = \frac{24}{y} \quad \blacksquare$$

Ⓑ $\frac{63}{a} = 9$

Solution Because 63 is divided by a, the product is 63 in the multiplication equation. Divide 63 by 9 in the other division equation.

$$9a = 63$$

$$\frac{63}{a} = 9$$

$$\frac{63}{9} = a \quad \blacksquare$$

Using Related Equations to Solve an Equation

When you find a related equation that has the variable alone on one side of the equation, you can simplify to find the solution.

Example 3   Solve using a related equation.

Ⓐ $9 + x = 12$

Solution

$9 + x = 12$ Use a related equation that has the variable alone on one side of the equation.

$x = 12 - 9$

$x = 3$ Subtract. ∎

Ⓑ $7y = 28$

Solution

$7y = 28$ Use a related equation that has the variable alone on one side of the equation.

$y = \dfrac{28}{7}$

$y = 4$ Divide. ∎

Problem Set

Write a complete set of related equations that contain the given equation.

1. $11 + 7 = 18$
2. $20 - 16 = 4$
3. $3 \cdot 4 = 12$
4. $\dfrac{44}{11} = 4$
5. $35 = 7k$
6. $3 = \dfrac{18}{e}$
7. $\dfrac{r}{5} = 4$
8. $3t = 60$
9. $6 + h = 13$
10. $4.5c = 9$

11. $n + 16 = 28$
12. $120 = 2 \cdot d$
13. $m = 1.8 + 0.2$
14. $p = \dfrac{24}{8}$
15. $g + \dfrac{1}{2} = 5\dfrac{1}{2}$
16. $42 - 12 = w$
17. $\dfrac{75}{w} = 15$
18. $5 + x = 11.2$
19. $b \cdot 10 = 35$
20. $\dfrac{90}{j} = 45$

Translate each sentence into an equation. Then write the two related equations.

21. The sum of a number and 19 is 25.
22. The product of 7 and a number is 84.

Write the related equation that has the variable by itself on one side of the equals sign. Then simplify the other side.

23. $14 + b = 27$

24. $\dfrac{32}{s} = 4$

25. $4n = 84$

26. $40 - f = 27$

27. $r + 21 = 81$

28. $\dfrac{a}{11} = 11$

29. $3n = 39$

30. $x - 50 = 15$

Solve each problem.

31. After selling x cans of soup from a 192-can shipment, a store had 51 cans left. Write and solve an equation to find how many cans x were sold.

32. A dozen eggs costs \$2.52. Write and solve an equation to find the cost of one egg.

*33. **Challenge** A child separated c crayons into 3 equal groups. There were 16 crayons in each group. Show how you could use related equations to find the value of c.

*34. **Challenge** When the Mason family began their trip, the odometer on their car read 46,792 miles. After driving x miles, the odometer read 47,912 miles.

A. Write an equation that represents the situation.

B. Identify the solution by writing the related equation that has the variable by itself on one side and then simplifying the other side.

C. Check your solution by substituting it back into the equation you wrote for part A.

Translating Words into Equations

Just as you can translate a phrase into an expression, you can translate a complete sentence into an equation.

If a sentence describes two equal quantities, it can be translated into an equation. The word *is* should usually be translated into an equals sign.

Translating Sentences into Equations

Example 1   Translate each sentence into an equation.

A Twenty-five times a number is 150.

Solution

Twenty-five times a number   is   150.

$25 \cdot n \qquad\qquad = \qquad 150$

$25n \qquad\qquad = \qquad 150 \ \blacksquare$

The word *times* indicates multiplication and the word *is* indicates an equals sign.

B Fourteen is the sum of a number and 6.

Solution

Fourteen   is   the sum of a number and 6.

$14 \qquad = \qquad\qquad n + 6 \ \blacksquare$

The word *sum* indicates addition and the word *is* indicates an equals sign.

C Two less than 5 times a number is 7.

Solution

$5n$ Translate *5 times a number.*

$5n - 2$ Translate *two less than 5 times a number.*

$5n - 2 = 7 \ \blacksquare$ Write the equation.

Translating Equations into Sentences

Example 2   Translate each equation into a sentence.

A $2 + (d + 3) = 10$

Solution   Possible answer:

Two increased by the sum of a number and 3 is 10. ■

B $2a = \dfrac{8}{a}$

Solution Possible answer:

Twice a number is the quotient of 8 and the number. ∎

Writing Equations and Identifying Solutions

Example 3 Translate each sentence into an equation. Then identify the solution, using the given replacement set.

A The product of 6 and a number is 42. Replacement set: $\{7, 36, 48\}$

Solution

The product of 6 and a number is 42.	The word *product* indicates multiplication.
$6s \qquad\qquad\quad = 42$	Write an equation.
$6 \cdot 7 \qquad\qquad = 42$	When $s = 7$, the equation is true.

The solution is $s = 7$. ∎

> **REMEMBER**
>
> Substitute each replacement-set value for the variable. Then decide which value makes the equation true.

B Nine is 3 more than twice a number. Replacement set: $\{2, 3, 6\}$

Solution

Nine is 3 more than twice a number.	The phrase *more than* indicates addition.
$9 \;\; = \qquad\quad 2n + 3$	Write an equation.
$9 \;\; = \qquad\quad 2 \cdot 3 + 3$	When $n = 3$, the equation is true.

The solution is $n = 3$. ∎

Application: Writing Formulas

A formula is an equation that describes a relationship among quantities.

Example 4 Write a formula that describes each relationship.

A If an object travels at a constant rate, the distance the object travels is the product of its rate and the amount of time it travels.

Solution Let d represent distance, r represent rate, and t represent time.

Distance is the product of rate and time.	Write a brief sentence.
$d = rt$	Translate the sentence into an equation. ∎

> **TIP**
>
> Distance and time are quantities. Rate is a ratio of those quantities. For example, if $d = 40$ miles and $t = 2$ hours, then
>
> $r = \dfrac{40 \text{ mi}}{2 \text{ h}} = \dfrac{20 \text{ mi}}{1 \text{ h}} = 20$ mi/h.

B The perimeter of a triangle is the sum of the lengths of its sides.

Solution Let P represent perimeter. Let a, b, and c represent the lengths of the sides.

Perimeter is the sum of the lengths of the sides.	Write a brief sentence.
$P = a + b + c$	Translate the sentence into an equation. ∎

Problem Set

Translate each sentence into an equation.

1. Two more than a number is 7.

2. The product of 4 and a number is 30.

3. Twice a number is 3 less than the number.

4. The quotient of a number and 5 is 11.

5. Twenty-two is the sum of 3 times a number and 7.

6. Four times the difference of a number and 1 is 18.

7. Six less than 5 times a number is 24.

8. A number decreased by 4 is the number divided by 2.

9. The sum of twice a number and one less than the number is 14.

10. Five times the sum of 2 and twice a number is 100.

Translate each equation into a sentence.

11. $8 - v = 3$

12. $21 = 3 \cdot (c + 9)$

13. $5m = \dfrac{30m}{6}$

14. $a + 2a = 3a$

15. $\dfrac{2x}{5} = 14$

16. $\dfrac{1}{2}t = 30$

Translate each sentence into an equation. Then identify the solution, using the given replacement set.

17. A certain amount more than 15 is 27. Replacement set: {9, 12, 42}

18. Two and five-tenths less than a number is 5.5. Replacement set: {2, 3, 7, 8}

19. Twenty-one is 3 times a number. Replacement set: {7, 18, 24, 63}

20. The quotient of a number and 6 is 30. Replacement set: {5, 24, 36, 180}

21. One less than 3 times a number is 26. Replacement set: {7, 8, 9}

22. Fifty-nine is the sum of 5 times a number and 4. Replacement set: {10, 11, 12}

23. The product of 3 and 12 more than a number is 45. Replacement set: {3, 5, 11}

*24. **Challenge** The quotient of 8 times a number and 1 more than the number is 6. Replacement set: {all whole numbers}

*25. **Challenge** The sum of 7 and a number is the same as the sum of 3 times the number increased by 5. Replacement set: {all whole numbers}

Write a formula that describes each relationship.

26. The area of a square is the length of one side of the square times itself.

27. The amount of interest owed on money borrowed is the product of the principal, which is the amount borrowed, the interest rate, written as a decimal, and the amount of time for which the money was borrowed, in years.

28. The height of a triangle can be found by dividing twice the area of the triangle by the length of its base.

29. A polygon is made up of three or more sides joined together. If the sides are the same length, as in a square, the polygon is a regular polygon. The measure of an interior angle of a regular polygon, in degrees, is the quotient of the product of 180 and 2 less than the number of sides and the number of sides.

*30. **Challenge** Translate each sentence into an equation. Then identify the solution of each equation by using mental math.

  A. The sum of two consecutive odd whole numbers is 48.

  B. The product of two consecutive whole numbers is 210.

Solving Problems

Problems are easier to solve when you have a plan.

THE 5-STEP PROBLEM-SOLVING PLAN

Step 1 *Identify*   Read the problem and identify the unknowns. What is given? What are you being asked to find? Write it down in words. If you can, estimate the answer.

Step 2 *Strategize*   Select and define variables and variable expressions for all the unknowns.

Step 3 *Set Up*   Write an equation, inequality, system of equations, or whatever other tools you need that model the problem that is being solved.

Step 4 *Solve*   Solve the model (equation, inequality, system, etc.). Answer the question.

Step 5 *Check*   Check your answer for reasonableness and accuracy with the original problem statement.

Application: Transportation

Example 1   Three times as many cars as trucks went over a bridge. Nineteen trucks went over the bridge. How many vehicles in all went over the bridge?

Solution   Use the problem-solving plan.

Identify   *Given:* number of cars = 3 times the number of trucks
    There were 19 trucks.
Need to find: total number of vehicles

Strategize   Let t = number of trucks. Then the number of cars = $3t$.

Set Up   cars + trucks = $3t + t$ Write an expression for the sum of the numbers of cars and trucks.

Solve

$3t + t = 3 \cdot 19 + 19$ Substitute 19 for t.

$\quad = 57 + 19$ Simplify.

$\quad = 76$

Seventy-six vehicles went over the bridge.

Check   Estimate to check for reasonableness. There were about 20 trucks. There were about $3 \cdot 20$, or 60 cars. $20 + 60 = 80$, which is close to 76. So, the answer is reasonable. ∎

> **TIP**
>
> You can solve the problem without using a variable, because the number of trucks is known. But writing variables and variable expressions is a useful skill; you will need it in later topics.

Application: Geometry

Example 2

A A playground is shaped like a square. Each side is 78 feet long. How many times did Maria run around the entire border of the playground if she ran 4992 feet?

Solution   Use the problem-solving plan.

Identify   *Given:* The playground is square. Maria runs 4992 feet.
      Need to find: how many times Maria ran around the border

Strategize   Let n = the number of times Maria ran around the border.

Set Up $4 \cdot 78 = 312$ feet   All 4 sides of a square have equal length.

      $312n = 4992$ Write an equation.

Solve

$$n = \frac{4992}{312}$$ Use a related equation to solve for n.

      $= 16$

Maria ran around the entire border 16 times.

Check   The distance around the playground is about 300 feet. Since $300 \cdot 16 = 4800$, the answer is reasonable. ■

B What are the possible lengths of a rectangle if the length must be 10 inches longer than the width and the area must be less than 35 square inches? Use only whole numbers for the dimensions.

Solution   Use the problem-solving plan.

Identify   *Given:* length = width + 10; area < 35
      Need to find: possible lengths for the longer side of the rectangle

> **REMEMBER**
>
> The area of a rectangle is the product of its length and width.

Strategize   Let w = width. Then length = $w + 10$.

Set Up $(w + 10) \cdot w < 35$ Area < 35, so length · width < 35.

Solve

$(w + 10) \cdot w < 35$	$(w + 10) \cdot w < 35$	$(w + 10) \cdot w < 35$	Substitute whole numbers for w, starting with 1.
$(1 + 10) \cdot 1 \overset{?}{<} 35$	$(2 + 10) \cdot 2 \overset{?}{<} 35$	$(3 + 10) \cdot 3 \overset{?}{<} 35$	
$11 < 35 \checkmark$	$24 < 35 \checkmark$	$39 \not< 35$	

The possible lengths are $1 + 10$ and $2 + 10$, or 11 inches and 12 inches.

Check   Using a length of 11 inches, the dimensions are 1 inch by 11 inches. Using a length of 12 inches, the dimensions are 2 inches by 12 inches. In each case, the length is 10 inches greater than the width and the area is less than 35 square inches. So, the answers are reasonable. ■

Problem Set

Solve each problem using the 5-step problem-solving plan.

1. In a zoo, there are 5 times as many monkeys as there are bears, and the number of bears is 2 fewer than the number of elephants. The zoo has 6 elephants. How many monkeys does the zoo have?

2. Joey has nickels and dimes in his pocket. The number of dimes is 3 times the number of nickels. If Joey has 8 nickels, what is the total value of the money he has in his pocket?

3. Shawna's book report must have a minimum number of words. She counted the number of words she already wrote and realized she still has to write at least 4 times as much as she already wrote. What is the minimum number of words the book report must have if Shawna already wrote 125 words?

4. The number of cars in a store's parking lot during a Special Saturday Sale is about 250 greater than the number in the lot on a regular day. If there are about 700 cars in the lot during the Special Saturday Sale, about how many cars are in the lot on a regular day?

5. What are the possible lengths of a rectangle if the width must be 8 inches less than the length and the area must be between 100 and 200 square inches? Use only whole numbers for the dimensions.

6. What are the possible lengths for the side of a square if the distance around the square must be less than 25 meters? Use only whole numbers for dimensions.

7. Mei drove a total of 504 miles in 9 hours. Find her average rate of speed given that distance is the product of rate and time.

8. It takes Francis about 25 minutes to walk to his best friend's house. He figured that he spent a total of 7 hours and 30 minutes walking back and forth to his friend's house last month. How many times did he walk to his friend's house last month?

9. A walking loop is made up of five connecting trails, where three of the trails are 1820 feet long and the other two are 965 feet long. How far does Mrs. Johansson walk if she walks the loop 2 times? 6 times?

10. The elevation at the start of a trail is 3780 feet and the elevation at the end of the trail is 5865 feet. Assuming the gain in elevation is fairly constant throughout the trail, about how many feet are gained every hour if it takes a hiker 3 hours to hike the trail? 5 hours?

11. The ages of three cousins are consecutive even whole numbers. The sum of the youngest and oldest ages is 16. How old is the oldest cousin?

12. The sum of the measures of the three angles in any triangle is 180°. If one of the angles is a 90° angle, what are the measures of the other two angles if the measure of the larger angle is 10° more than the measure of the smaller angle?

13. At a museum, adult tickets to a special exhibit cost $5 and children's tickets cost $2.50. A group of children and adults has budgeted $50 for the exhibit. Two adults must enter the exhibit. How many children could they take with them? How many fewer children could they take if the price of the children's ticket is raised by $0.50?

14. Donald drove a total of 279 miles at an average rate of 62 miles per hour. How long did the trip take?

15. Doug is 1 year older than twice Cheryl's age. Ed is 3 times as old as Doug, and he is between 70 and 90 years old. Find the possible whole number ages that Cheryl can be.

16. A bird feeder is shaped like a rectangular prism. Its base measures 6.3 cm by 3.8 cm and its height is 16.6 cm. Alonzo bought a box of bird seed measuring 40 cm by 18 cm by 9 cm. About how many times can Alonzo fill the bird feeder completely?

UNIT 2

Addition and Subtraction

As values go up and down, addition and subtraction can help you make sense of the changes.

If you have two oranges and a friend gives you three oranges, how many do you have? If you then give four oranges to your friend, how many are you left with? This sort of addition and subtraction problem with passing fruit back and forth is the type of simple math you have done since you were very young. When you expand your addition and subtraction skills to negative numbers and decimals, you can solve many more complicated problems.

Big Ideas

▶ The laws of arithmetic can be used to simplify algebraic expressions and equations.

▶ A number is any entity that obeys the laws of arithmetic; all numbers obey the laws of arithmetic. The laws of arithmetic can be used to simplify algebraic expressions.

Unit Topics

▶ Integers on a Number Line

▶ Adding Integers

▶ Subtracting Integers

▶ Decimals on a Number Line

▶ Adding Decimals

▶ Subtracting Decimals

▶ Addition and Subtraction Properties

▶ Equations Involving Addition and Subtraction

▶ Addition and Subtraction Applications

Integers on a Number Line

A number line goes in two directions. To the right of zero are positive numbers. To the left of zero are negative numbers.

Nonzero **opposites** are two numbers that are the same distance from zero on a number line. A **number line** can be used to compare and order numbers. Every number has its own corresponding point on a number line.

The set of **integers** is {..., −3, −2, −1, 0, 1, 2, 3, ...}. It is the set of whole numbers and their opposites.

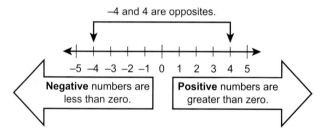

The opposite of zero is zero. Zero is neither positive nor negative.

THINK ABOUT IT

Zero is a whole number and an integer.

Identifying Coordinates of Points on a Number Line

A **coordinate** is a number that indicates the location of a point on a number line. The **origin** is the point on a number line with coordinate 0.

Example 1 State the coordinate of each indicated point.

A Point *A*

Solution Point *A* is the origin. The coordinate of point *A* is 0. ■

B Point *B*

Solution Point *B* is 3 units to the right of the origin. The coordinate of point *B* is 3. ■

C Point *C*

Solution Point *C* is 4 units to the left of the origin. The coordinate of point *C* is −4. ■

TIP

A number with no symbol in front is positive. So, 3 represents positive 3. Some books use +3 to represent positive 3.

(continued)

D Point D

Solution   Point D is 7 units to the left of the origin. The coordinate of point D is -7. ■

Graphing Integers on a Number Line

To graph an integer on a number line, begin at the origin, and then count the correct number of units right or left. Draw a dot to represent the point, and label the point with its coordinate.

Example 2   Graph each number on a number line.

A 6

Solution   Since 6 is positive, it is to the right of the origin. Start at zero and count 6 units to the right.

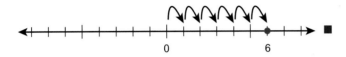

B -3

Solution   Since -3 is negative, it is to the left of the origin. Start at zero and count 3 units to the left.

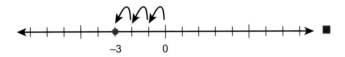

Comparing Numbers

Graphing numbers on a number line can help you compare them. Numbers increase in value as you move to the right. Numbers decrease in value as you move to the left. So, when comparing two numbers, the number to the left is less and the number to the right is greater.

Example 3   Use a number line to compare the integers. Use $<$, $>$, or $=$.

A 2 and -4

Solution

Because -4 is to the left of 2, you know that -4 is less than 2. So you can write either $-4 < 2$ or $2 > -4$. ■

B -6 and -2

Solution

Because -6 is to the left of -2, you know that -6 is less than -2. So you can write either $-6 < -2$ or $-2 > -6$. ■

Absolute Value

The **absolute value** of a number is its distance from zero. Absolute value is indicated by the | | symbol. For example, read |−4| as *the absolute value of negative four.*

Example 4

A Find |−4|.

Solution

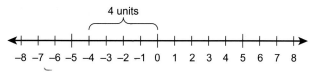

Since −4 is 4 units from zero, |−4| = 4. ■

B Find |6|.

Solution

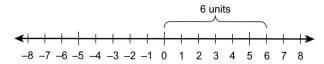

Since 6 is 6 units from zero, |6| = 6. ■

Opposite Numbers

At the beginning of the lesson, you learned that numbers are opposites if they are the same distance from zero, but in different directions on a number line. Another property of opposites is that they have different signs (except for zero), but the same absolute value. For example, 12 and −12 are opposites because they have different signs, but |12| = 12 and |−12| = 12.

The − sign is used to indicate *opposite*. You can read −2 as either *negative two* or the *opposite of two*. Read −(−2) as the *opposite of negative two*. The opposite of −2 is 2, so write −(−2) = 2 and read it as *the opposite of negative two equals two.*

Example 5 Write the opposite of each integer.

A 3

Solution The opposite of 3 is −3. ■

B −10

Solution The opposite of −10 is 10. Or, −(−10) = 10. ■

C 0

Solution The opposite of 0 is 0. ■

TIP

The same sign is used for *opposite, negative,* and *subtraction.*

THINK ABOUT IT

All numbers have opposites, not just integers. For example, the opposite of 3.4 is −3.4.

Identifying Integer Solutions of Absolute Value Open Sentences

You can use a number line to help identify integer solutions of simple equations and inequalities involving absolute value.

Example 6   Identify all integer solutions of the equation or inequality.

Ⓐ $|x| = 7$

Solution   The absolute value of x is 7, so all values of x are 7 units from zero on a number line.

The integer solutions of $|x| = 7$ are -7 and 7. ■

Ⓑ $|x| < 3$

Solution   The absolute value of x is less than 3, so all values of x are less than 3 units from zero on a number line.

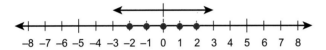

The integer solutions of $|x| < 3$ are $-2, -1, 0, 1,$ and 2. ■

Application: Weather

Example 7   The temperatures for five cities on a particular day are shown in the table. Plot the temperatures on a number line. Then list the cities in order from coldest to warmest.

City	Temperature (°C)
Ottawa, Canada	-6
Los Angeles, CA	11
Seward, AK	-7
Houston, TX	6
Washington, DC	-1

Solution

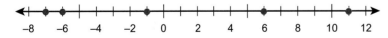

The cities from coldest to warmest are Seward, Ottawa, Washington, Houston, and Los Angeles. ■

Problem Set

State the coordinate of the indicated point on the number line below.

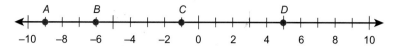

1. Point A

2. Point B

3. Point C

4. Point D

Graph each of the following numbers on a number line.

5. -7

6. 0

7. 3

8. -6

Compare the following integers. Use $<$, $>$, or $=$.

9. 3 and -1

10. -8 and 4

11. -5 and 0

12. -2 and -6

For each value of *n*, find

A. the absolute value of *n*: $|n|$
B. the opposite of *n*: $-n$

13. $n = 10$

14. $n = -15$

15. $n = -4$

16. $n = 8$

Complete the statement with $<$, $>$, or $=$.

17. $|-4|$ ▢ 4

18. $|-3|$ ▢ $|-8|$

19. -6 ▢ $|-10|$

20. $-|-5|$ ▢ 1

Identify all integer solutions of the equation or inequality.

21. $|x| = 5$

22. $|x| = -3$

23. $|r| < 6$

24. $|x| < 1$

25. $|a| < -2$

26. $|n| > -1$

27. $|x| \leq 2$

28. $|s| \leq 1$

Solve each problem.

29. Students are playing a game in which they draw cards and then add or subtract the integer shown on the card. The students' scores at the end of the game are shown in the chart below. List the students in order from the lowest scoring student to the highest scoring student.

Name	Score
Alana	4
Haley	−7
Trent	0
Buan	−2
Jared	2

30. The lowest recorded temperature (in degrees Celsius) for each month for Boise, Idaho are shown in the chart below. Name the months that had temperatures lower than the low temperature in April but higher than the low temperature in February.

Lowest Recorded Temperature Years on Record: 47	
Month	**°C**
Jan.	−27
Feb.	−26
Mar.	−14
Apr.	−7
May	−5
June	--
July	1
Aug.	1
Sept.	−5
Oct.	−11
Nov.	−19
Dec.	−31

31. A group of friends were playing miniature golf. Their scores at the end of the game are shown in the chart below. The player with the lowest score wins the game. List the players in order of finish, starting with the winning player.

Name	Score
Olivia	−2
Emilio	3
Ramon	0
Leticia	−1
Max	−4

32. Order the numbers below from least to greatest.

$$-7, |-4|, 3, -|6|, 0, -|-5|$$

Adding Integers

You can use a number line to add integers.

USING A NUMBER LINE TO ADD INTEGERS

Start at 0.
For **positive integers,** move **right.**
For **negative integers,** move **left.**
The ending point of each move is the starting point for the next move.
The ending point of the last move is the answer.

> **TIP**
>
> In any addition expression, the numbers being added are called *addends.*

Using a Number Line to Add Integers

Example 1 Find each sum.

A $3 + (-7)$

Solution Start at 0. Move 3 units right. From 3, move 7 units left.

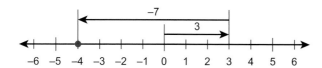

> **TIP**
>
> You can start with either integer.
>
> $3 + (-7) = -7 + 3$

$3 + (-7) = -4$ ∎

B $-4 + (-2)$

Solution Start at 0. Move 4 units left. From -4, move 2 units left.

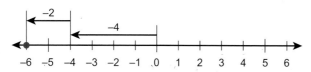

$-4 + (-2) = -6$ ∎

Using Rules to Add Integers

In addition to a number line, you can also use rules to add integers.

RULES FOR ADDING TWO INTEGERS

If the **signs are the same,** add the absolute values of the integers. The sum has the same sign as the addends.

If the **signs are different,** find the difference of the absolute values. The sum has the same sign as the addend with the greater absolute value

(continued)

Example 2 Find each sum.

Ⓐ $-20 + (-13)$

Solution Both addends are negative. The sum will be negative.

$$-20 + (-13) = -(|-20| + |-13|) \qquad \text{The sum is negative.}$$
$$= -(20 + 13) \qquad \text{Evaluate the absolute values.}$$
$$= -33 \qquad \text{Add.} \blacksquare$$

Ⓑ $-25 + 35$

Solution The addends have different signs. Because $|35|$ is greater than $|-25|$, the sum will be positive.

$$-25 + 35 = +(|35| - |-25|) \qquad \text{The sum is positive.}$$
$$= 35 - 25 \qquad \text{Evaluate the absolute values.}$$
$$= 10 \qquad \text{Subtract.}$$

Check Use a number line.

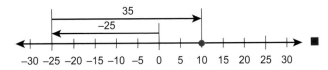

Evaluating Expressions

Evaluate variable expressions by substituting values for the variables and then simplifying.

Example 3

Ⓐ Evaluate $a + b$ when $a = 5$ and $b = -1$.

Solution

$$a + b = 5 + (-1) \qquad \text{Substitute 5 for } a \text{ and } -1 \text{ for } b.$$
$$= 4 \qquad \text{Add.} \blacksquare$$

Ⓑ Evaluate $x + y + z$ when $x = -43, y = -17,$ and $z = -10$.

Solution

$$x + y + z = -43 + (-17) + (-10) \qquad \text{Substitute } -43 \text{ for } x,$$
$$-17 \text{ for } y, \text{ and } -10 \text{ for } z.$$
$$= -60 + (-10) \qquad \text{Add from left to right.}$$
$$= -70 \ \blacksquare$$

Comparing Expressions

Example 4 Select the symbol ($<$, $>$, or $=$) that makes a true statement.

Ⓐ $3 + (-4)$ ▨ $5 + (-2)$

Solution

$3 + (-4)$ ▨ $5 + (-2)$ Evaluate the expression on each side.

    -1 $<$ 3 Since -1 is less than 3, use the $<$ symbol.

$3 + (-4) < 5 + (-2)$ ∎

Ⓑ $8 + (-20)$ ▨ $-7 + (-10)$

Solution

$8 + (-20)$ ▨ $-7 + (-10)$ Evaluate the expression on each side.

   -12 $>$ -17 Since -12 is greater than -17, use the $>$ symbol.

$8 + (-20) > -7 + (-10)$ ∎

Ⓒ $-3 + 8 + (-11)$ ▨ $10 + (-16)$

Solution

$-3 + 8 + (-11)$ ▨ $10 + (-16)$ Evaluate the expression on each side.

     -6 $=$ -6 Since -6 is equal to -6, use the $=$ symbol.

$-3 + 8 + (-11) = 10 + (-16)$ ∎

> **TIP**
>
> To compare -12 and -17, plot them on a number line. The lesser number is on the left and the greater number is on the right.

Addition Properties

Two useful properties for addition are given below.

ADDITION PROPERTIES

Property	Symbols	Examples
Identity Property for Addition The sum of any number and zero is equal to the number. Zero is called the **additive identity.**	$a + 0 = a$ $0 + a = 0$	$-5 + 0 = -5$ $0 + 8 = 8$
Property of Inverses for Addition The sum of any number and its opposite is equal to zero. Opposites are also called **additive inverses.**	$a + (-a) = 0$ $-a + a = 0$	$3 + (-3) = 0$ $-10 + 10 = 0$ $-7 + (-(-7)) = 0$

(continued)

Example 5 Find the value of the variable that makes the statement true.

Ⓐ $x + 5 = 0$

Solution The property of inverses for addition states that the sum of any number and its opposite is 0. Because the sum is 0, you know that x is the opposite of 5. So $x = -5$. ∎

Ⓑ $-4 + x = -4$

Solution The identity property for addition states that the sum of any number and 0 is equal to the same number. Because -4 plus x is equal to -4, you know that x is 0. So $x = 0$. ∎

Application: Banking

Example 6 The table shows deposits and withdrawals in a new bank account. How much is in the account at the end of the week?

Day	Deposit or Withdrawal
Monday	+$50
Wednesday	−$27
Thursday	+$30
Friday	−$13

Solution

$$50 + (-27) + 30 + (-13) = 23 + 30 + (-13)$$
$$= 53 + (-13)$$
$$= 40$$

At the end of the week, the account contains $40. ∎

Problem Set

Use a number line to find each sum.

1. $-7 + (-2)$

2. $4 + (-5)$

3. $-6 + 2$

4. $8 + (-3)$

Find each sum.

5. $17 + (-12)$

6. $-27 + 28$

7. $-22 + (-74)$

8. $45 + (-58)$

9. $-15 + (-25)$

10. $-100 + 42$

Evaluate when $a = -6$, $b = 2$, and $c = -7$.

11. $a + b$

12. $c + b$

13. $a + c$

14. $a + b + c$

Select the symbol ($<$, $>$, or $=$) that makes a true statement.

15. $8 + (-7) \quad\blacksquare\quad 7 + (-8)$

16. $-12 + (-4) \quad\blacksquare\quad -20 + (-6)$

17. $9 + (-15) \quad\blacksquare\quad -2 + (-4)$

18. $9 + (-20) \quad\blacksquare\quad 15 + (-3)$

Find the value of the variable that makes the statement true.

19. $x + (-7) = 0$

20. $-3 = -3 + x$

21. $x + (-15) = -13 + (-2)$

22. $4 + (-1) + x = 0$

Evaluate when $x = -12$, $y = 27$, and $z = -32$.

23. $|x| + y$

24. $|x + y|$

25. $|y + z|$

26. $y + |z|$

27. $x + |z|$

28. $|x + y + z|$

Solve each problem.

29. The drama club was planning an after-play celebration. The chart below shows the amount of money the club expects to gain (positive number) and the costs of each item for the party (negative numbers).

    A. Will the drama club have enough money to pay for the party costs?

    B. If so, how much money will they have left over? If not, how much more money will they need?

    C. Explain your answer.

Income from tickets	800
Cost of food	−523
Cost of decorations	−125
Cost of plates, cups	−80

30. This month, Nahla deposited $425 in her bank account. She withdrew $320, then deposited $210. What is the amount of money in her account after those transactions?

Subtracting Integers

In simple arithmetic, subtraction is the same as "taking away." In algebra, subtraction is the same as adding the opposite.

To subtract an integer, you add its opposite.

SUBTRACTING INTEGERS

Properties	Symbols	Examples
To **subtract** an integer, **add its opposite.**	$a - b = a + (-b)$ $a - (-b) = a + b$	$1 - 5 = 1 + (-5)$ $10 - (-4) = 10 + 4$

Subtracting Integers

Example 1   Find each difference.

A $2 - 7$

Solution

$2 - 7 = 2 + (-7)$ Rewrite as adding the opposite of 7.

$\qquad = -5$ ∎

B $3 - (-5)$

Solution

$3 - (-5) = 3 + 5$ Add the opposite of -5.

$\qquad = 8$ ∎

C $-4 - 11$

Solution

$-4 - 11 = -4 + (-11)$ Add the opposite of 11.

$\qquad = -15$ ∎

D $-47 - (-7)$

Solution

$-47 - (-7) = -47 + 7$ Add the opposite of -7.

$\qquad = -40$ ∎

THINK ABOUT IT

The rules for adding and subtracting integers apply to adding and subtracting all real numbers. For example,

$-3.2 - 4.5 = -3.2 + (-4.5)$

$\qquad = -7.7$

Evaluating Expressions

Evaluate variable expressions by substituting values for the variables.

Example 2

Ⓐ Evaluate $a - b$ when $a = -1$ and $b = -6$.

Solution

$$
\begin{aligned}
a - b &= -1 - (-6) && \text{Substitute } -1 \text{ for } a \text{ and } -6 \text{ for } b. \\
&= -1 + 6 && \text{Add the opposite of } -6. \\
&= 5 \ \blacksquare
\end{aligned}
$$

Ⓑ Evaluate $20 - x - y$ when $x = 14$ and $y = -6$.

Solution

$$
\begin{aligned}
20 - x - y &= 20 - 14 - (-6) && \text{Substitute 14 for } x \text{ and } -6 \text{ for } y. \\
&= 20 + (-14) + 6 && \text{Rewrite using addition.} \\
&= 6 + 6 && \text{Add from left to right.} \\
&= 12 \ \blacksquare
\end{aligned}
$$

Ⓒ Evaluate $c - d + f$ when $c = -2$, $d = 18$, and $f = -11$.

Solution

$$
\begin{aligned}
c - d + f &= -2 - 18 + (-11) && \text{Substitute } -2 \text{ for } c, 18 \text{ for } d, \text{ and} \\
& && -11 \text{ for } f. \\
&= -2 + (-18) + (-11) && \text{Rewrite using addition.} \\
&= -20 + (-11) && \text{Add from left to right.} \\
&= -31 \ \blacksquare
\end{aligned}
$$

> **TIP**
>
> When substituting a negative value for a variable, use parentheses. That will help you avoid confusion between subtraction signs and negative signs.

Application: Geography

Example 3   Driskill Mountain, Louisiana, has an elevation of 535 feet. For large portions of the city of New Orleans, the average elevation is -9 feet. What is the difference between those two elevations?

Solution   Subtract the lower elevation from the higher elevation.

$$
\begin{aligned}
535 - (-9) &= 535 + 9 \\
&= 544
\end{aligned}
$$

The difference between the elevations is 544 feet. $\blacksquare$

Problem Set

Find each difference.

1. $-9 - (-10)$
2. $4 - (-9)$
3. $10 - (-10)$
4. $-6 - 8$
5. $5 - (-8)$
6. $0 - (-2)$
7. $-25 - (-31)$
8. $-46 - 37$

9. $13 - 23$
10. $50 - (-37)$
11. $-44 - (-34)$
12. $-20 - 30$
13. $51 - 59$
14. $18 - (-33)$
15. $-46 - (-77)$
16. $19 - 34$

Evaluate each expression for the given values of the variables.

17. $3 - y$ when $y = -4$
18. $b - (-8)$ when $b = -3$
19. $u - (-15)$ when $u = 10$
20. $27 - k$ when $k = -14$
21. $10 - w - 4$ when $w = -2$

22. $-8 - p - 5$ when $p = -5$
23. $1 - 9 - x$ when $x = -4$
24. $6 - q - (-7)$ when $q = 10$
25. $a - b + 7$ when $a = -4$ and $b = 6$
26. $8 - s + t$ when $s = -5$ and $t = -1$

Find the value of x that makes the equation true.

27. $7 - x = 24$

28. $30 - x = -15$

Solve each problem.

29. The highest recorded temperature in South Dakota is 120° F. The lowest recorded temperature is −58° F. What is the difference between these temperatures?

30. The highest elevation in Africa is Kilimanjaro, Tanzania, at 5895 meters. The lowest elevation in Africa is Lake Asal, Djibouti, at −156 meters. What is the difference between these two elevations?

Decimals on a Number Line

Integers are not the only numbers on a number line. Between any two integers, you can find countless other numbers.

You have seen that the set of whole numbers and their opposites is called *the integers*. Integers graphed on a number line look like this:

There are also numbers between integers that can be written in decimal form. The diagram below shows some of the decimals between −1 and 1.

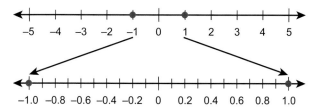

In fact, there are decimals between any two decimals you choose, no matter how close they are. For example, one decimal between 0.01 and 0.02 is 0.013. This property is described as *density* on a number line.

Identifying Decimal Coordinates of Points on a Number Line

Example 1 State the coordinate of each labeled point.

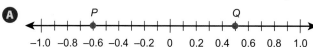

Solution Point P is 0.6 to the left of 0, so its coordinate is −0.6. Point Q is to the right of 0 and halfway between 0.4 and 0.6, so its coordinate is 0.5. ■

(continued)

B

Solution   The tick marks on this number line are 0.2 apart. Reading to the left from 0, the tick marks represent -0.2, -0.4, -0.6, -0.8, and so on. Point C is halfway between -1.6 and -2.0, so its coordinate is -1.8. Point D is halfway between 0 and 0.4, so its coordinate is 0.2. ■

Graphing Decimals on a Number Line

To set up a number line, decide what numbers to represent with equally spaced tick marks. This is called choosing a *scale*. Given a particular number to graph, you can choose different scales, but some scales are more appropriate than others. It is a good idea to include one or more integers in your scale because they are good reference points. It is often a good idea to include 0 because it separates negative numbers and positive numbers.

Example 2

A Graph 1.4 on a number line.

Solution   You can choose a scale in which tick marks are spaced 0.2 apart. Include several tick marks to the left of 0 and several tick marks to the right of 1.4. From 0, count by 0.2 until you get to 1.4. Draw a dot to represent the point for 1.4. Label 0, 1.0, and 1.4.

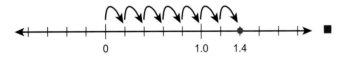

REMEMBER

People often read the decimal 1.4 as *one point four*, but more formally, it can be read as *one and four-tenths*.

B Graph -0.7 on a number line.

Solution   Because -0.7 is negative, it is to the left of the origin. Start at 0 and count 0.7 to the left. If your tick marks are spaced 0.2 apart, count three full spaces and another half space. Plot -0.7 halfway between -0.6 and -0.8.

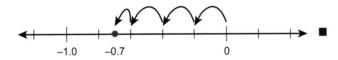

THINK ABOUT IT

For Example 2B, an alternate choice for a scale could have tick marks spaced 0.1 apart. Using that scale, -0.7 would be graphed directly on a tick mark.

C Graph -12.68 on a number line.

Solution   The given number is in hundredths, but it would not be practical to use a scale in hundredths, containing 0. Such a scale would contain too many tick marks. It makes sense to use a scale that shows the integers -12 and -13 because -12.68 is between those two integers. You can draw the tick marks spaced 0.25 apart. Plot -12.68 between -12.50 and -12.75, closer to -12.75.

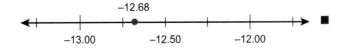

Comparing Decimals

Graphing decimals on a number line can help you compare them. Remember, when comparing two numbers, the number to the left is less than the number to the right.

Example 3   Compare the decimals. Use $<$, $>$, or $=$.

A   Compare -1.2 and 0.1.

Solution

Every negative number is less than every positive number, so you know that -1.2 is less than 0.1. You can write either $-1.2 < 0.1$ or $0.1 > -1.2$. ■

B   Compare -0.4 and -2.4.

Solution

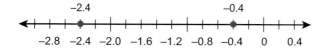

Because -2.4 is to the left of -0.4, you know that -2.4 is less than -0.4. You can write either $-2.4 < -0.4$ or $-0.4 > -2.4$. ■

C   Compare -5.2 and -4.8.

Solution

Because -5.2 is to the left of -4.8, you know that -5.2 is less than -4.8. You can write either $-5.2 < -4.8$ or $-4.8 > -5.2$. ■

> **TIP**
>
> To graph -5.2 and -4.8 on a number line, use -5.0 as a reference point.

Ordering Decimals

You can also use a number line to help you order decimals from least to greatest. First plot the decimals. Then list them in order from left to right.

Example 4

A   Write 0.8, -0.6, 0.4, and -1.0 in order from least to greatest.

Solution

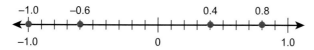

From least to greatest, the decimals are -1.0, -0.6, 0.4, and 0.8. ■

(continued)

B Write 0.3, −8.6, −6.2, and 2.8 in order from least to greatest.

Solution

From least to greatest, the decimals are −8.6, −6.2, 0.3, and 2.8. ■

Application: Science

Example 5 Students conducting an experiment measured the temperature of some different liquids. The data are shown in the table. List the liquids in order from coldest to warmest.

Liquid	Temperature (°C)
A	−7.2
B	5.0
C	−0.4
D	2.4
E	−5.5

Solution

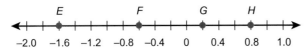

The liquids in order from coldest to warmest are A, E, C, D, B. ■

Problem Set

. . . .

State the coordinate of each indicated point on the number line below.

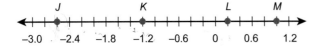

1. Point *E*

2. Point *F*

3. Point *G*

4. Point *H*

State the coordinate of each indicated point on the number line below.

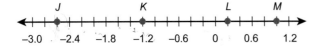

5. Point *J*

6. Point *K*

7. Point *L*

8. Point *M*

State the coordinate of each indicated point on the number line below.

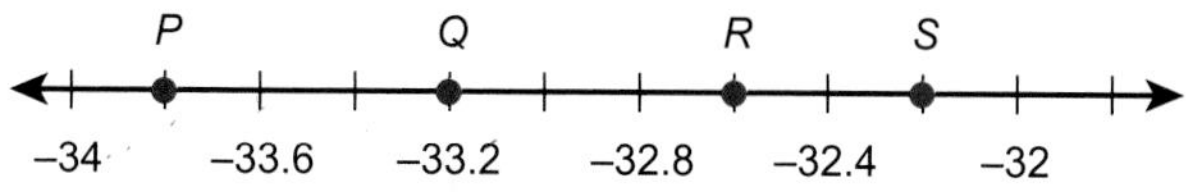

9. Point *P*

10. Point *Q*

11. Point *R*

12. Point *S*

Graph the following decimals on a number line.

13. -2.4

14. 0.9

15. -8.65

16. 1.3

17. 0.1

18. -0.2

Select the symbol ($<$, $>$, or $=$) that makes a true statement.

19. -2.4 ▨ 1.2

20. -0.6 ▨ -0.8

21. -1.24 ▨ -1.35

22. -8.75 ▨ -8.25

23. 4.95 ▨ 4.9

24. -7.342 ▨ -7.348

Write the decimals in order from least to greatest.

25. $1.3, -1.4, 0.9, -0.3$

26. $-1, 2.2, 0.2, -0.4$

27. $-0.5, 0.03, -1.9, 1.7$

28. $0.04, -0.5, -0.58, 0.002$

Solve each problem.

29. The temperatures of several cities are shown in the chart below. Put the cities in order of temperature from the coldest to the warmest.

City	Temperature C°
Oak Park	0.2
College City	-1.6
Snow Town	-1.4
Green Valley	-1.45

*30. **Challenge** Write the decimals in order from least to greatest.

$|-4.3|, -3.2, -|4.1|, 0.6, -|-0.5|$

Adding Decimals

Adding decimals on a number line is similar to adding integers.

Using a Number Line to Add Decimals

Like with integers, a negative decimal can be shown with a line segment pointing to the left, while a positive decimal can be shown with a segment pointing to the right.

Example 1 Find each sum.

A $-1.6 + (-0.8)$

Solution Start at 0. Move 1.6 units left. From -1.6, move 0.8 unit left.

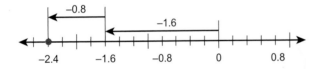

$-1.6 + (-0.8) = -2.4$ ■

B $0.5 + (-1.8)$

Solution Start at 0. Move 0.5 unit right. From 0.5, move 1.8 units left.

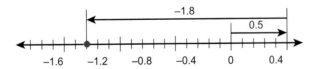

$0.5 + (-1.8) = -1.3$ ■

> **REMEMBER**
>
> Check the scale of the number line you are using. The distance between tick marks in Example 1A is 0.2. The distance between tick marks in Example 1B is 0.1.

Adding Decimals Vertically

When you add decimals vertically, remember to align the decimal points. Use zeros as placeholders when necessary.

Example 2 Find each sum.

A $34.14 + 12.6$

Solution

34.14	Align the decimal points.
+12.60	Write a zero as a placeholder.
46.74	Add. ■

B $0.85 + 11.678$

Solution

$$\begin{array}{r} \overset{1\ \ 1}{0.850} \\ +11.678 \\ \hline 12.528 \end{array}$$

0.850   Align the decimal points. Write a zero as a placeholder.

12.528   Regroup as needed. Add. ■

Using Rules to Add Decimals

The rules for adding positive and negative decimals are the same as the rules for adding positive and negative integers.

> **RULES FOR ADDING TWO DECIMALS**
>
> If the **signs are the same,** add the absolute values of the decimals. Use the same sign as the decimals.
>
> If the **signs are different,** find the difference of the absolute values. Use the sign of the decimal with the greater absolute value.

Example 3   Find each sum.

A $-6.7 + (-1.3)$

Solution   Both signs are negative. The answer will be negative.

$$-6.7 + (-1.3) = -(|-6.7| + |-1.3|) \qquad \text{Add the absolute values.}$$
$$= -(6.7 + 1.3)$$
$$= -8.0 \qquad \text{The sum has the same sign as}$$
$$\text{the addends.} \ ■$$

B $-27.8 + 14.3$

Solution   The signs are different. Because $|-27.8|$ is greater than $|-4.3|$, the answer will be negative.

$$-27.8 + 14.3 = -(|-27.8| - |-14.3|) \qquad \text{Subtract the smaller absolute value from the greater}$$
$$= -(27.8 - 14.3) \qquad\qquad\quad \text{absolute value. The sum has the sign of the decimal}$$
$$= -13.5 \qquad\qquad\qquad\quad\ \text{with the greater absolute value.} \ ■$$

Evaluating Expressions with Decimals

Evaluate variable expressions by substituting values for the variables.

Example 4

A   Evaluate $a + b$ when $a = 1.5$ and $b = -2.8$.

Solution

$$a + b = 1.5 + (-2.8) \qquad \text{Substitute 1.5 for } a \text{ and } -2.8 \text{ for } b. \text{ Subtract}$$
$$= -1.3 \qquad\qquad\quad\ \text{absolute values. Use the sign of the greater}$$
$$\text{absolute value.} \ ■$$

(continued)

B Evaluate $-0.6 + r + z$ when $r = -5.09$ and $z = -1.2$.

Solution

$$-0.6 + r + z = -0.6 + (-5.09) + (-1.2) \quad \text{Substitute } -5.09 \text{ for } r \text{ and } -1.2 \text{ for } z.$$

$$= -6.89 \quad \text{Add absolute values vertically.} \rightarrow$$

$$\begin{array}{r} 0.60 \\ 5.09 \\ +1.20 \\ \hline 6.89 \end{array}$$

The sum is -6.89. ■

C Evaluate $c + d + f$ when $c = -2.2$, $d = -5.1$, and $f = 10.5$.

Solution

$$c + d + f = -2.2 + (-5.1) + 10.5 \quad \text{Substitute } -2.2 \text{ for } c, -5.1 \text{ for } d, \text{ and } 10.5 \text{ for } f.$$

$$= -7.3 + 10.5 \quad \text{Add from left to right.}$$

$$= 3.2 \ ■$$

Using Related Equations to Solve Subtraction Equations

You can use related equations to solve subtraction equations. Just find a related equation with the variable alone on one side of the equation.

Example 5 Solve each equation.

A $x - 3.2 = 6.04$

Solution

$$x - 3.2 = 6.04 \quad \text{Write the given subtraction equation.}$$

$$x = 3.2 + 6.04 \quad \text{Write the related addition equation.}$$

$$x = 9.24 \quad \text{Add.} \ ■$$

B $n - (-0.9) = 1.25$

Solution

$$n - (-0.9) = 1.25 \quad \text{Write the given subtraction equation.}$$

$$n = -0.9 + 1.25 \quad \text{Write the related addition equation.}$$

$$n = 0.35 \quad \text{Add.} \ ■$$

> **REMEMBER**
>
> To add decimals, align the decimal points. Write zeros as placeholders if needed. Use the correct rule regarding positive and negative signs.

Application: Animals

Example 6 Jess is tracking the movement of a garden snail toward a plant. The table shows the snail's progress each minute. A positive number indicates movement forward. A negative number indicates movement backward. What is the net forward progress of the snail toward the plant?

Solution The net forward progress is the sum of the positive and negative numbers.

$$1.9 + (-0.5) + 2.3 + 1.1 = 1.4 + 2.3 + 1.1 \quad \text{Add from left to right.}$$

$$= 3.7 + 1.1$$

$$= 4.8$$

Minute	Distance Traveled (feet)
1	+1.9
2	−0.5
3	+2.3
4	+1.1

The net forward progress of the snail toward the plant is 4.8 feet. ■

Problem Set

Find each sum.

1. $-1.4 + (-0.2)$

2. $-0.5 + 1.7$

3. $1.3 + (-2.4)$

4. $-1.8 + (-1.2)$

5. $-3.4 + 1.5$

6. $25.34 + 16.17$

7. $-10.25 + (-11.98)$

8. $-23.512 + 14.001$

9. $-0.66 + 0.14$

10. $6.13 + (-5.64)$

11. $15 + (-5.2) + (-1.4)$

12. $8.3 + (-0.044)$

13. $8.623 + 4.5$

14. $0.55 + (-6.8) + 2.05$

15. $0.02 + (-0.9)$

16. $-0.98 + (-0.06)$

17. $35 + (-0.023)$

18. $-0.985 + 0.87$

19. $-14.75 + (-2.25) + (-10.5)$

20. $0.011 + (-0.6) + 0.11 + (-2.03)$

Evaluate each expression by substituting values for the variables.

21. $x + y$ when $x = -1.7$ and $y = -5.4$

22. $p + q$ when $p = -5.7$ and $q = 3.4$

23. $d + e$ when $d = 1.78$ and $e = -3.24$

24. $t + (-1.5) + s$ when $t = 1.23$ and $s = -4.01$

25. $-7.2 + m + n$ when $m = 14.78$ and $n = 0.875$

26. $u + v + (-2.15)$ when $u = -0.003$ and $v = -5.64$

Find the value of the variable that makes the equation true.

27. $-3.6 - a = -8.4$

28. $x - (-5.25) = 7.25$

29. $z - 2.4 = 4.2$

30. $2x - 3.5 = x - 3.5$

31. $4a - 2.5 = a - 10$

Solve each problem.

32. A garden in the shape of a triangle is shown below. What is the distance around the garden?

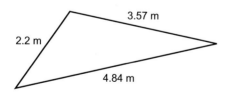

3.57 m

2.2 m

4.84 m

33. The table shows deposits and withdrawals in a new bank account. How much is in the account at the end of March?

Beginning Balance: $350

Jan.	+$125.67
Feb.	-$45.85
Mar.	-$102.00

Subtracting Decimals

Before subtracting decimals that involve negative numbers, review subtracting decimals vertically.

Subtracting Decimals Vertically

Remember to align the decimal points when you subtract, just as you do when you add. Use zeros as placeholders when necessary.

Example 1   Find each difference.

A 129.52 − 14.2

Solution

$$
\begin{array}{r}
129.52 \\
-\ 14.20 \\
\hline
115.32
\end{array}
$$

Align the decimal points.
Write a zero as a placeholder.
Subtract. ■

> **TIP**
>
> You can check your subtraction by adding.
>
> $$
> \begin{array}{r}
> 115.32 \\
> +\ 14.20 \\
> \hline
> 129.52
> \end{array}
> $$

B 20.56 − 8.473

Solution

$$
\begin{array}{r}
20.560 \\
-\ 8.473 \\
\hline
12.087
\end{array}
$$

Align the decimal points. Write a zero as a placeholder.

Regroup as needed. Subtract. ■

Using a Rule to Subtract Decimals

The rule for subtracting any number, including a decimal, is the same as the rule for subtracting an integer.

SUBTRACTING A NUMBER

To **subtract** a number, **add its opposite**.

Example 2   Subtract.

A 2.3 − 4.5

Solution

$$
\begin{aligned}
2.3 - 4.5 &= 2.3 + (-4.5) \\
&= -(|-4.5| - |2.3|) \\
&= -(4.5 - 2.3) \\
&= -2.2 \ ■
\end{aligned}
$$

Write subtraction as adding the opposite.

The signs of 2.3 and −4.5 are different, so subtract the absolute values. The difference has the sign of the number with the greater absolute value.

B $24.3 - (-11.5)$

Solution

$$24.3 - (-11.5) = 24.3 + 11.5$$
$$= 35.8 \ \blacksquare$$

Write subtraction as adding the opposite of -11.5.

C $-0.04 - (-10.1)$

Solution

$$-0.04 - (-10.1) = -0.04 + 10.1$$

Write subtraction as adding the opposite.

$$= |10.1| - |-0.04|$$
$$= 10.1 - 0.04$$

The signs of -0.04 and 10.1 are different, so subtract the absolute values. ⟶

$$\begin{array}{r} 10.10 \\ -\ 0.04 \\ \hline 10.06 \end{array}$$

$$= 10.06$$

The difference has the sign of the number with the greater absolute value. $\blacksquare$

Using Related Equations to Solve Addition Equations

Because addition and subtraction are inverse operations, you can solve an addition equation by subtracting. To solve a simple addition equation, write the related subtraction equation that has the variable alone on one side of the equation.

Example 3   Solve each equation.

A $r + 7.5 = -3$

Solution

$$r + 7.5 = -3$$

Write the given addition equation.

$$r = -3 - (7.5)$$
$$r = -10.5$$

Write the related subtraction equation that has the variable alone on one side of the equation. Then subtract. $\blacksquare$

B $-2.4 + t = 1.05$

Solution

$$-2.4 + t = 1.05$$

Write the given addition equation.

$$t = 1.05 - (-2.4)$$
$$t = 1.05 + 2.4$$
$$t = 3.45 \ \blacksquare$$

Write the related subtraction equation that has the variable alone on one side of the equation. Then simplify.

> **TIP**
>
> For the addition equation $-2.4 + t = 1.05$, the two related subtraction equations are $t = 1.05 - (-2.4)$ and $-2.4 = 1.05 - t$.

C $x + (-0.85) = -1$

Solution

$$x + (-0.85) = -1$$

Write the given addition equation.

$$x = -1 - (-0.85)$$
$$x = -1 + 0.85$$
$$x = -0.15 \ \blacksquare$$

Write the related subtraction equation that has the variable alone on one side of the equation. Then simplify.

Evaluating Expressions with Decimals

Example 4

Ⓐ Evaluate $a - b$ when $a = 3.1$ and $b = -4.6$.

Solution

$$a - b = 3.1 - (-4.6) \qquad \text{Substitute 3.1 for } a \text{ and } -4.6 \text{ for } b.$$
$$= 3.1 + 4.6 \qquad\qquad \text{Add the opposite of } -4.6.$$
$$= 7.7 \ \blacksquare$$

Ⓑ Evaluate $b - a$ when $a = 3.1$ and $b = -4.6$.

Solution

$$b - a = -4.6 - 3.1 \qquad\qquad \text{Substitute } -4.6 \text{ for } b \text{ and 3.1 for } a.$$
$$= -4.6 + (-3.1) \qquad \text{Add the opposite of 3.1.}$$
$$= -7.7 \ \blacksquare$$

Ⓒ Evaluate $u - 3.5 - s$ when $u = -4$ and $s = -0.1$.

Solution

$$u - 3.5 - s = -4 - 3.5 - (-0.1) \qquad \text{Substitute } -4 \text{ for } u \text{ and } -0.1 \text{ for } s.$$
$$= -4.0 + (-3.5) + 0.1 \qquad \text{Write } -4 \text{ as } -4.0. \text{ Add the opposite}$$
$$= -7.5 + 0.1 \qquad\qquad\quad \text{of 3.5 and the opposite of } -0.1.$$
$$\qquad\qquad\qquad\qquad\qquad\quad \text{Add from left to right.}$$
$$= -7.4 \ \blacksquare$$

> **THINK ABOUT IT**
>
> **For any numbers *a* and *b*, *a* − *b* and *b* − *a* are opposites. This property is illustrated in Examples 4A and 4B.**

Application: Climatology

Example 5   Air pressure is measured by inches of mercury in a barometer. According to one study, the lowest recorded sea-level air pressure is 25.69 inches and the highest is 32.01 inches. What is the difference between these measurements?

Solution   Subtract the decimals.

$$\begin{array}{r} 32.01 \\ -25.69 \\ \hline 6.32 \end{array}$$

The difference is 6.32 inches. $\blacksquare$

Problem Set

. . . .

Find each difference.

1. $6.7 - 4.1$
2. $4.3 - 0.7$
3. $7.5 - (-6.9)$
4. $87.5 - 42.1$
5. $15.7 - (-2.6)$
6. $-7.45 - 2.17$
7. $-2.33 - (-1.05)$
8. $-4.037 - 1.057$
9. $-14.76 - 12.28$
10. $1.5 - 0.08$

11. $0.48 - 4.9$
12. $3.055 - (-0.26)$
13. $-0.1 - (-0.08)$
14. $658.23 - (-414.5)$
15. $-180 - 14.27$
16. $-56.87 - 23.25$
17. $62.1 - (-76)$
18. $-1.357 - (-2)$
19. $341.27 - (-78.5)$
20. $-79.432 - 54.6$

Evaluate each expression by substituting values for the variables.

21. $m - n$ when $m = -6.2$ and $n = 3.6$
22. $u - v$ when $u = 14.25$ and $v = -5.8$
23. $x - y$ when $x = 1.3$ and $y = 7.4$

24. $-7.1 - s - t$ when $s = 9.8$ and $t = -10.3$
25. $p - 14.832 - q$ when $p = 12.035$ and $q = -8.75$
26. $w - x - (-17.2)$ when $w = 134.7$ and $x = -4.003$

Find the value of the variable that makes the equation true.

27. $m + (-16.2) = 8.7$
28. $8.4 + b = -22.9$
29. $c + 3.4 = 4.3$

30. $3r + 1.5 = r + 4.5$
31. $6d + 8.7 = d + 8.7$

Solve each problem.

32. Gwen is sketching the layout of a flower garden shown below. The perimeter of her flower garden is 18.39 m. Gwen is going to fence in only the solid sides of the figure. She will not fence in the side indicated by the dashed line measuring 4.04 m. What is the total length of the sides that Gwen will fence in?

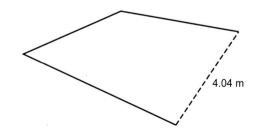

4.04 m

33. The temperature of a liquid was taken at different intervals. The temperature at one point was 1.35°C . When taken next, the temperature was -2.4°C. What is the change in the temperature of the liquid?

Addition and Subtraction Properties

You have already learned some properties of addition. Three more useful properties of addition are given below.

ADDITION PROPERTIES

Properties	Symbols	Examples
Commutative Property Numbers can be added in any order.	$a + b = b + a$	$2 + (-5) = -5 + 2$ $-3 = -3$ ✓
Associative Property For three or more numbers, their sum is always the same, no matter how the numbers are grouped.	$(a + b) + c = a + (b + c)$	$(-1 + 7) + 4 = -1 + (7 + 4)$ $6 + 4 = -1 + 11$ $10 = 10$ ✓
Opposite of a Sum The opposite of the sum of two numbers is equal to the sum of the opposites.	$-(a + b) = -a + (-b)$	$-(5 + 3) = -5 + (-3)$ $-8 = -8$ ✓

Identifying Addition Properties

Example 1   Identify the property shown.

Ⓐ $-3 + 4 = 4 + (-3)$

Solution   The order of the numbers being added is changed. The property shown is the commutative property of addition. ∎

Ⓑ $5 + (-8 + 10) = (5 + (-8)) + 10$

Solution   The numbers being added are grouped differently. The property shown is the associative property of addition. ∎

Ⓒ $15 + (-7) + 5 = 15 + 5 + (-7)$

Solution   The order of -7 and 5 is changed. The property shown is the commutative property of addition. ∎

> **TIP**
> Parentheses do not always indicate the associative property. In Example 1C, parentheses are used to separate a negative sign from addition signs.

D $-(-1 + 7) = 1 + (-7)$

Solution   The equation states that the opposite of the sum of -1 and 7 is equal to the sum of 1 and -7. The property shown is the property of the opposite of a sum. ■

Using Addition Properties

Using the associative and commutative properties of addition can make some expressions easier to evaluate with mental math.

Example 2   Use properties to rewrite each expression, then evaluate.

A $-87 + (-68) + (-13)$

Solution

$$\begin{aligned}
-87 + (-68) + (-13) &= -68 + (-87) + (-13) \\
&= -68 + (-87 + (-13)) \\
&= -68 + (-100) \\
&= -168 \ \blacksquare
\end{aligned}$$

Use the commutative property to change the order of -87 and -68. Then use the associative property to group -87 and -13.

B $-36 + 419 + 136$

Solution

$$\begin{aligned}
-36 + 419 + 136 &= -36 + 136 + 419 \\
&= 100 + 419 \\
&= 519 \ \blacksquare
\end{aligned}$$

Use the commutative property to change the order of 419 and 136. Then add from left to right.

Rewriting Subtraction as Addition to Use Addition Properties

The commutative and associative properties do not apply to subtraction. Examples to illustrate this are shown below.

$$3 - 1 \neq 1 - 3 \qquad (8 - 2) - 5 \neq 8 - (2 - 5)$$
$$2 \neq -2 \qquad\qquad 6 - 5 \neq 8 - (-3)$$
$$1 \neq 11$$

However, by rewriting a subtraction expression as addition of the opposite, you can use the commutative and associative properties of addition.

(continued)

Example 3 Rewrite each expression using addition only. Then use addition properties so that you can evaluate the expression by mental math.

A $-18 + 34 - 12$

Solution

$$\begin{aligned}
-18 + 34 - 12 &= -18 + 34 + (-12) &&\text{To subtract 12, add } -12.\\
&= -18 + (-12) + 34 &&\text{Use the commutative property to change the order}\\
&= -30 + 34 &&\text{of 34 and } -12.\ \text{Then add from left to right.}\\
&= 4\ \blacksquare
\end{aligned}$$

B $42 - 27 + 8 - 3$

Solution

$$\begin{aligned}
42 - 27 + 8 - 3 &= 42 + (-27) + 8 + (-3) &&\text{Rewrite both subtractions as additions.}\\
&= 42 + 8 + (-27) + (-3) &&\text{Use the commutative property to change the}\\
&= (42 + 8) + (-27 + (-3)) &&\text{order of } -27 \text{ and 8. Then use the associative}\\
&= 50 + (-30) &&\text{property to group numbers that are easier}\\
&= 20\ \blacksquare &&\text{numbers to add.}
\end{aligned}$$

Solving Equations by Recognizing Properties of Addition

Example 4 Solve each equation.

A $(7 + 4.14) + 8.2 = 7 + (y + 8.2)$

Solution By the associative property, $(7 + 4.14) + 8.2 = 7 + (4.14 + 8.2)$, so $y = 4.14$. $\blacksquare$

B $2 + (-0.4) + 5.06 = 2 + c + (-0.4)$

Solution By the commutative property, $2 + (-0.4) + 5.06 = 2 + 5.06 + (-0.4)$, so $c = 5.06$. $\blacksquare$

C $-(-5 + 4) = 5 + x$

Solution By the property of the opposite of a sum, you know that $-(-5 + 4) = 5 + (-4)$, so $x = -4$. $\blacksquare$

> **REMEMBER**
>
> The opposite of a negative number is positive.
> In Example 4C, the opposite of -5 is 5.

Application: Inventory

Example 5 An inventory is a record of the number or amount of something. A librarian keeps track of the change in her inventory of books as shown in the table. What is the net change in inventory for the week? Explain your steps.

Day of the Week	Change in Inventory
Monday	+30
Tuesday	−27
Wednesday	14
Thursday	26
Friday	−3

Solution

$$30 + (-27) + 14 + 26 + (-3) = 30 + (-27) + (-3) + 14 + 26$$
$$= 30 + (-27 + (-3)) + (14 + 26)$$
$$= 30 + (-30) + 40$$
$$= 0 + 40$$
$$= 40$$

The commutative property is used to change the order of the addends so that −27 and −3 are together from left to right. Then the associative property is used to group −27 and −3 as well as 14 and 26. Then the additions inside grouping symbols are performed. Finally, the numbers are added from left to right. The net change in inventory is +40. ∎

Problem Set

Identify the property shown.

1. $-(6 + 2) = -6 + (-2)$
2. $14 + (-7) = -7 + 14$
3. $-4 + (-3 + (-10)) = (-4 + (-3)) + (-10)$
4. $12 + (-7) + (-8) = 12 + (-8) + (-7)$
5. $-(-7 + 3) = 7 + -3$
6. $(3.6 + 5.2) + 1.8 = 3.6 + (5.2 + 1.8)$

Use properties and mental math to evaluate each expression.

7. $42 + (-16) + 28$
8. $(63 + (-45)) + 5$
9. $-24 + 33 + (-6)$
10. $-45 + (17 + (-55))$
11. $(1 + (-15)) + -35$
12. $-94 - 51 + (-6)$
13. $-46 + 87 + 46$
14. $-62 + ((-18) - (-2))$
15. $6.2 + (-4 + 0.8)$
16. $1.3 + (-2.5) + 0.7$
17. $8.34 - (-6.32) - 0.34$
18. $-55.2 + (-6.8 - 15.1)$
19. $(9.8 - 0.3) + 12.3$
20. $2.25 + (-0.75 + (-0.37))$

Use the properties of addition to solve each equation.

21. $-(8 + 5) = -8 + m$

22. $(5 + 8) + 12 = 5 + (8 + a)$

23. $25 + (-6) + (-5) = 25 + (-5) + c$

24. $(4.2 + (-3.8)) + 2 = q + ((-3.8) + 2)$

25. $-(7 + y) = -7 + (-3)$

26. $-7 + 0.1 + (-3) = 0.1 + b + (-3)$

Find the value of the variable that makes the equation true.

27. $7 + x + (-17) = 2$

28. $-(5 + y) = 6$

Solve each problem.

29. Spiro made the following deposits and withdrawals in his bank account:

$$-25.00, +13.10, +50.00, -5.10$$

What is the net amount of these transactions?

30. Hana's score in a game is determined by the sum of the numbers she selects. If Hana's numbers are $-7, 14, 7, -3,$ and 6, what is her score?

31. A stock price starts at $24, falls $2, rises $3, falls $2, and rises $3. What is the current stock price?

32. A football team gained 6 yards, lost 3 yards, gained 15 yards, lost 2 yards, lost 2 yards, and gained 7 yards. What is the net gain or loss?

Equations Involving Addition and Subtraction

To solve equations, you need to understand equivalent equations.

Equivalent equations are equations with the same solution or solutions. Related equations are equivalent, but you can also use properties of equality to create equivalent equations.

Properties	Symbols	Examples
Addition Property of Equality If you add the same number to both sides of an equation, you obtain an equivalent equation.	If $a = b$, then $a + c = b + c$ and $c + a = c + b$.	If $n = 3$, then $n + 2 = 3 + 2$. If $x - 4 = 9$, then $x - 4 + 4 = 9 + 4$.
Subtraction Property of Equality If you subtract the same number from both sides of an equation, you obtain an equivalent equation.	If $a = b$, then $a - c = b - c$.	If $r = 7$, then $r - 5 = 7 - 5$. If $x + 3 = 12$, then $x + 3 - 3 = 12 - 3$.
Substitution Property of Equality A value or expression may replace an equal value or expression.	If $a = b$, then either may replace the other in any expression.	If $x = 6$, then you can rewrite the expression $x - 10$ as $6 - 10$.

Solving Addition and Subtraction Equations

Addition and subtraction are *inverse operations*. To solve an equation, use inverse operations to obtain one or more simpler equations that are equivalent. When you obtain the simplest equivalent equation, you have the solution.

If a **number is subtracted from a variable** in an equation, you can **add that same number** to both sides of the equation to undo the subtraction.

If a **number is added to a variable** in an equation, you can **subtract that same number** from both sides of the equation to undo the addition.

(continued)

Example 1 Solve each equation. Check your answer.

A $x - 10 = -4$

Solution

$$x - 10 = -4$$

$$\underline{+10 \quad +10}$$ To undo the subtraction, add 10 to both sides.

$$x - 10 + 10 = -4 + 10$$

$$x + 0 = 6$$ Opposites sum to zero.

$$x = 6$$

Check

$$x - 10 = -4$$

$$6 - 10 \overset{?}{=} -4$$ Substitute 6 for x.

$$-4 = -4 \checkmark \blacksquare$$

B $x + 15 = -10$

Solution

$$x + 15 = -10$$

$$\underline{-15 \quad -15}$$ To undo the addition, subtract 15 from both sides.

$$x + 15 - 15 = -10 - 15$$

$$x = -25$$

Check

$$x + 15 = -10$$

$$-25 + 15 \overset{?}{=} -10$$ Substitute -25 for x.

$$-10 = -10 \checkmark \blacksquare$$

Solving Equations Involving Decimals

Use the same strategies to solve equations with decimals that you use with integers.

Example 2 Solve.

A $x + 5.3 = 15$

Solution

$$x + 5.3 = 15$$

$$\underline{-5.3 \quad -5.3}$$ Subtract 5.3 from both sides.

$$x + 5.3 - 5.3 = 15 - 5.3$$

$$x = 9.7 \blacksquare$$

B $23 = d - 9.5$

Solution

$$23 = d - 9.5$$
$$\underline{+9.5 \quad +9.5} \qquad \qquad \text{Add 9.5 to both sides.}$$
$$23 + 9.5 = d - 9.5 + 9.5$$
$$32.5 = d \quad \blacksquare$$

Simplifying Before Solving

With some equations, it is easier to simplify one side of the equation before you perform an inverse operation.

Example 3   Solve each equation.

A $-5.2 + x + 3.8 = 13$

Solution

$$-5.2 + x + 3.8 = 13$$
$$x + (-5.2) + 3.8 = 13 \qquad \text{Use the associative property to rearrange}$$
$$\qquad \qquad \qquad \qquad \qquad \qquad \text{the addends.}$$
$$x + (-1.4) = 13 \qquad \text{Add } -5.2 \text{ and } 3.8 \text{ to simplify the left side.}$$
$$x - 1.4 = 13$$
$$\underline{+1.4 \quad +1.4} \qquad \text{Add 1.4 to both sides.}$$
$$x - 1.4 + 1.4 = 13 + 1.4$$
$$x = 14.4 \quad \blacksquare$$

B $0 = -9.1 - (d + 3)$

Solution

$$0 = -9.1 - (d + 3)$$
$$0 = -9.1 + [-(d + 3)] \qquad \text{To subtract } (d + 3) \text{, add its opposite, } -(d + 3).$$
$$0 = -9.1 + (-d) + (-3) \qquad \text{Apply the property of the opposite of a sum.}$$
$$0 = -12.1 + (-d) \qquad \text{Add } -9.1 \text{ and } -3 \text{ to simplify the right side.}$$
$$\underline{+12.1 \quad +12.1} \qquad \qquad \text{Add 12.1 to both sides.}$$
$$0 + 12.1 = -12.1 + (-d) + 12.1$$
$$12.1 = -d$$
$$-12.1 = d \qquad \qquad \text{If the opposite of } d \text{ equals 12.1, then } d \text{ equals } -12.1. \quad \blacksquare$$

Application: Landscape Design

Example 4 A landscaper has 20 meters of border for a garden. She has planned the lengths of three sides, as shown in the diagram. What length is needed for the fourth side so that she can use the entire border?

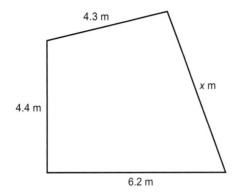

Solution

$$6.2 + 4.4 + 4.3 + x = 20.0$$

$$14.9 + x = 20.0$$

$$\underline{-14.9 \quad -14.9}$$

$$14.9 + x - 14.9 = 20.0 - 14.9$$

$$x - 14.9 + 14.9 = 20.0 - 14.9$$

$$x = 5.1$$

The length of the fourth side should be 5.1 meters. ■

Problem Set

Solve.

1. $x - 16 = -36$

2. $m + (-12) = -8$

3. $23 = y + 6$

4. $-1 = b + (-3)$

5. $k - 7 = -24$

6. $m + (-13) = -19$

7. $-1 = a + 15$

8. $z + 11 = 21$

9. $x + 7 = 0$

10. $g + 11 = 9$

11. $x + (-14) = 5$

12. $k - 16 = -27$

13. $-31 = z + (-17)$

14. $-13 + s = -18$

15. $a - 5.1 = 1.7$

16. $y + 6.2 = -2.4$

17. $-8.4 = k + 0.6$

18. $a + 0.4 = -6.4$

19. $z + (-0.1) = 7.9$

20. $4.5 = g - 0.5$

21. $-2.2 = m + 0.8$

22. $-5 + y + (-6) = 5$

23. $7 + a + (-2) = 14$

24. $2 = y + (-4) + 11$

25. $-17 = -11 + z + (-8)$

26. $b + (-6) + 13 = 25$

27. $17 = -18 + 17 + b$

28. $14 + g + 3 = -36$

Do the following for each problem:

A. Write an equation that models the problem.
B. Solve the equation.
C. Answer the question.

29. The sum of a number and 14 is −26. What is the number?

30. Sam purchased a calculator and a backpack. The total for the two items (without tax) is $151.48. The cost of the backpack is $65.49. What is the cost of the calculator?

31. Maggie wants to increase the number of cards in her collection to 325 cards. She now has 275 cards. How many cards does she need to buy?

32. The temperature is now −5°F. The temperature has dropped 12°F since midnight. What was the temperature at midnight?

33. The cost of an item is $8.39. If the item is bought with a coupon, the cost is $7.14. How much was the coupon worth?

34. **Challenge** If the mass of a rock were 4 kg heavier, its mass would be 3 kg more that twice what it is. What is the mass of the rock?

Addition and Subtraction Applications

Positive and negative numbers are used in many real world applications.

Application: Nutrition

Example 1   The table shows the amount of fiber in several kinds of fruit.

Ⓐ How much fiber is in a serving that contains 100 grams of apple, 100 grams of banana, and 100 grams of orange?

Solution The apple has 2.3 grams, the banana has 2.7 grams, and the orange has 1.8 grams. Add: $2.3 + 2.7 + 1.8 = 6.8$. The serving has a total of 6.8 grams of fiber. ■

Ⓑ How much more fiber is in 100 grams of grapes than in 100 grams of pear?

Solution Subtract: $2.2 - 2.1 = 0.1$.

The grapes have 0.1 gram more fiber than the pear. ■

Fruit (100 grams)	Grams of Fiber
Apple	2.3
Apricot	2.1
Banana	2.7
Cherry	1.2
Grapes	2.2
Lemon	1.8
Orange	1.8
Peach	1.4
Pear	2.1

Application: Elevation

Example 2   Mount Whitney, California, has an approximate elevation of 4418 meters. The lowest point in Death Valley, California, has an elevation of -86 meters. The shoreline of the Dead Sea, which is located on the border of Israel and Jordan, has an elevation of -413 meters.

Ⓐ What is the difference in elevation between Mount Whitney and the lowest point in Death Valley?

Solution Subtract the lower elevation from the higher elevation.

$$4418 - (-86) = 4418 + 86$$
$$= 4504$$

The difference in elevation between Mount Whitney and the lowest point in Death Valley is 4504 meters. ■

B What is the difference in elevation between the lowest point in Death Valley and the shoreline of the Dead Sea?

Solution Subtract the lower elevation from the higher elevation.

$$-86 - (-413) = -86 + 413$$
$$= 327$$

The difference in elevation between the lowest point in Death Valley and the shoreline of the Dead Sea is 327 meters. ∎

THINK ABOUT IT

In Example 2, subtracting elevations in the opposite order would have resulted in negative values, which is fine. When you get your solution, be sure to interpret any positive or negative signs.

Application: Temperature

Example 3 The U.S. record for the greatest temperature change in 24 hours occurred on January 23, 1916, in Browning, Montana. The temperature dropped from 44°F to −56°F. What was the change in temperature?

Solution Subtract the initial temperature from the final temperature.

$$-56 - 44 = -56 + (-44)$$
$$= -100$$

The change in temperature was −100°F, which was a decrease of 100°F. ∎

Application: Sports

Example 4 As of September 6, 2006, the indoor world record of 6.15 meters for the pole vault was held by Sergei Bubka of the Ukraine. The indoor world record of 2.43 meters for the high jump was held by Javier Sotomayor of Cuba. What is the difference in these heights?

Solution Subtract 2.43 from 6.15.

$$\begin{array}{r} \overset{5\ 11}{6.\cancel{1}5} \\ -2.43 \\ \hline 3.72 \end{array}$$ Align decimal points. Regroup 1 whole as 10 tenths, and add 10 tenths to 1 tenth to make 11 tenths. Subtract.

The difference in the heights is 3.72 meters. ∎

Application: Ballooning

Example 5 The changes in the height of a hot air balloon were recorded at different times during a flight. Given that the balloon started and ended at the same height, what is the missing change in height, x?

Change in Height (Feet)	+1200	+775	−845	x	−475	+320	−620

(continued)

Solution Because the balloon started and ended at the same height, the sum of all the decreases and increases is zero.

$$1200 + 775 + (-845) + x + (-475) + 320 + (-620) = 0$$

$$2295 + (-1940) + x = 0$$

$$355 + x = 0$$

$$x = -355$$

The missing change in height is a decrease of 355 feet. ∎

Application: Biology

Example 6 The table shows the weights of four different monarch butterflies. Order the butterflies from least to greatest weight. Then find the difference in weight between the heaviest and the lightest.

Butterfly	Weight (grams)
A	0.313
B	0.504
C	0.6
D	0.53

Solution

To compare the weights, write them all with the same number of decimal places.

A 0.313
B 0.504
C 0.600
D 0.530

In order from least to greatest weights, the butterflies are A, B, D, C.

To find the difference in weight, subtract.

$$
\begin{array}{r}
0.\overset{5}{\cancel{6}}\overset{9}{\cancel{0}}\overset{10}{\cancel{0}} \\
-0.3\,1\,3 \\
\hline
0.2\,8\,7
\end{array}
$$

The difference in weight between the heaviest and lightest butterfly is 0.287 gram. ∎

Application: Personal Banking

Example 7 The table shows Priti's bank account information. What is the missing amount? Is it a deposit or withdrawal? Explain how you know.

Beginning balance: $268.42	
Deposits	**Withdrawals**
$145.30	$275.00
$75.82	$155.10
Missing amount = x	
Ending balance: $53.82	

Solution

$$268.42 + 145.30 + 75.82 - 275.00 - 155.10 + x = 53.82$$

$$59.44 + x = 53.82 \qquad \text{Simplify the left side.}$$

$$59.44 + x - 59.44 = 53.82 - 59.44 \qquad \text{Then subtract 59.44 from both sides.}$$

$$x = -5.62$$

The missing amount is -5.62. It is a withdrawal of $5.62 because it is a negative number. ∎

Application: Amusement Park

Example 8 A roller coaster car starts at ground level, then rises 50 feet, drops 35 feet, rises x feet, and drops 12 feet. After the 12-foot drop, it is 13 feet above the ground. What is the missing rise x?

Solution

$$50 - 35 + x - 12 = 13$$

$$x + 3 = 13$$

$$x + 3 - 3 = 13 - 3$$

$$x = 10$$

The missing rise is 10 feet. ∎

Problem Set

· ·

Solve each problem. Assume all differences requested are positive differences.

The lowest elevation for each continent is shown in the table. Use the information to answer questions 1–6.

Continent	Lowest Elevation (meters)
Africa	−156
North America	−86
South America	−40
Antarctica	−2538
Asia	−411
Australia	−12
Europe	−28

1. List the elevations in order from least to greatest.

2. What is the difference between the highest and the lowest elevation shown?

3. What is the difference between the lowest elevations for Africa and Europe?

4. Which two continents have the smallest difference between their lowest elevations?

5. The highest elevation in Asia is 8850 meters. What is the difference between the highest and lowest elevation in Asia?

6. The highest elevation in South America is 6960 meters. What is the difference between the highest and lowest elevation in South America?

The lowest recorded temperatures for several cities are shown in the table. Use the information to answer questions 7–12.

City, State	Lowest Temperature (°F)
Juneau, AK	−22
Los Angeles, CA	23
Denver, CO	−30
Bismarck, ND	−44
Philadelphia, PA	−7

7. List the temperatures in order from lowest to highest.

8. What is the difference between the warmest and coldest temperature shown?

9. What is the difference between the Juneau temperature and the Los Angeles temperature?

10. Which two cities have the smallest difference in temperatures shown?

11. The difference between the Denver temperature and another temperature in the table is 23°F. Write an equation to represent this situation. Solve the equation. What city has the other temperature?

12. Which two cities have a difference of 37°?

13. The table shows Amal's bank account information. What is the missing amount? Is it a deposit or a withdrawal? Explain how you know.

Beginning balance: $426.30	
Deposits	**Withdrawals**
$251.25	$177.00
$68.24	$27.30
Missing amount $= x$	
Ending balance: $135.50	

14. On July 21, 2007, Alan Webb set a U.S. record for the mile run at 3 minutes 46.91 seconds. He broke the previous record of 3 minutes 47.69 seconds that had been set by Steve Scott in 1982. What is the difference in these records?

15. A traffic helicopter hovered over an interstate to report on traffic. The changes in height of the helicopter were recorded. Given that the helicopter started and ended at the same height, what is the missing change in height x?

Change in height: Increase/Decrease (feet)				
+108	−375	+182	x	−134

16. As of September 6, 2006, the world indoor shot put record for men was 22.66 meters, held by Randy Barnes of the United States. The record for women was 22.5 meters, held by Helena Fibingerova of Czechoslovakia. How much longer was Barnes's throw than Fibingerova's?

17. The highest recorded temperature in the United States is 134°F, recorded in California. The lowest recorded temperature in the United States is −80°F, recorded in Alaska. What is the difference between these temperatures?

18. The difference between the elevations in a particular area is 46 feet. If the higher elevation is 32 feet, what is the lower elevation?

Use the following information for problems 19–21.

Sam and Ella were playing a game by drawing cards. A black card represents a positive number. A red card represents a negative number. Each selected 5 cards. The results are shown below.

Sam	Ella	Anju	Ben
+7	−8	+4	−10
−5	+2	−3	−2
−3	−1	−9	+8
+10	+6	+5	−7

19. What is the total score for each player?

20. List the players in order from the lowest score to the highest score.

21. What is the difference between the highest and lowest score?

UNIT 3   Multiplication and Division

Skaters work as a pair to put on quite a show. Multiplication and division work as a pair to solve many types of problems.

Isaac Newton's third law of motion is often paraphrased as "for every action, there is an equal and opposite reaction." Just as forces come in pairs, so can mathematical operations. Multiplication and division are inverse operations. They undo each other and can both be used to solve many types of problems.

Big Ideas

▶ A number is any entity that obeys the laws of arithmetic; all numbers obey the laws of arithmetic. The laws of arithmetic can be used to simplify algebraic expressions.

▶ Expressions, equations, and inequalities express relationships between different entities.

Unit Topics

▶ Multiplying Integers and Decimals

▶ Dividing Integers and Decimals

▶ Multiplication and Division Properties

▶ Rounding and Estimation

▶ Equations Involving Multiplication and Division

▶ Multiplication and Division Applications

Multiplying Integers and Decimals

The result of multiplying two or more **factors** together is the **product**.

Multiplying Integers

To find the product of two or more nonzero numbers, use these rules.

RULES FOR MULTIPLYING NONZERO NUMBERS

Step 1 Ignore the signs of the numbers. Multiply as usual.
Step 2 Give the product a sign:
- The product of two positive factors is positive.
- The product of two negative factors is positive.
- The product of a negative factor and a positive factor is negative.

> **TIP**
> The rules can also be stated this way:
> If the signs are the same, the product is positive.
> If the signs are different, the product is negative.

SIGN OF THE PRODUCT $a \cdot b$

		a	
		positive	**negative**
b	**positive**	$+$	$-$
	negative	$-$	$+$

Example 1 Multiply.

A $3 \cdot 8$

Solution

$3 \cdot 8 = 24$ Multiply. Both factors are positive.
The product is positive. ■

B $-4 \cdot (-7)$

Solution

$-4 \cdot (-7) = +28$ Multiply. Both factors are negative.
The product is positive. ■

(continued)

C $-9 \cdot 5$

Solution

$-9 \cdot 5 = -45$ Multiply. One factor is negative. The other is positive.
The product is negative. ■

Multiplying Decimals

Use the same rules to multiply decimals.

Example 2   Multiply.

A $-0.2 \cdot (-6.5)$

Solution

$$
\begin{array}{r}
\overset{1}{6.5} \\
\times\ 0.2 \\
\hline
1.30
\end{array}
$$
     Multiply 0.2×6.5.

$-0.2 \cdot (-6.5) = 1.30$ Both factors are negative. The product is positive. ■

B $4.2 \cdot (-1.3)$

Solution

$$
\begin{array}{r}
4.2 \\
\times 1.3 \\
\hline
126 \\
420 \\
\hline
-5.46
\end{array}
$$
     Multiply $4.2 \cdot 1.3$.

$4.2 \cdot (-1.3) = -5.46$ One factor is positive. The other factor is negative. The product is negative. ■

Multiplying Three or More Factors

To find the product of three or more factors, multiply one pair of factors. Then multiply their product by the next factor. Keep going until you have used every factor.

Example 3   Multiply.

A $-8 \cdot 2 \cdot (-3)$

Solution

$-8 \cdot 2 \cdot (-3) = -16 \cdot (-3)$ Multiply the first two factors.

           $= 48$ Multiply the product by the third factor. ■

THINK ABOUT IT

You can choose any pair of factors to multiply first. The final answer will be the same. For example,

$$-8 \cdot 2 \cdot (-3) = -8 \cdot (-6)$$
$$= 48$$

Simplifying and Evaluating Expressions

Example 4 Simplify.

$3 + (-2) \cdot 6$

Solution

$3 + (-2) \cdot 6 = 3 + (-12)$ Multiply. The product is negative.

$\qquad\qquad\qquad = -9$ Add. ∎

Example 5 Evaluate $3x - 4$ when $x = -7$.

Solution

$3x - 4 = 3 \cdot (-7) - 4$ Substitute -7 for x.

$\qquad\quad = -21 - 4$ Multiply.

$\qquad\quad = -25$ Subtract. ∎

TIP

When simplifying an expression, only do one step at a time.

Determining the Sign of the Product of Several Factors

When you multiply three or more nonzero factors, you can determine the sign of the product by counting the number of negative factors. Every pair of negative factors makes a positive, which means that

If the number of negative factors is even, the product is positive.

If the number of negative factors is odd, the product is negative.

Example 6 Give the sign of the product.

Ⓐ $-6 \cdot 0.5 \cdot (-2) \cdot (-4) \cdot (-1)$

Solution

$-6 \cdot 0.5 \cdot (-2) \cdot (-4) \cdot (-1)$ There are four negative factors. The product is positive. ∎

Ⓑ $(-3)^5$

Solution

$(-3)^5 = (-3) \cdot (-3) \cdot (-3) \cdot (-3) \cdot (-3)$ There are five negative factors. The product is negative. ∎

REMEMBER

An exponent tells how many times the base is used as a factor.

Problem Set

Multiply.

1. $12 \cdot 3$

2. $-4 \cdot (-2)$

3. $6 \cdot (-5)$

4. $7 \cdot (-2)$

5. $-8 \cdot (-15)$

6. $+5 \cdot (-13)$

7. $-9 \cdot (-8)$

8. $19 \cdot (-27)$

9. $+73 \cdot (+3)$

10. $-20 \cdot 6$

11. $-0.6 \cdot (-7)$

12. $3.4 \cdot (-1.5)$

13. $-2.4 \cdot (-3.2)$

14. $-5.6 \cdot 1.3$

15. $3.5 \cdot (-2.6)$

16. $15,000 \cdot (-2.5)$

17. $-2 \cdot 8 \cdot (-3)$

18. $-6 \cdot (-3) \cdot (-5)$

19. $2.5 \cdot (-2) \cdot 3$

20. $-8 \cdot (-4) \cdot (-5)$

21. $3.5 \cdot 4 \cdot (-5)$

Give the sign of the product. Write *positive* or *negative*.

22. $-5 \cdot (-3) \cdot (-2)$

23. $4 \cdot (-9) \cdot 7 \cdot (-4) \cdot (-7) \cdot 9$

24. $-1 \cdot (-1) \cdot (-1) \cdot (-1) \cdot (-1) \cdot (-1) \cdot (-1)$

25. -2^4

Simplify.

26. $20 - (-3) \cdot (-2)$

27. $-3 \cdot (-6) + (-5) \cdot 2$

28. $[4 - (-2) \cdot 3] \div 2$

29. $-4 \cdot (-1 + 6)$

30. $-3 \cdot 2 + (-2) \cdot 4$

31. $[(-6) \cdot (-8)] \div [(-3) \cdot (-2)]$

Evaluate.

32. $4t$ when $t = -16$

33. $-2a$ when $a = -4.1$

34. mn when $m = -3$ and $n = 8$

35. $4n + 9$ when $n = -3$

36. $st - 4$ when $s = 6$ and $t = -2$

37. $abc + 4$ when $a = -6$, $b = 2$, and $c = -3$

Dividing Integers and Decimals

The result of division is the **quotient**.

Dividing Integers and Decimals

If you can divide positive numbers, you can divide positive and negative numbers. The rules for the sign of a quotient are the same as the rules for the sign of a product.

RULES FOR DIVIDING NONZERO NUMBERS

Step 1   Ignore the signs of the numbers. Divide as usual.
Step 2   Give the quotient a sign:
  • The quotient of two positive numbers is positive.
  • The quotient of two negative numbers is positive.
  • The quotient of a negative number and a positive number is negative.

TIP

The rules for multiplying and dividing nonzero numbers are the same.

SIGN OF THE QUOTIENT $a \div b$

		a	
		positive	**negative**
b	**positive**	+	−
	negative	−	+

Example 1   Divide.

Ⓐ $-12 \div 3$

Solution

$-12 \div 3 = -4$ Divide. One number is negative. The other number is positive. The quotient is negative. ∎

Ⓑ $-5.5 \div (-1.1)$

Solution

$-5.5 \div (-1.1) = 5$ Divide. Both numbers are negative. The quotient is positive. ∎

Ⓒ $6 \div 1.5$

Solution

$6 \div 1.5 = 4$ Divide. Both numbers are positive. The quotient is positive. ∎

Simplifying and Evaluating Expressions

Example 2   Simplify.

$$\frac{12}{-4 + 2}$$

Solution

$$\frac{12}{-4 + 2} = \frac{12}{-2} \qquad \text{Simplify the denominator.}$$

$$= -6 \qquad \text{Divide.} \quad \blacksquare$$

Example 3   Evaluate $0.6b \div (0.2 - 0.5)$ when $b = 4$.

Solution

$$
\begin{aligned}
0.6b \div (0.2 - 0.5) &= (0.6 \cdot 4) \div (0.2 - 0.5) & \text{Substitute 4 for } b. \\
&= (0.6 \cdot 4) \div (-0.3) & \text{Subtract inside parentheses.} \\
&= 2.4 \div (-0.3) & \text{Multiply.} \\
&= -8 & \text{Divide.} \quad \blacksquare
\end{aligned}
$$

Finding the Mean of Signed Numbers

The **mean** or **average** of a set of values is found by adding the numbers, then dividing by the number of values.

Example 4   Find the mean.

$-3, 5, 0, 2, -1.5, -4$

Solution

$$
\begin{aligned}
\frac{-3 + 5 + 0 + 2 + (-1.5) + (-4)}{6} &= \frac{-1.5}{6} & \begin{array}{l}\text{Write a division expression} \\ \text{and simplify the numerator.}\end{array} \\
&= -\frac{1}{4} & \text{Divide.} \quad \blacksquare
\end{aligned}
$$

Problem Set

Divide.

1. $21 \div (-3)$

2. $-45 \div 9$

3. $30 \div (-6)$

4. $-121 \div 11$

5. $-81 \div (-9)$

6. $-100 \div 10$

7. $-32 \div 8$

8. $63 \div (-7)$

9. $-4.5 \div (-5)$

10. $4.5 \div 9$

11. $-7.2 \div (-0.9)$

12. $3.6 \div 6$

13. $-3.2 \div 3.2$

14. $10{,}000 \div (-0.1)$

15. $-0.560 \div (-0.8)$

16. $-6.5 \div (-0.25)$

17. $3.75 \div (-0.125)$

18. $-8.14 \div 0.2$

Simplify.

19. $\dfrac{3 - 9}{-2}$

20. $\dfrac{6 + (-4)}{-9 + 7}$

21. $(-5 \cdot (-5)) \div (1 - 6)$

*22. **Challenge** $[(3 - 5) \div 0.2] \div 5$

Evaluate.

23. $\dfrac{t + 5}{-6}$ when $t = 25$

24. $\dfrac{-1.2r}{6}$ when $r = -3$

25. $b \div 5c$ when $b = -60$ and $c = -1$

26. $\dfrac{m - 1.1}{n + 1.1}$ when $m = 5.6$ and $n = -0.6$

Find the mean of the set of numbers.

27. $-5, -6, -2, 0, 3$

28. $10, -12, -4, -6, 8, -10$

29. $-3, -6, 5, 12, 8, -7, -2, 3$

30. $-1.7, 2.5, -3.5, -1.1$

Multiplication and Division Properties

When you multiply or divide with 0, 1, or -1, you can use properties of multiplication and division to simplify.

MULTIPLICATION AND DIVISION PROPERTIES INVOLVING 0, 1, AND -1

Property	Symbols	Examples
Identity Property of Multiplication The product of any number and 1 is equal to the number. The number 1 is called the **multiplicative identity**.	$a \cdot 1 = a$ $1 \cdot a = a$	$5 \cdot 1 = 5$ $1 \cdot (-3) = -3$
Zero Property of Multiplication The product of any number and zero is equal to zero.	$a \cdot 0 = 0$ $0 \cdot a = 0$	$(-2) \cdot 0 = 0$ $0 \cdot 6 = 0$
Negative One Property of Multiplication The product of any number and -1 is equal to the opposite of the number.	$a \cdot (-1) = -a$ $(-1) \cdot a = -a$	$(-5) \cdot (-1) = 5$ $(-1) \cdot 4 = -4$
Identity Property of Division The quotient of any number and 1 is equal to the number.	$\dfrac{a}{1} = a$	$\dfrac{6}{1} = 6$ $\dfrac{(-2)}{1} = -2$
Division Into Zero Property Zero divided by any non-zero number is equal to zero.	$\dfrac{0}{a} = 0$ (when $a \neq 0$)	$\dfrac{0}{(-3)} = 0$ $\dfrac{0}{4} = 0$
Negative One Property of Division The quotient of any number and -1 is equal to the opposite of the number.	$a \div (-1) = -a$ $\dfrac{a}{(-1)} = -a$	$4 \div (-1) = -4$ $\dfrac{(-2)}{(-1)} = 2$

THINK ABOUT IT

The number 0 does not have a sign. It is not positive or negative. The expression -0 is equivalent to 0.

Using Multiplication and Division Properties of 0, 1, and −1 to Simplify Expressions

Example 1 Simplify.

Ⓐ $-5 \cdot 0$

Ⓑ $\dfrac{-3}{-1}$

Ⓒ $bc \cdot 1$

Solution

$-5 \cdot 0 = 0$

Use the zero property of multiplication. ∎

Solution

$\dfrac{-3}{-1} = -(-3) = 3$

The quotient of a number and −1 is the opposite of the number. ∎

Solution

$bc \cdot 1 = bc$

Use the identity property of multiplication. ∎

> **REMEMBER**
>
> The **opposite** of 3 is −3 because 3 lies three units to the right of zero and −3 lies three units to the left of zero.

Using the Commutative and Associative Properties of Multiplication to Simplify Expressions

Like addition, multiplication is commutative and associative for all real numbers.

MULTIPLICATION PROPERTIES

Property	Symbols	Examples
Commutative Property of Multiplication In a product, you can multiply the numbers in any order.	$a \cdot b = b \cdot a$	$4 \cdot 6 = 6 \cdot 4$
Associative Property of Multiplication Changing the grouping of the numbers in a product does not change the product.	$(a \cdot b) \cdot c = a \cdot (b \cdot c)$	$(2 \cdot 3) \cdot 5 = 2 \cdot (3 \cdot 5)$

You can use properties to rearrange and group numbers so you can use mental math to simplify expressions.

Example 2 Use properties and mental math to simplify.

Ⓐ $5 \cdot 3 \cdot (-6)$

Solution

$5 \cdot 3 \cdot (-6) = 5 \cdot (-6) \cdot 3$ Use the commutative property of multiplication.

$\qquad\qquad = -30 \cdot 3$ Multiply.

$\qquad\qquad = -90$ Multiply. ∎

(continued)

B $(4.65 \cdot 2) \cdot 5$

Solution

$(4.65 \cdot 2) \cdot 5 = 4.65 \cdot (2 \cdot 5)$	Use the associative property of multiplication.
$= 4.65 \cdot 10$	Multiply inside parentheses.
$= 46.5$	Multiply. ∎

C $2x \cdot 6y^2$

Solution

$2x \cdot 6y^2 = 2 \cdot x \cdot 6 \cdot y^2$	Use multiplication symbols.
$= 2 \cdot 6 \cdot x \cdot y^2$	Use the commutative property of multiplication.
$= (2 \cdot 6) \cdot (x \cdot y^2)$	Use the associative property of multiplication.
$= 12 \cdot xy^2$	Multiply.
$= 12xy^2$	Write without multiplication symbols. ∎

> **REMEMBER**
>
> When you multiply a constant by a variable, you do not have to show the multiplication symbol.
>
> $2x = 2 \cdot x$
>
> $6y^2 = 6 \cdot y^2$

Using the Multiplicative Inverse

A **reciprocal** or **multiplicative inverse** is a number by which a given number must be multiplied to get a result of 1. The reciprocal of a nonzero number a is $\frac{1}{a}$. The reciprocal of a nonzero number $\frac{a}{b}$ is $\frac{b}{a}$.

> **RECIPROCAL PROPERTY OF MULTIPLICATION**
>
> For $a, b \neq 0$:   **Examples**
>
> $a \cdot \dfrac{1}{a} = 1$ $3 \cdot \dfrac{1}{3} = 1$
>
> $\dfrac{a}{b} \cdot \dfrac{b}{a} = 1$ $-\dfrac{4}{3} \cdot -\dfrac{3}{4} = 1$

> **THINK ABOUT IT**
>
> The number 0 does not have a reciprocal. There is no number you can multiply by 0 to get a product of 1.

You can use these properties to simplify expressions.

Example 3   Simplify.

A $6 \cdot \dfrac{1}{6}$

Solution

$6 \cdot \dfrac{1}{6} = 1$ The numbers 6 and $\frac{1}{6}$ are reciprocals. Their product is 1. ∎

B $b \cdot c \cdot \dfrac{1}{b}$

Solution

$b \cdot c \cdot \dfrac{1}{b} = b \cdot \dfrac{1}{b} \cdot c$	Use the commutative property of multiplication.
$= 1 \cdot c$	Use the reciprocal property of multiplication.
$= c$	Use the identity property of multiplication. ∎

C $\frac{2}{5} \cdot \frac{5}{2} \cdot (-4)$

Solution

$\frac{2}{5} \cdot \frac{5}{2} \cdot (-4) = 1 \cdot (-4)$ Use the reciprocal property of multiplication.

                $= -4$ Use the identity property of multiplication. ∎

Using Multiplcation and Division Properties to Solve Equations

To **solve** an equation is to find the values of the variables that make the equation true. These values are called **solutions** to the equation. You can use properties to figure out the solution to an equation.

Example 4   Solve the equation.

A $8 \cdot \frac{1}{n} = 1$

Solution

$8 \cdot \frac{1}{n} = 1$

$8 \cdot \frac{1}{8} = 1$ The product of 8 and $\frac{1}{8}$ is 1. The solution is $n = 8$. ∎

> **TIP**
>
> For Example 4A, ask "What number must I multiply by 8 to get 1?"

B $4 \cdot 3 \cdot t = 7 \cdot 3 \cdot 4$

Solution

$4 \cdot 3 \cdot t = 7 \cdot 3 \cdot 4$

$4 \cdot 3 \cdot t = 4 \cdot 3 \cdot 7$ Use the commutative property of multiplication.

$4 \cdot 3 \cdot 7 = 4 \cdot 3 \cdot 7$ The solution is $t = 7$. ∎

C $\frac{b}{7} = 0$

Solution

$\frac{b}{7} = 0$

$\frac{0}{7} = 0$ The quotient of 0 and 7 is 0. The solution is $b = 0$. ∎

> **THINK ABOUT IT**
>
> You could solve Example 4C using a related equation.
>
> $$\frac{b}{7} = 0$$
>
> $$b = 0 \cdot 7 = 0$$

D $(-4 \cdot b) \cdot 6 = -4 \cdot (6 \cdot 3)$

Solution

$(-4 \cdot b) \cdot 6 = -4 \cdot (6 \cdot 3)$

$(-4 \cdot b) \cdot 6 = -4 \cdot (3 \cdot 6)$ Use the commutative property of multiplication.

$(-4 \cdot b) \cdot 6 = (-4 \cdot 3) \cdot 6$ Use the associative property of multiplication.

$(-4 \cdot 3) \cdot 6 = (-4 \cdot 3) \cdot 6$ The solution is $b = 3$. ∎

Problem Set

Name the property that shows the equation is true. Assume that no variable equals zero.

1. $7 \cdot 1 = 7$

2. $3 \cdot (4 \cdot 6) = (3 \cdot 4) \cdot 6$

3. $\dfrac{4}{5} \cdot \dfrac{5}{4} = 1$

4. $[5 \cdot (-6)] \cdot 1 = 5 \cdot (-6)$

5. $1 = 5 \cdot \dfrac{1}{5}$

6. $3bc = 3cb$

7. $(7 - 4b) \cdot 0 = 0$

8. $-2 \cdot h = h \cdot (-2)$

9. $9 \cdot 0 = 0$

10. $-2m(n - 7) = -2(n - 7)m$

Simplify. Identify the property or properties you use.

11. $3.5 \cdot 0$

12. $(6 - 9) \cdot 1$

13. $(7 \cdot 2) \cdot 5$

14. $\dfrac{2}{3} \cdot \dfrac{3}{2}$

15. $\dfrac{5 \cdot 0}{3 - 6}$

16. $5 \cdot 19 \cdot 2$

17. $3b \cdot 4c$

18. $\dfrac{5 \cdot (-6)}{5 - 6}$

19. $\dfrac{7}{8} \cdot \dfrac{r}{5} \cdot \dfrac{8}{7}$

*20. Challenge $\left[\dfrac{3}{n} \cdot 5rs\right]\left[(-1) \cdot \dfrac{n}{3}\right]$

Use multiplication and division properties to solve.

21. $\dfrac{k}{-3} = 0$

22. $\dfrac{5}{8}b = 0$

23. $\dfrac{2}{3} \cdot \dfrac{m}{2} = 1$

24. $(5 \cdot 3) \cdot 6 = 6 \cdot (3 \cdot r)$

25. $3 \cdot (9 \cdot 8) = (3 \cdot b) \cdot 8$

26. $6 \cdot \dfrac{f}{6} = 1$

27. $-5.2 \cdot 3.6 \cdot z = -5.2 \cdot 2.1 \cdot 3.6$

28. $\dfrac{0}{b} = 0$

*29. Challenge $\left(\dfrac{10 - r}{6}\right) \cdot \dfrac{6}{8} = 1$

*30. Challenge $\dfrac{3x}{-1} = 12$

Rounding and Estimation

To estimate, you usually need to round numbers.

To round a number to a specified place value, use the rules for rounding.

> **RULES FOR ROUNDING A NUMBER TO A SPECIFIED PLACE**
>
> **Step 1** Identify the digit in the specified place.
> **Step 2** Look at the digit in the next place to the right.
> **Step 3** If the digit to the right is greater than or equal to 5, increase the digit in the specified place by 1. If the digit to the right is less than 5, do not change the digit in the specified place.
> **Step 4** Drop all digits to the right of the specified place.

Rounding Numbers

Example 1 Round each value to the nearest hundredth, tenth, unit, and ten.

A 42.738

Solution

Nearest hundredth	42.738	$8 \geq 5$, so round to 42.74.
Nearest tenth	42.738	$3 < 5$, so round to 42.7.
Nearest unit	42.738	$7 \geq 5$, so round to 43.
Nearest ten	42.738	$2 < 5$, so round to 40. ∎

B 3.551

Solution

Nearest hundredth	3.551	$1 < 5$, so round to 3.55.
Nearest tenth	3.551	$5 \geq 5$, so round to 3.6.
Nearest unit	3.551	$5 \geq 5$, so round to 4.
Nearest ten	03.551	$3 < 5$, so round to 0. ∎

> **REMEMBER**
> The symbol $\geq$ means *greater than or equal to.*

One way to estimate the value of an expression is to round every number in the expression and then perform the indicated operations. Even when you use a calculator, it is still a good idea to estimate to see if your answer is reasonable. If your answer is not reasonable, you may have pressed an incorrect calculator key.

Estimating the Value of an Expression

Example 2

A Estimate $163.74 + 78.3 - 19.095$ by rounding to the nearest ten.

Solution Round each number to the nearest ten. Then perform the indicated operations.

$$163.74 + 78.3 - 19.095 \rightarrow 160 + 80 - 20$$
$$= 220$$

So, the estimate for $163.74 + 78.3 - 19.095$ is 220. ■

B Estimate $\$3.84 + \$16.26 + \$5.14$ by rounding to the nearest dollar.

Solution Round each amount to the nearest dollar. Then perform the indicated operations.

$$\$3.84 + \$16.26 + \$5.14 \rightarrow \$4 + \$16 + \$5$$
$$= \$25$$

So, the estimate for $\$3.84 + \$16.26 + \$5.14$ is $\$25$. ■

Determining Whether an Answer Is Reasonable

You can use estimation to determine whether a solution to a problem is reasonable.

THINK ABOUT IT

If your estimate is close to the answer, then the answer is reasonable.

Example 3

Determine whether each answer is reasonable. Explain.

A $398 + 187 + 492$

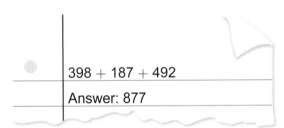

398 + 187 + 492

Answer: 877

Solution Estimate by rounding to the nearest hundred.

$$398 + 187 + 492 \rightarrow 400 + 200 + 500$$
$$= 1100$$

Because the estimate is 1100, the answer 877 *is not* reasonable. ■

B 4.8×9.2

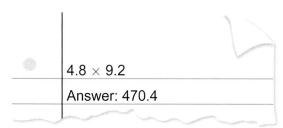

4.8×9.2

Answer: 470.4

Solution   Estimate by rounding to the nearest unit.

$4.8 \times 9.2 \rightarrow 5 \times 9$

$\qquad = 45$

Because the estimate is 45, the answer 470.4 *is not* reasonable. ∎

C $180.96 \div 8.7$

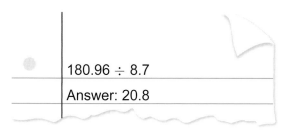

$180.96 \div 8.7$

Answer: 20.8

Solution   Estimate by rounding to the nearest ten.

$180.96 \div 8.7 \rightarrow 180 \div 10$

$\qquad = 18$

Because the estimate is 18, the answer 20.8 *is* reasonable. ∎

> **TIP**
>
> You can use *compatible numbers* to get a better estimate in Example 3C. Round 8.7 to 9 instead of rounding it to 10.
>
> $$180 \div 9 = 20$$
>
> **Twenty is a better estimate than 18.**

Application: Estimating Capacity

Example 4

An aquarium in the shape of a rectangular prism has dimensions 3 feet 2 inches, 2 feet 1 inch, and 2 feet. Estimate the capacity of the aquarium in gallons.

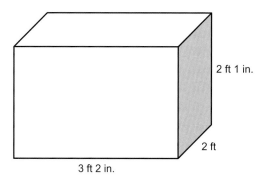

2 ft 1 in.

2 ft

3 ft 2 in.

Solution   One cubic foot holds approximately 7.48 gallons.

Round dimensions to the nearest foot as needed.

3 feet 2 inches $\rightarrow$ 3 feet

2 feet 1 inch $\rightarrow$ 2 feet

(continued)

Round 7.48 to 7.5 to get an approximation of the number of gallons in a cubic foot. Multiply the approximate volume in cubic feet by 7.5.

approximate volume in cubic feet   Approximate number of gallons per cubic foot

$$
\begin{aligned}
& 3 \ \times\ 2\ \times\ 2\ \times\ 7.5 \\
=\ & (\ 3\ \ \times\ 2\ )\ \times\ (\ 2\ \ \times\ 7.5\ ) \quad \leftarrow \text{ Group compatible factors.} \\
=\ & \quad (\ 6\ ) \quad\ \times \quad\ (\ 15\ ) \qquad \leftarrow \text{ Multiply inside grouping symbols.} \\
=\ & \qquad\qquad 90
\end{aligned}
$$

The aquarium holds approximately 90 gallons. ∎

TIP

Capacity and volume are different ways to look at the same concept—the amount of space inside an object. A gallon is a unit of capacity; a cubic foot is a unit of volume.

Application: Using Percent to Estimate

Example 5

Based on various studies, from 7% to 11% of people are left-handed. Use these results to guess the number of left-handers in a middle school that has 827 students.

Solution   For estimating, it makes sense to use 10% for two reasons: it is between 7% and 11%, and it is easy to compute with. Round 827 to 800.

$$10\% \text{ of } 800 = 0.10 \times 800 = 80$$

Based on the studies, 80 is a good guess of the number of left-handers in the middle school. ∎

THINK ABOUT IT

10% is somewhat more than halfway between 7% and 11%, but 800 is somewhat less than 827. So the estimating strategy is sound.

Problem Set

Round each value to the nearest hundredth, tenth, unit, and ten.

1. 6.25

2. 93.548

3. 326.004

4. 62.519

Estimate by rounding each number to the given place, then simplifying.

5. Round to the nearest ten.
   $326.5 + 62.48 + 48.62$

6. Round to the nearest tenth.
   $62.59 - 31.27$

7. Round to the nearest dollar.
   $\$5.82 + \$13.89 - \$11.09$

8. Round to the nearest hundred.
   $628 - 85 - 131$

9. Round to the nearest hundredth.
   $0.026 + 0.041 + 0.52$

10. Round to the nearest unit.
    $695.324 - 299.67$

11. Round to the nearest dime.
    $\$58.64 - \$32.19$

12. Round to the nearest ten.
    $72 + 2.05 - 38.62 + 12.489$

Select the most reasonable estimated answer.

13. $62.2 + 48.7$
   A. 50
   B. 90
   C. 110
   D. 180

14. $809 \div 78$
   A. 4
   B. 10
   C. 24
   D. 30

15. $11,862 \div 196$
   A. 6
   B. 60
   C. 600
   D. 6000

16. 5.9×32.8
   A. 10
   B. 70
   C. 120
   D. 180

17. $9.21 - 3.92$
   A. 4
   B. 5
   C. 6
   D. 7

18. 0.492×0.031
   A. 0.015
   B. 0.15
   C. 1.5
   D. 15

Determine whether each answer is reasonable. Explain.

19. $872 + 94 + 349$

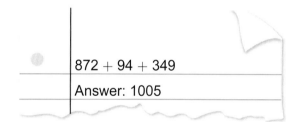

$872 + 94 + 349$
Answer: 1005

20. $0.265 - 0.018$

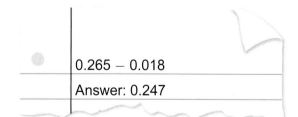

$0.265 - 0.018$
Answer: 0.247

21. 32.5×84.9

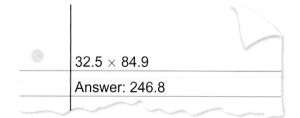

32.5×84.9
Answer: 246.8

22. $235.98 \div 62.1$

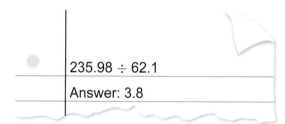

$235.98 \div 62.1$
Answer: 3.8

23. $72.518 + 12.84 + 162.7$

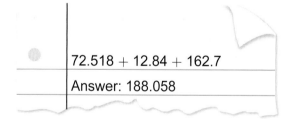

$72.518 + 12.84 + 162.7$
Answer: 188.058

24. 2.51×3.84

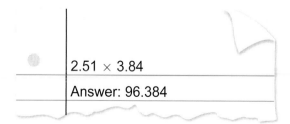

2.51×3.84
Answer: 96.384

25. $5.76 \div 0.72$

$5.76 \div 0.72$

Answer: 8

26. $61 + 84 + 59 + 18 + 47$

$61 + 84 + 59 + 18 + 47$

Answer: 222

Solve.

27. A brick mold in the shape of a rectangular prism measures 2.25 inches $\times$ 3.5 inches $\times$ 8 inches. What is the approximate volume of the brick?

28. The land for a new playground is in the shape of a triangle with a base of 52.8 meters and a height of 178 meters. What is the approximate area of the land?

29. A bedroom in the shape of a rectangle measures 11 feet 3 inches by 15 feet 8 inches. New carpet for the bedroom costs $4.89 per square foot. What is the approximate cost of new carpet for the bedroom?

30. A family's restaurant bill is $42.17. They want to leave a 20% tip for the waiter. About how much should they leave?

31. A political party estimates that their candidate will receive between 28% and 33% of the votes during an election. If 639 people vote, about how many votes can the candidate expect to receive?

32. A room has four walls that are each 14 feet 2 inches long and 8 feet high. If one can of paint covers about 325 square feet, about how many cans of paint will be needed to paint each wall with two coats of paint?

Equations Involving Multiplication and Division

If you divide both sides of an equation by the same nonzero number, the equation will still be true. You can use the division property of equality to solve equations.

Using the Division Property of Equality to Solve Equations

You can use the division property of equality to find equivalent equations. The point of this sort of transformation is to find an equation that makes the solution easy to see.

Example 1 Solve.

A $5 \cdot r = -30$

Solution

$5 \cdot r = -30$

$\dfrac{5 \cdot r}{5} = \dfrac{-30}{5}$ Divide both sides of the equation by 5.

$1 \cdot r = -6$ Simplify.

$r = -6$ Use the identity property of multiplication. ■

B $2.1 = -7b$

Solution

$2.1 = -7b$

$\dfrac{2.1}{-7} = \dfrac{-7b}{-7}$ Divide both sides of the equation by -7.

$-0.3 = 1 \cdot b$ Simplify.

$-0.3 = b$ Use the identity property of multiplication. ■

Using the Multiplication Property of Equality to Solve Equations

If you multiply both sides of an equation by the same number, the equation will still be true. You can use the multiplication property of equality to solve equations.

MULTIPLICATION PROPERTY OF EQUALITY

For a, b, and n: **Example**

If $\quad a = b$ If $\quad\quad \frac{x}{5} = 3$

then $\quad an = bn$ then $\quad \frac{x}{5} \times 5 = 3 \times 5$

$$x = 15$$

All three of these are equivalent equations.

Example 2   Solve.

A $\frac{b}{3} = 10$

Solution

$$\frac{b}{3} = 10$$

$\frac{b}{3} \cdot 3 = 10 \cdot 3$ $\quad$ Multiply both sides of the equation by 3.

$b \cdot 1 = 30$ $\quad\quad$ Simplify.

$\quad b = 30$ $\quad\quad$ Use the identity property of multiplication. ■

B $3 = \frac{w}{0.65}$

Solution

$$3 = \frac{w}{0.65}$$

$3 \cdot 0.65 = \frac{w}{0.65} \cdot 0.65$ $\quad$ Multiply both sides of the equation by 0.65.

$1.95 = w \cdot 1$ $\quad\quad$ Simplify.

$1.95 = w$ $\quad\quad$ Use the identity property of multiplication. ■

Using the Reciprocal to Solve an Equation

When the variable in an equation is multiplied by a fraction, multiply both sides by the reciprocal of the fraction to solve. Multiplying by the reciprocal is the same as dividing.

Example 3   Solve.

$\frac{2}{3}p = -6$

Solution

$$\frac{2}{3}p = -6$$

$\frac{2}{3} \cdot \frac{3}{2} \cdot p = -6 \cdot \frac{3}{2}$ Multiply both sides of the equation by $\frac{3}{2}$.

$1 \cdot p = -9$ Simplify. The product of reciprocals is 1.

$p = -9$ Use the identity property of multiplication. ■

REMEMBER

$$-6 \cdot \frac{3}{2} = -\frac{6}{1} \cdot \frac{3}{2}$$

$$= -\frac{\overset{3}{\cancel{6}}}{1} \cdot \frac{3}{\underset{1}{\cancel{2}}}$$

$$= -\frac{9}{1}$$

$$= -9$$

Application: Science

Example 4   Scientists estimate the fish population in a lake every year. In 2008, the estimate was 22,500. The estimate for 2008 was three times the estimate for 2005. What was the estimate for 2005?

Solution

Use the words to write an equation. The unknown quantity is the estimate for 2005.

TIP

When modeling a problem, the words "is" and "was" can often be translated to equals signs.

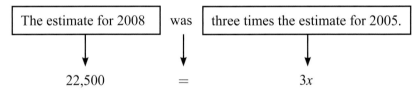

Solve the equation.

$22,500 = 3x$

$\dfrac{22,500}{3} = \dfrac{3x}{3}$ Divide both sides of the equation by 3.

$7500 = x$ Simplify both sides of the equation. ■

Problem Set

Solve.

1. $-2r = 4$

2. $4z = 12$

3. $2b = 10$

4. $6p = -72$

5. $\frac{2}{3}m = -8$

6. $\frac{a}{16} = -20$

7. $-2x = -15$

8. $6x = 42$

9. $\frac{g}{3} = -0.7$

10. $\frac{y}{4} = 3$

11. $-7 = \frac{j}{2}$

12. $\frac{y}{-2} = -6$

13. $-8 = \frac{b}{-3}$

14. $-5x = -30$

15. $-72 = -8x$

16. $\frac{3}{8}t = -27$

17. $\frac{y}{5} = -6$

18. $-\frac{9}{10}b = -18$

19. $\frac{1}{4}z = -2$

20. $12t = 48$

21. $\frac{7}{8}b = 7$

22. $15 = 4x$

23. $\frac{k}{3.2} = -4$

24. $\frac{2}{3}q = -\frac{2}{3}$

25. $-4.5 = 0.9w$

26. $5 = \frac{n}{-0.15}$

27. $\frac{5}{6} = -\frac{10}{13}p$

Do the following for each problem:

A Write an equation.
B. Solve the equation.
C. Answer the question.

28. A carpenter cut a board into 3 pieces of equal length. One of the pieces was 15.2 cm long. What was the length of the board?

29. Mrs. Williams has 24 students in her class this year. The number of students she has this year is 120% of the number she had last year. How many students were in Mrs. Williams's class last year?

30. Raisins make up $\frac{2}{5}$ of Rhonda's trail mix. If she makes a batch of trail mix using $\frac{1}{8}$ lb of raisins, what is the weight of the entire batch?

Multiplication and Division Applications

Many relationships can be described with multiplication or division.

Using Formulas

A **formula** is an equation that defines the relationship between two or more measurable quantities. To use a formula, substitute numbers for all but one of the variables and simplify.

Example 1 Solve.

A The formula $P = 4s$ gives the perimeter P of a square in which each side measures s units. What is the perimeter of a square with side length 13.6 cm?

Solution

$P = 4s$ Write the formula.

$\quad = 4 \cdot 13.6$ Substitute the known value for s.

$\quad = 54.4$ Multiply.

The perimeter of the square is 54.4 cm. ∎

> **TIP**
>
> The letters chosen to represent measurements in a formula are often related to the quantities they represent. Here *s* represents side length and *P* represents Perimeter.

B A teacher uses the formula $G = 100 \cdot \frac{c}{t}$ to find the grade G assigned to a student with c correct answers on a test with t questions. What is the grade assigned to a student with 9 correct answers on a test with 12 questions?

Solution

$G = 100 \cdot \dfrac{c}{t}$ Write the formula.

$\quad = 100 \cdot \dfrac{9}{12}$ Substitute the known values for c and t.

$\quad = 100 \cdot 0.75$ Write the fraction as a decimal.

$\quad = 75$ Simplify.

The student's grade is 75. ∎

(continued)

C The percent change PC in the price of an item is found using the formula $PC = \frac{n - r}{r}$, where n is the new price and r is the original price. What is the percent change when the price of a gallon of milk goes from \$2.50 to \$2.25?

Solution

$$PC = \frac{n - r}{r} \qquad \text{Write the formula.}$$

$$= \frac{\$2.25 - \$2.50}{\$2.50} \qquad \text{Substitute known values for } n \text{ and } r.$$

$$= \frac{-\$0.25}{\$2.50} \qquad \text{Simplify the numerator.}$$

$$= -0.1 \qquad \text{Simplify.}$$

$$= -10\% \qquad \text{Change decimal to percent.}$$

The percent change is -10%. The price of milk decreased by 10%. ■

THINK ABOUT IT

When the price decreases, the percent change is negative. When the price increases, the percent change is positive.

Using Properties of Equality with Formulas

When you look at a formula, you see that one variable is the **output** and one or more other variables are the **inputs**. For example, in the formula $P = 4s$, the perimeter P is the output. The side length s is the input. This form of the formula is most useful when you know s and want to find P.

What you have learned about solving equations using multiplication and division can help you use formulas when they are not written with the unknown variable as the output.

Example 2 Solve.

A The formula $d = rt$ gives the distance d traveled in time t at rate r. How long will it take Harry to cycle 39 miles if he maintains a constant speed of 12 miles per hour?

Solution

$$d = rt \qquad \text{Write the formula.}$$

$$39 = 12t \qquad \text{Substitute known values for } d \text{ and } r.$$

$$\frac{39}{12} = \frac{12t}{12} \qquad \text{Divide both sides by 12.}$$

$$3.25 = t \qquad \text{Simplify.}$$

It will take Harry 3.25 hours to cycle 39 miles. ■

B The formula $A = \dfrac{bh}{2}$ gives the area A of a triangle with base length b and height h. What is the height in a triangular garden that has an area of 33.15 square meters and a base length of 6.5 meters?

Solution

$$A = \frac{bh}{2}$$ Write the formula.

$$33.15 = \frac{6.5h}{2}$$ Substitute known values for A and b.

$$33.15 \cdot \frac{2}{6.5} = \frac{6.5h}{2} \cdot \frac{2}{6.5}$$ Multiply both sides by the reciprocal of the coefficient of h.

$$10.2 = h$$ Simplify.

The height of the garden is 10.2 m. ■

Literal Equations

A **literal equation** is an equation with one or more variables. A formula is one kind of literal equation. You can use the properties of equality to solve a literal equation for one of its variables.

Example 3

A Solve the formula $I = prt$ for t.

Solution

$$I = prt$$

$$\frac{I}{pr} = t$$ Divide both sides by pr. ■

B Solve the formula $P = 2l + 2w$ for w.

Solution

$$P = 2l + 2w$$

$$P - 2l = 2l - 2l + 2w$$ Subtract $2l$ from both sides to isolate $2w$.

$$P - 2l = 2w$$ Simplify.

$$\frac{P - 2l}{2} = \frac{2w}{2}$$ Divide both sides by 2.

$$\frac{P - 2l}{2} = w$$ Simplify. ■

> **TIP**
>
> When you solve a literal equation for one of its variables, treat the other variables like constants. If the equation $I = prt$ were $24 = 6 \cdot 2 \cdot t$, how would you solve for t?
>
> **Divide both sides by 12.**

Problem Set

· ·

The formula $A = s \cdot s$ gives the area A of a square with side length s. Find the area of the square with the given side length.

1. $s = 7$ in.

2. $s = 14$ m

3. $s = 2.4$ cm

The formula $P = 8s$ gives the perimeter P of a regular octagon with side length s. Find the perimeter of the regular octagon with the given side length.

4. $s = 2$ cm

5. $s = 6$ m

6. $s = 3.1$ ft

The formula $A = \dfrac{bh}{2}$ gives the area A of a triangle with base length b and height h. Find the area of the triangle with the given base length and height.

7. $b = 5$ cm; $h = 2$ cm

8. $b = 8$ ft; $h = \dfrac{3}{4}$ ft

9. $b = 5.2$ m; $h = 3.1$ m

The formula $d = rt$ gives the distance d that is traveled in time t at rate r. Find the distance that is traveled in the given time at the given rate.

10. $r = 50$ mph; $t = 3$ h

12. $r = 14$ feet per second; $t = 2.25$ sec

11. $r = 35$ meters per second; $t = 4.3$ sec

13. $r = 80$ km per hour; $t = 0.25$ h

The percent change PC in the price of an item is found using the formula $PC = \dfrac{n - r}{r}$, where n is the new price and r is the original price. Find the percent change for the given new and original prices.

14. new price: $2.40
original price: $3.00

16. new price: $14,100
original price: $15,000

15. new price: $820.80
original price: $720

Solve the literal equation for the given variable.

17. $d = rt$
Solve for r.

18. $C = 3.14d$
Solve for d.

19. $A = \dfrac{bh}{2}$
Solve for b.

20. $x = \dfrac{4}{5}y$
Solve for y.

21. $F = ma$
Solve for a.

22. $I = prt$
Solve for p.

23. $R = \dfrac{V}{I}$
Solve for V.

*24. Challenge $S = 2B + ph$
Solve for B.

Solve.

25. The formula $P = 2l + 2w$ gives the perimeter P of a rectangle with length l and width w. The perimeter of a rectangle is 24 inches. Its length is 3 inches. What is its width?

26. The formula $I = prt$ gives the interest I on an investment of p dollars at rate r for time t. If a certain investment yielded $49 interest when invested at 2% for 7 years, what was the amount of the investment? Hint: Use 0.02 for r.

27. The formula $d = rt$ gives the distance d traveled in time t at rate r. A motorcycle traveled 67.2 miles in 1.2 hours. What was its average rate of speed?

28. The formula $c = 2.54n$ can be used to convert a measurement of c centimeters to an equivalent measure of n inches. Henry is 170 centimeters tall. What is his height in inches? Round to the nearest tenth of an inch.

* 29. **Challenge** The formula $S = 2lw + 2wh + 2lh$ gives the surface area S of a rectangular prism with length l, height h, and width w. The surface area of a rectangular prism is 88 square inches. Its length is 6 inches and its height is 2 inches. What is its width?

* 30. **Challenge** The formula $B = \dfrac{703}{4900}w$ gives the body mass index (BMI) B for a person 5 feet 10 inches tall weighing w pounds. Joe is 5 feet 10 inches tall with a BMI of 24. What is his weight? Round your answer to the nearest tenth of a pound.

UNIT 4   Fractions

A carpenter needs to know how to use fractions to make the right cut.

Every fraction can be written as a decimal and every decimal can be written as a fraction. As a result, you could do just about all math with only fractions or only decimals, but decimals are used for certain applications just as fractions are used for others. For example, carpenters use fractions and mixed numbers quite a bit. Anybody building a house or a deck deals with lots of fractions.

Big Ideas

▶ Ratios, fractions, percents, and decimals can be used to compare one value to another.

▶ A number is any entity that obeys the laws of arithmetic; all numbers obey the laws of arithmetic.

Unit Topics

▶ Equivalent Fractions

▶ Multiplying Fractions

▶ Dividing Fractions

▶ Common Denominators

▶ Adding and Subtracting Fractions

▶ Working with Improper Fractions and Mixed Numbers

▶ Multiplying and Dividing Mixed Numbers

▶ Equations with Fractions and Mixed Numbers

Equivalent Fractions

A fraction is a number that represents a comparison of two values.

More than one fraction can name the same number.

Equivalent fractions, such as $\frac{1}{3}$ and $\frac{2}{6}$, are fractions with the same value.

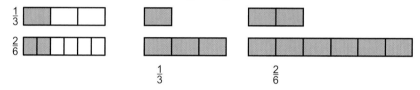

Writing Fractions in Lowest Terms

A fraction is in **lowest terms** when the numerator and denominator have no common factors other than 1. The fraction $\frac{2}{6}$ is not in lowest terms because the numerator and denominator have a common factor of 2.

$$\frac{2}{6} = \frac{1 \cdot 2}{3 \cdot 2}$$

To write a fraction in lowest terms, divide common factors from both the numerator and denominator until no common factors other than 1 remain.

Dividing is the same as multiplying by the reciprocal. When you divide the numerator and denominator by the same value, it is the same as multiplying by a fraction with the same value in the numerator and denominator, which is the same as multiplying by a form of 1.

Example 1   Write each fraction in lowest terms.

A $\frac{24}{30}$

B $\frac{-4}{12}$

Solution

Divide the numerator and denominator by 6.

$$\frac{24}{30} = \frac{24 \div 6}{30 \div 6}$$

$$= \frac{4}{5} \blacksquare$$

Solution

Divide the numerator and denominator by 4.

$$\frac{-4}{12} = \frac{-4 \div 4}{12 \div 4}$$

$$= \frac{-1}{3} \blacksquare$$

Determining if Fractions Are Equivalent

Example 2 Determine if the fractions are equivalent fractions.

Ⓐ $\frac{3}{18}$ and $\frac{6}{24}$

Solution Write each fraction in lowest terms.

$$\frac{3}{18} = \frac{3 \div 3}{18 \div 3} \qquad \frac{6}{24} = \frac{6 \div 6}{24 \div 6}$$

$$= \frac{1}{6} \qquad\qquad = \frac{1}{4}$$

The fractions are not equivalent fractions. ∎

Ⓑ $\frac{25}{45}$ and $\frac{10}{18}$

Solution Write each fraction in lowest terms.

$$\frac{25}{45} = \frac{25 \div 5}{45 \div 5} \qquad \frac{10}{18} = \frac{10 \div 2}{18 \div 2}$$

$$= \frac{5}{9} \qquad\qquad = \frac{5}{9}$$

The fractions are equivalent fractions. ∎

Simplifying Algebraic Fractions

To simplify a fraction with a variable, write the numerator and denominator as products of factors and then divide out the factors that appear in each part.

Example 3 Simplify each fraction.

Ⓐ $\frac{5b}{20}$

Solution The numerator and denominator have a common factor of 5. Write each part as a product with a factor of 5.

$$\frac{5b}{20} = \frac{\cancel{5} \cdot b}{\cancel{5} \cdot 4} \qquad \text{Divide out the common factor of 5.}$$

$$= \frac{b}{4} \quad \blacksquare$$

Ⓑ $\frac{3}{14d}$

Solution There are no common factors. The fraction is simplified. ∎

> **TIP**
>
> Simplify a fraction by writing the fraction in lowest terms.

> **THINK ABOUT IT**
>
> Simplified algebraic fractions may need to be simplified even further after a value is substituted for the variable.

Using Equivalent Fractions to Solve Equations

Example 4 Determine the value of x that makes each equation true.

Ⓐ $\dfrac{1}{2} = \dfrac{x}{8}$

Solution In equivalent fractions, the same factor appears in both the numerator and denominator. To make the denominators equal, think about what number times 2 equals 8. Then, multiply the numerator and denominator by that number.

$$\dfrac{1 \times 4}{2 \times 4} = \dfrac{4}{8} \longrightarrow \dfrac{1}{2} = \dfrac{4}{8}$$

The value of x is 4. ■

Ⓑ $\dfrac{24}{42} = \dfrac{4}{x}$

Solution To make equivalent fractions, think about what number you can divide 24 by to get 4. Then, divide the numerator and denominator by that number.

$$\dfrac{24 \div 6}{42 \div 6} = \dfrac{4}{7} \longrightarrow \dfrac{24}{42} = \dfrac{4}{7}$$

The value of x is 7. ■

Ⓒ $\dfrac{x}{5} = \dfrac{9}{15}$

Solution To make equivalent fractions, think about what number you can multiply 5 by to get 15. Then, multiply the numerator and denominator by that number.

$$\dfrac{x \cdot 3}{5 \cdot 3} = \dfrac{9}{15} \longrightarrow \text{If } x \cdot 3 = 9, \text{ then } x = 3.$$

The value of x is 3. ■

THINK ABOUT IT

You can also use division in Example 4C.

$$\dfrac{x}{5} = \dfrac{9}{15} = \dfrac{9 \div 3}{15 \div 3} = \dfrac{3}{5}$$

Application: Entertainment

Example 5 Use the chart to determine if the same fraction of attendees at a movie each day was children.

Solution Write and compare fractions where the numerator is the number of children and the denominator is the total number of people.

Attendees	Sat.	Sun.
Children	21	15
Adults	35	25

Saturday: $\dfrac{21}{21 + 35} = \dfrac{21}{56} = \dfrac{21 \div 7}{56 \div 7}$ Sunday: $\dfrac{15}{15 + 25} = \dfrac{15}{40} = \dfrac{15 \div 5}{40 \div 5}$

$$= \dfrac{3}{8} \qquad\qquad\qquad\qquad = \dfrac{3}{8}$$

The same fraction of attendees each day was children. ■

Problem Set

. . . .

Write each fraction in lowest terms.

1. $\dfrac{4}{10}$

4. $\dfrac{8}{14}$

7. $\dfrac{18}{-20}$

10. $-\dfrac{56}{84}$

2. $\dfrac{5}{30}$

5. $\dfrac{26}{36}$

8. $\dfrac{36}{63}$

11. $\dfrac{48}{52}$

3. $\dfrac{7}{28}$

6. $\dfrac{-15}{20}$

9. $\dfrac{27}{32}$

12. $\dfrac{72}{120}$

Determine if the fractions are equivalent fractions.

13. $\dfrac{1}{3}$ and $\dfrac{3}{9}$

15. $\dfrac{4}{10}$ and $\dfrac{2}{6}$

17. $\dfrac{10}{35}$ and $\dfrac{18}{70}$

19. $\dfrac{35}{45}$ and $\dfrac{21}{36}$

14. $\dfrac{3}{6}$ and $\dfrac{9}{18}$

16. $\dfrac{15}{40}$ and $\dfrac{12}{32}$

18. $\dfrac{12}{15}$ and $\dfrac{20}{25}$

20. $\dfrac{6}{27}$ and $\dfrac{10}{36}$

Simplify each fraction.

21. $\dfrac{3x}{24}$

22. $\dfrac{10}{12k}$

23. $\dfrac{7w}{15}$

24. $\dfrac{-6a}{-8}$

Determine the value of the variable that makes each equation true.

25. $\dfrac{1}{3} = \dfrac{x}{9}$

28. $\dfrac{1}{z} = \dfrac{6}{30}$

31. $\dfrac{28}{42} = \dfrac{b}{6}$

33. $\dfrac{x}{9} = \dfrac{36}{54}$

26. $\dfrac{2}{5} = \dfrac{6}{n}$

29. $\dfrac{x}{40} = \dfrac{1}{8}$

32. $\dfrac{17}{c} = \dfrac{34}{40}$

34. $\dfrac{84}{100} = \dfrac{42}{z}$

27. $\dfrac{3}{7} = \dfrac{15}{y}$

30. $\dfrac{4}{8} = \dfrac{a}{4}$

Solve each problem.

35. A nail is $\dfrac{14}{16}$ inch long. Write this length in lowest terms.

36. A coin collection consists of 32 pennies and 28 dimes. What fraction of the collection is made up of pennies?

37. A chef used 10 of the 2 dozen eggs that were in the refrigerator. What fraction of the eggs did the chef use? Write the fraction in lowest terms.

38. On Monday, a photographer took 16 portraits and 12 of them were of children. On Tuesday, he took 24 portraits and 20 of them were of children. Determine if the same fraction of portraits taken each day were of children.

39. Of the 135 registered voters who were surveyed in June, 54 of them said they would vote for Mrs. Mitchell for mayor. In October, 32 of the 80 registered voters surveyed said they would vote for her. Determine if the same fraction of voters who said they would vote for Mrs. Mitchell is the same for each survey.

*40. **Challenge** Naomi read 200 out of 240 pages in her book. Antonio read the same fraction of pages of his book. If his book has 210 pages, how many pages did he read?

Multiplying Fractions

You can use a diagram to understand what one fraction times another fraction represents.

This figure illustrates $\frac{1}{3}$ of a whole.

One-half of the shaded square is $\frac{1}{2}$ of $\frac{1}{3}$, or $\frac{1}{2} \cdot \frac{1}{3}$.

This is $\frac{1}{6}$ of the whole.

Multiplying Fractions

The example above suggests that when you multiply two fractions, you can multiply the numerators and the denominators. In fact, that's true.

MULTIPLYING FRACTIONS

Property

$$\frac{a}{b} \cdot \frac{c}{d} = \frac{ac}{bd}$$

$b \neq 0, d \neq 0$

Example

$$\frac{2}{3} \cdot \frac{5}{7} = \frac{2 \cdot 5}{3 \cdot 7} = \frac{10}{21}$$

It is customary to write the product of fractions in lowest terms.

Example 1   Find each product and simplify.

Ⓐ $\frac{1}{2} \cdot \frac{4}{5}$

Solution

$$\frac{1}{2} \cdot \frac{4}{5} = \frac{1 \cdot 4}{2 \cdot 5}$$ Multiply the numerators and the denominators.

$$= \frac{4}{10}$$

$$= \frac{2}{5}$$ Write the fraction in lowest terms. ∎

(continued)

B $-\dfrac{2}{3} \cdot \dfrac{6}{10}$

Solution

$-\dfrac{2}{3} \cdot \dfrac{6}{15} = -\dfrac{2 \cdot 6}{3 \cdot 15}$ Multiply the numerators and the denominators.

$= -\dfrac{12}{45}$

$= -\dfrac{4}{15}$ Write the fraction in lowest terms. ∎

C $\dfrac{5}{8} \cdot \dfrac{x}{3}$

Solution

$\dfrac{5}{8} \cdot \dfrac{x}{3} = \dfrac{5x}{8 \cdot 3}$ Multiply the numerators and the denominators.

$= \dfrac{5x}{24}$ Simplify. The fraction is in lowest terms already. ∎

Multiplying by Simplifying First

Common factors in either numerator can be divided out with common factors in either denominator. You can combine the fractions, then simplify; or you can simplify before combining the fractions. It is common practice to simplify first.

Example 2   Divide out common factors. Then multiply.

A $\dfrac{3}{8} \cdot \dfrac{4}{5}$

Solution

$\dfrac{3}{8} \cdot \dfrac{4}{5} = \dfrac{3}{\overset{}{\underset{2}{8}}} \cdot \dfrac{\overset{1}{4}}{5}$ Divide out the common factor of 4.

$= \dfrac{3 \cdot 1}{2 \cdot 5} = \dfrac{3}{10}$ Multiply $3 \cdot 1$ and $2 \cdot 5$. ∎

B $\dfrac{8}{15} \cdot \left(-\dfrac{10}{12}\right)$

Solution   Write each fraction in lowest terms.

$\dfrac{8}{15} \cdot \left(-\dfrac{10}{12}\right) = \dfrac{\overset{2}{8}}{\underset{3}{15}} \cdot \left(-\dfrac{\overset{2}{10}}{\underset{3}{12}}\right)$ Divide out the common factor of 4 in 8 and 12 and the common factor of 5 in 10 and 15.

$= -\dfrac{2 \cdot 2}{3 \cdot 3} = -\dfrac{4}{9}$ Multiply $2 \cdot 2$ and $3 \cdot 3$. ∎

Application: Cooking

Example 3 Keisha wants to bake 24 soft pretzels, but the recipe she has makes 48 soft pretzels.

Ⓐ What fraction of each ingredient should she use?

Ⓑ The recipe calls for $\frac{3}{4}$ cup of flour. How much flour should Keisha use?

Solution

Ⓐ $\dfrac{\text{soft pretzels wanted}}{\text{total recipe makes}} = \dfrac{24}{48} = \dfrac{1}{2}$

Ⓑ Find $\frac{1}{2}$ of $\frac{3}{4}$.

$$\frac{1}{2} \cdot \frac{3}{4} = \frac{3}{8}$$

Keisha should use $\frac{3}{8}$ cup of flour. ∎

Problem Set

Find each product and simplify.

1. $\dfrac{1}{8} \cdot \dfrac{1}{2}$

2. $\dfrac{1}{2} \cdot \dfrac{2}{3}$

3. $-\dfrac{3}{5} \cdot \dfrac{3}{4}$

4. $\dfrac{3}{4} \cdot \dfrac{1}{4}$

5. $\dfrac{7}{8} \cdot \dfrac{3}{4}$

6. $-\dfrac{5}{11} \cdot \left(-\dfrac{2}{3}\right)$

7. $\dfrac{4}{5} \cdot \dfrac{3}{8}$

8. $\dfrac{9}{10} \cdot \left(-\dfrac{5}{6}\right)$

9. $-\dfrac{4}{7} \cdot \left(-\dfrac{3}{10}\right)$

10. $\dfrac{4}{9} \cdot \dfrac{w}{5}$

11. $\dfrac{x}{3} \cdot \dfrac{2}{y}$

12. $\dfrac{4}{a} \cdot \dfrac{a}{b}$

Divide out common factors. Then multiply.

13. $\dfrac{2}{5} \cdot \dfrac{1}{2}$

14. $\dfrac{3}{6} \cdot \dfrac{1}{4}$

15. $\dfrac{3}{5} \cdot \dfrac{5}{10}$

16. $-\dfrac{7}{8} \cdot \dfrac{4}{5}$

17. $\dfrac{6}{14} \cdot \dfrac{7}{8}$

18. $-\dfrac{3}{4} \cdot \left(-\dfrac{10}{11}\right)$

19. $\dfrac{12}{15} \cdot \dfrac{3}{4}$

20. $\dfrac{6}{7} \cdot \left(-\dfrac{1}{6}\right)$

21. $-\dfrac{5}{2} \cdot \left(-\dfrac{2}{5}\right)$

22. $\dfrac{15}{20} \cdot \dfrac{10}{12}$

23. $\dfrac{8}{9} \cdot \dfrac{12}{16}$

24. $-\dfrac{3}{4} \cdot \dfrac{4}{3}$

25. $\dfrac{9}{14} \cdot \dfrac{14}{15}$

26. $\dfrac{1}{a} \cdot \dfrac{a}{7}$

27. $\dfrac{c}{d} \cdot \dfrac{d}{c}$

28. $\dfrac{2}{9} \cdot \left(-\dfrac{b}{6}\right)$

29. $\dfrac{e}{9} \cdot \dfrac{3}{f}$

30. $\dfrac{250c}{25} \cdot \dfrac{h}{50d}$

Solve each problem.

31. Lydell wants to make 36 granola bars, but the recipe he has makes 60 granola bars.

    A. What fraction of each ingredient should he use?

    B. The recipe calls for $\frac{2}{3}$ cup of brown sugar. How much brown sugar should Lydell use?

32. Victoria needs to make 30 fruit cups for her class party. The recipe she has will make 36 fruit cups.

    A. What fraction of each ingredient should she use?

    B. The recipe she has calls for $\frac{3}{4}$ cup of pears. How many pears should Victoria use?

33. So far, Dianne has walked $\frac{1}{4}$ of a trail that is $\frac{7}{8}$ mile long. How far has she walked?

34. This figure illustrates $\frac{2}{5}$ of a whole.

    Describe how this figure can be used to illustrate each of the given fractions.

    A. $\frac{2}{5}$ C. $\frac{2}{3}$

    B. $\frac{3}{5}$ D. $\frac{3}{2}$

35. A bottle contains $\frac{1}{2}$ gallon of juice. Catalina drank $\frac{1}{5}$ of the juice. How much juice did Catalina drink?

36. Ismael completed $\frac{3}{5}$ of the levels of a video game. His friend Ari completed $\frac{2}{3}$ of the number of levels that Ismael completed. What fraction of the game has Ari completed?

37. Thirty out of 32 students passed the last mathematics test.

    A. What fraction of the students passed the test?

    B. Out of the students who passed the test, $\frac{1}{6}$ earned a grade of A. What fraction of students earned a grade of A?

*38. **Challenge** Use a figure to illustrate that $\frac{2}{3}$ of $\frac{2}{3}$ is $\frac{4}{9}$.

Dividing Fractions

Division separates a number into equal groups.

Sometimes the divisor and dividend are fractions.

This figure illustrates $\frac{2}{3}$ of a whole.

This is $\frac{1}{6}$ of the whole.

There are four $\frac{1}{6}$s in $\frac{2}{3}$. That is, $\frac{2}{3} \div \frac{1}{6} = 4$.

Finding Reciprocals of Fractions

The reciprocal of $\dfrac{a}{b} = \dfrac{1}{\frac{a}{b}}$ The reciprocal of any number is 1 over the number.

$$= \dfrac{1}{\frac{a}{b}} \cdot \dfrac{b}{b}$$ Multiply the numerator and denominator by b so there will no longer be a fraction in the bottom.

$$= \dfrac{1 \cdot b}{a \cdot \not{b}}{\not{b}}$$

$$= \dfrac{b}{a}$$ Simplify.

> **REMEMBER**
>
> The reciprocal is also called the *multiplicative inverse*.

> **RECIPROCAL OF A FRACTION**
>
> **For any nonzero a and b:**   **Example**
>
> $$\dfrac{a}{b} = \dfrac{b}{a}$$ $$\dfrac{2}{3} = \dfrac{3}{2}$$

Example 1   Find the reciprocal of each number.

Ⓐ $\dfrac{9}{10}$

Ⓑ $\dfrac{1}{5}$

Solution   The reciprocal is $\dfrac{10}{9}$. ∎

Solution   The reciprocal is $\dfrac{5}{1}$, or 5. ∎

To divide fractions, multiply the divisor by the **reciprocal** of the dividend.

(continued)

> **TIP**
>
> To find a reciprocal, "flip" the fraction. Check your answer by multiplying.
>
> $$\dfrac{9}{10} \cdot \dfrac{10}{9} = \dfrac{90}{90} = 1$$

Property	Example
$\dfrac{a}{b} \div \dfrac{c}{d} = \dfrac{a}{b} \cdot \dfrac{d}{c} = \dfrac{ad}{bc}$	$\dfrac{2}{3} \div \dfrac{1}{6} = \dfrac{2}{3} \cdot \dfrac{6}{1} = \dfrac{12}{3} = 4$
$b \neq 0, c \neq 0, d \neq 0$	

REMEMBER

In $x \div y$, x is the *dividend* and y is the *divisor*.

Dividing Fractions

Example 2   Find each quotient and simplify.

A $\dfrac{1}{2} \div \dfrac{4}{6}$

Solution

$$\dfrac{1}{2} \div \dfrac{4}{6} = \dfrac{1}{2} \cdot \dfrac{6}{4} \qquad \text{Multiply by the reciprocal.}$$

$$= \dfrac{1 \cdot 6}{2 \cdot 4} \qquad \text{Multiply the numerators and the denominators.}$$

$$= \dfrac{6}{8}$$

$$= \dfrac{3}{4} \qquad \text{Write in lowest terms.} \quad \blacksquare$$

B $-8 \div \dfrac{1}{4}$

Solution

$$-8 \div \dfrac{1}{4} = -8 \cdot \dfrac{4}{1} \qquad \text{Multiply by the reciprocal.}$$

$$= -8 \cdot 4 \qquad \text{Write } \dfrac{4}{1} \text{ as 4.}$$

$$= -32 \qquad \text{Multiply.} \quad \blacksquare$$

TIP

In Example 2B, you can also write $-\dfrac{8}{1} \cdot \dfrac{4}{1}$ in the second step.

C $\dfrac{2}{3} \div 6$

Solution

$$\dfrac{2}{3} \div 6 = \dfrac{2}{3} \cdot \dfrac{1}{6} \qquad \text{Multiply by the reciprocal.}$$

$$= \dfrac{2 \cdot 1}{3 \cdot 6} \qquad \text{Multiply the numerators and the denominators.}$$

$$= \dfrac{2}{18}$$

$$= \dfrac{1}{9} \qquad \text{Write in lowest terms.} \quad \blacksquare$$

D $\dfrac{5}{x} \div \dfrac{10}{y}$

Solution

$$\dfrac{5}{x} \div \dfrac{10}{y} = \dfrac{\overset{1}{\cancel{5}}}{x} \cdot \dfrac{y}{\underset{2}{\cancel{10}}}$$ 　Multiply by the reciprocal. Divide out the common factor of 5.

$$= \dfrac{y}{2x}$$ 　Multiply. ∎

Application: Sewing

Example 3　Three-fourths yard of fabric is divided into 6 sections, each with equal length. How long is each section?

Solution　Divide: $\dfrac{3}{4} \div 6 = \dfrac{\overset{1}{\cancel{3}}}{4} \cdot \dfrac{1}{\underset{2}{\cancel{6}}}$ 　Multiply by the reciprocal. Divide out the common factor of 3.

$$= \dfrac{1}{8}$$ 　Multiply.

Each section is $\dfrac{1}{8}$ yard long.

Check　If each section is $\dfrac{1}{8}$ yard long, then the total length should be $6 \cdot \dfrac{1}{8} = \dfrac{6}{8} = \dfrac{3}{4}.$ The solution checks. ∎

Problem Set

Find the reciprocal of each number.

1.　6

2.　$\dfrac{1}{8}$

3.　$-\dfrac{2}{3}$

4.　-15

5.　$\dfrac{8}{9}$

6.　$\dfrac{5}{12}$

7.　$\dfrac{x}{y}$

8.　$\dfrac{3}{h}$

Find each quotient and simplify.

9.　$\dfrac{1}{5} \div \dfrac{1}{2}$

10.　$\dfrac{5}{6} \div \dfrac{5}{6}$

11.　$3 \div \dfrac{1}{3}$

12.　$\dfrac{1}{3} \div \dfrac{4}{5}$

13.　$\dfrac{5}{8} \div 8$

14.　$\dfrac{5}{12} \div 10$

15.　$-\dfrac{1}{8} \div \left(-\dfrac{3}{4}\right)$

16.　$\dfrac{6}{7} \div 5$

17.　$-20 \div \dfrac{2}{3}$

18.　$\dfrac{1}{a} \div \dfrac{3}{a}$

19.　$1 \div \dfrac{1}{2}$

20.　$-\dfrac{3}{4} \div \dfrac{3}{2}$

21.　$\dfrac{4}{9} \div \dfrac{3}{5}$

22.　$\dfrac{3}{8} \div \dfrac{6}{11}$

23.　$\dfrac{a}{4} \div a$

24.　$\dfrac{2}{13} \div \dfrac{1}{13}$

25.　$\dfrac{4}{5} \div (-3)$

26.　$2b \div \dfrac{1}{2}$

27.　$\dfrac{2}{k} \div \dfrac{m}{k}$

28.　$-\dfrac{15}{32} \div \left(-\dfrac{1}{2}\right)$

29. $\dfrac{14}{27} \div \dfrac{2}{3}$

31. $\dfrac{3}{x} \div \dfrac{4}{x}$

33. $3 \div \dfrac{1}{2} \div \dfrac{1}{2}$

30. $\dfrac{5}{a} \div \dfrac{15}{b}$

32. $\dfrac{17}{20} \div (-34)$

34. $\dfrac{3}{4} \cdot \dfrac{2}{5} \div (-4)$

Solve each problem.

35. A chef cuts a banana in half and sets one half to the side. He cuts the remaining half into four equal sections. What fraction of the whole banana is each piece?

36. Three girls took turns running equal parts of a relay race. The total length of the race was $\dfrac{9}{10}$ km. How far did each girl run if each girl ran the same distance?

37. A wire that is $\dfrac{7}{16}$ foot long is divided into 7 equal sections. How long is each section?

38. A 6-foot long board is divided into sections that are each $\dfrac{1}{3}$ foot long. How many sections are there?

39. Use a model to show that $3 \div \dfrac{1}{3} = 9$.

*40. **Challenge** Which division problem is illustrated by the model? Explain.

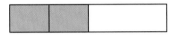

Common Denominators

A common denominator enables you to compare, add, or subtract fractions.

Some multiples of 4 and 6 are shown below. The common multiples are in red.

$$4 : 4, 8, 12, 16, 20, 24, 28, 32, 36, \ldots$$

$$6 : 6, 12, 18, 24, 30, 36, 42, \ldots$$

DEFINITIONS

The **least common multiple (LCM)** is the least number that is a common multiple of all numbers in a set. The **least common denominator (LCD)** is the least common multiple of two or more denominators.

TIP

To find the LCM, you can also list multiples of the greater number until you find one that is a multiple of the smaller number.

The LCD of $\frac{3}{4}$ and $\frac{5}{6}$ is 12 because the LCM of 4 and 6 is 12.

Finding the Least Common Denominator

Example 1   Find the LCD of each pair of fractions.

A $\frac{2}{5}$ and $\frac{3}{8}$

Solution   Find the LCM of 5 and 8.

multiples of 5 : 5, 10, 15, 20, 25, 30, 35, 40, . . .

multiples of 8 : 8, 16, 24, 32, 40, . . .

The LCD is 40. ■

B $\frac{1}{6}$ and $\frac{5}{9}$

Solution   Find the LCM of 6 and 9.

multiples of 6 : 6, 12, 18, . . .

multiples of 9 : 9, 18, 27, . . .

The LCD is 18. ■

THINK ABOUT IT

The product of the denominators is always a common multiple. It may or may not be the least common multiple.

(continued)

C $-\dfrac{5}{84}$ and $-\dfrac{7}{12}$

Solution Disregard negative signs. Because 84 is a multiple of 12, the LCM of 84 and 12 is 84.

The LCD is 84. ■

Expressing Fractions with the Same Denominator

Any fraction can be renamed to an equivalent fraction by multiplying both the numerator and denominator by the same number. When you multiply the numerator and denominator by the same number, you are multiplying the original fraction by a form of 1. This results in an equivalent fraction.

REMEMBER

Equivalent fractions are fractions with the same value.

Example 2 Express each set of fractions using the same denominator.

A $\dfrac{3}{4}$ and $\dfrac{2}{3}$

Solution The LCD is 12. Rename both fractions with a denominator of 12.

$$\dfrac{3}{4} = \dfrac{3}{4} \cdot \dfrac{3}{3} \qquad \dfrac{2}{3} = \dfrac{2}{3} \cdot \dfrac{4}{4}$$

$$= \dfrac{3 \cdot 3}{4 \cdot 3} \qquad \dfrac{2}{3} = \dfrac{2 \cdot 4}{3 \cdot 4}$$

$$= \dfrac{9}{12} \qquad\qquad = \dfrac{8}{12}$$

The fractions are $\dfrac{9}{12}$ and $\dfrac{8}{12}$. ■

THINK ABOUT IT

In Example 2, we are using the LCD. Other fractions are possible, such as $\dfrac{18}{24}$ and $\dfrac{16}{24}$ for Example 3A.

B $-\dfrac{1}{6}$ and $\dfrac{5}{24}$

Solution The LCD is 24. Rename $-\dfrac{1}{6}$ with a denominator of 24.

$$-\dfrac{1}{6} = -\dfrac{1}{6} \cdot \dfrac{4}{4}$$

$$= -\dfrac{1 \cdot 4}{6 \cdot 4}$$

$$= -\dfrac{4}{24}$$

The fractions are $-\dfrac{4}{24}$ and $\dfrac{5}{24}$. ■

C $\frac{11}{18}$, $\frac{1}{54}$, and $\frac{2}{27}$

Solution   The LCD is 54. Rename $\frac{11}{18}$ and $\frac{2}{27}$.

$$\frac{11}{18} = \frac{11}{18} \cdot \frac{3}{3} \qquad \frac{2}{27} = \frac{2}{27} \cdot \frac{2}{2}$$

$$= \frac{11 \cdot 3}{18 \cdot 3} \qquad\qquad = \frac{2 \cdot 2}{27 \cdot 2}$$

$$= \frac{33}{54} \qquad\qquad = \frac{4}{54}$$

The fractions are $\frac{33}{54}$, $\frac{1}{54}$, and $\frac{4}{54}$. ∎

Comparing Fractions

When fractions have a common denominator, you can compare them by comparing the numerators. For example, $\frac{4}{7} > \frac{3}{7}$ because $4 > 3$. When the fractions have unlike denominators, rename one or both fractions so that they have a common denominator. Then compare the numerators.

Example 3   Compare the fractions using $>$, $<$, or $=$.

A $\frac{11}{20}$ and $\frac{2}{5}$

Solution   Rename $\frac{2}{5}$ with a denominator of 20.

$$\frac{2}{5} = \frac{2 \cdot 4}{5 \cdot 4} \qquad \text{Multiply the numerator and denominator by 4.}$$

$$= \frac{8}{20}$$

Compare $\frac{11}{20}$ and $\frac{8}{20}$. Because $11 > 8$, $\frac{11}{20} > \frac{8}{20}$, and $\frac{11}{20} > \frac{2}{5}$. ∎

TIP

Any common denominator, not necessarily the LCD, can be used to compare fractions.

B $-\frac{3}{7}$ and $-\frac{2}{5}$

Solution   Rename both fractions with a denominator of 35.

$$-\frac{3}{7} = -\frac{3 \cdot 5}{7 \cdot 5} \qquad -\frac{2}{5} = -\frac{2 \cdot 7}{5 \cdot 7}$$

$$= -\frac{15}{35} \qquad\qquad = -\frac{14}{35}$$

Because $-15 < -14$, $-\frac{15}{35} < -\frac{14}{35}$, and $-\frac{3}{7} < -\frac{2}{5}$. ∎

(continued)

C $\dfrac{9}{15}$ and $\dfrac{6}{10}$

Solution Rename both fractions with a denominator of 30.

$$\dfrac{9}{15}=\dfrac{9\cdot 2}{15\cdot 2} \qquad \dfrac{6}{10}=\dfrac{6\cdot 3}{10\cdot 3}$$

$$=\dfrac{18}{30} \qquad\qquad =\dfrac{18}{30}$$

Because $\dfrac{18}{30}=\dfrac{18}{30}, \dfrac{9}{15}=\dfrac{6}{10}.$ ■

THINK ABOUT IT

The fractions in Example 3C can also be compared by simplifying each fraction.

$$\dfrac{3}{5}=\dfrac{3}{5}$$

Application: Competition

Example 4

A Jordan ran $\dfrac{7}{8}$ mile and Miguel ran $\dfrac{4}{5}$ mile. Who ran farther?

Solution Compare $\dfrac{7}{8}$ and $\dfrac{4}{5}$ using the LCD of 40.

Jordan: $\dfrac{7}{8}=\dfrac{7\cdot 5}{8\cdot 5}$ \qquad Miguel: $\dfrac{4}{5}=\dfrac{4\cdot 8}{5\cdot 8}$

$$=\dfrac{35}{40} \qquad\qquad =\dfrac{32}{40}$$

Jordan ran farther. ■

B Three neighbors had a tomato-growing contest. The weights of their best tomatoes are shown in the table. List the weights from greatest to least.

Margo	Julie	Hank
$\dfrac{11}{16}$ lb	$\dfrac{1}{2}$ lb	$\dfrac{3}{4}$ lb

Solution Compare the fractions using the LCD of 16.

Margo: $\dfrac{11}{16}$ \qquad Julie: $\dfrac{1}{2}=\dfrac{1\cdot 8}{2\cdot 8}$ \qquad Hank: $\dfrac{3}{4}=\dfrac{3\cdot 4}{4\cdot 4}$

$$=\dfrac{8}{16} \qquad\qquad =\dfrac{12}{16}$$

The weights from greatest to least are $\dfrac{3}{4}$ lb, $\dfrac{11}{16}$ lb, and $\dfrac{1}{2}$ lb. ■

Problem Set

Find the LCD of each pair of fractions.

1. $\frac{2}{3}$ and $\frac{1}{2}$

2. $\frac{1}{3}$ and $\frac{1}{4}$

3. $\frac{3}{4}$ and $\frac{7}{9}$

4. $\frac{3}{10}$ and $\frac{1}{2}$

5. $\frac{3}{8}$ and $\frac{2}{7}$

6. $-\frac{4}{9}$ and $\frac{11}{12}$

7. $\frac{3}{5}$ and $\frac{3}{8}$

8. $\frac{1}{18}$ and $\frac{7}{24}$

9. $-\frac{5}{14}$ and $-\frac{1}{3}$

10. $\frac{2}{15}$ and $\frac{5}{6}$

Express each set of fractions using the same denominator.

11. $\frac{1}{2}$ and $\frac{3}{4}$

12. $\frac{2}{5}$ and $\frac{1}{2}$

13. $-\frac{2}{3}$ and $\frac{3}{5}$

14. $\frac{5}{6}$ and $\frac{2}{3}$

15. $\frac{4}{7}$ and $\frac{3}{5}$

16. $-\frac{11}{12}$ and $-\frac{7}{8}$

17. $\frac{1}{8}$ and $\frac{3}{16}$

18. $\frac{4}{15}$ and $\frac{9}{10}$

19. $\frac{1}{2}, \frac{1}{3},$ and $\frac{1}{4}$

20. $\frac{5}{6}, \frac{9}{10},$ and $\frac{2}{5}$

Compare the fractions using >, <, or =.

21. $\frac{3}{5}$ and $\frac{4}{7}$

22. $\frac{7}{8}$ and $\frac{8}{10}$

23. $\frac{5}{12}$ and $\frac{3}{5}$

24. $\frac{6}{10}$ and $\frac{9}{15}$

25. $-\frac{6}{7}$ and $-\frac{11}{12}$

26. $\frac{13}{20}$ and $\frac{2}{3}$

27. $-\frac{5}{18}$ and $-\frac{3}{10}$

28. $\frac{6}{27}$ and $\frac{10}{36}$

Solve each problem.

29. Johan finished $\frac{3}{4}$ of his math problems while Maria finished $\frac{7}{9}$ of her math problems. Who finished a greater fraction of math problems?

30. The Cherry Tree Trail is $\frac{13}{16}$ mile long and the Weeping Willow Trail is $\frac{7}{10}$ mile long. Which trail is longer?

31. A biologist took the weights of a blue jay and a northern cardinal. The blue jay weighed $\frac{3}{16}$ pound and the cardinal weighed $\frac{3}{32}$ pound. Which bird was heavier?

32. The heights of four plants are shown in the table. List the plants from shortest to tallest.

Plant	A	B	C	D
Height in Meters	$\frac{3}{10}$	$\frac{2}{5}$	$\frac{1}{4}$	$\frac{1}{2}$

Adding and Subtracting Fractions

To add and subtract fractions, start by expressing each fraction with the same denominator.

ADDING AND SUBTRACTING FRACTIONS

Like Fractions (same denominator)	Unlike Fractions (different denominators)
• Add or subtract the numerators. • Keep the same denominator. • Simplify if possible.	• Write equivalent fractions as needed so that the fractions have the same denominator. • Then add or subtract the like fractions.

Adding and Subtracting Like Fractions

Example 1

Find each sum or difference. Write the answer in simplest form.

A $\dfrac{2}{7} + \dfrac{4}{7}$

Solution

$\dfrac{2}{7} + \dfrac{4}{7} = \dfrac{2+4}{7}$ Add the numerators. Keep the same denominator.

$= \dfrac{6}{7}$ Simplify. The fraction is already in lowest terms. ∎

B $\dfrac{5}{8} - \left(-\dfrac{1}{8}\right)$

Solution

$\dfrac{5}{8} - \left(-\dfrac{1}{8}\right) = \dfrac{5-(-1)}{8}$ Subtract the numerators. Keep the same denominator.

$= \dfrac{6}{8}$

$= \dfrac{3}{4}$ Simplify by writing in lowest terms. ∎

REMEMBER

To subtract a number, add its opposite.

$$5 - (-1) = 5 + 1 = 6$$

Adding and Subtracting Unlike Fractions

Example 2

Find the sum. Write the answer in simplest form.

$$-\frac{5}{6} + \frac{2}{3}$$

Solution   The least common denominator of $-\frac{5}{6}$ and $\frac{2}{3}$ is 6.

$$-\frac{5}{6} + \frac{2}{3} = -\frac{5}{6} + \frac{4}{6}$$

Write $\frac{2}{3}$ as the equivalent fraction $\frac{4}{6}$ so that the fractions to be added have the same denominator.

$$= \frac{-5 + 4}{6}$$

Then add the like fractions $-\frac{5}{6}$ and $\frac{4}{6}$. ■

$$= \frac{-1}{6} = -\frac{1}{6}$$

Improper Fractions and Mixed Numbers

A fraction can represent a number greater than one.

This figure illustrates $\frac{3}{2}$.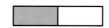

Each shaded area is one-half. There are three one-halves.

Another way to write the number illustrated by the diagram is $1\frac{1}{2}$ because there is one whole and one half rectangle shaded.

> **DEFINITION**
>
> An **improper fraction** is a fraction where the numerator is greater than or equal to the denominator. A **mixed number** is a number consisting of both a whole number and a fraction, or the opposite of such a number.

> **CONVERTING IMPROPER FRACTIONS TO MIXED NUMBERS**
>
> **Step 1** Divide the numerator by the denominator.
> **Step 2** Use the quotient as the whole number and the remainder as the numerator.
> **Step 3** Keep the original denominator.

Example 3   Convert each improper fraction to a mixed number.

A $\frac{23}{8}$

Solution

$$8)\overline{23} \quad \frac{2\ R\ 7}{}$$

Divide the numerator by the denominator.

$$2\frac{7}{8}$$

Use the quotient as the whole number and the remainder as the numerator. ■

> **TIP**
>
> Be careful when using a calculator. Most calculators will give the quotient as a decimal.
>
> $$23 \div 8 = 2.875$$
> $$45 \div 6 = 7.5$$

(continued)

B $-\frac{45}{6}$

Solution

$$\begin{array}{r} -7 \text{ R } 3 \\ -6\overline{)45} \end{array}$$ Divide the numerator by the denominator.

$-7\frac{3}{6} = -7\frac{1}{2}$ Use the quotient as the whole number and the remainder as the numerator. ∎

Subtracting Unlike Fractions and Converting to a Mixed Number

Example 4

Find the difference. Write the answer as a mixed number in simplest form.

$$-\frac{3}{20} - \frac{14}{15}$$

Solution The least common denominator of $-\frac{3}{20}$ and $\frac{14}{15}$ is 60.

$-\frac{3}{20} - \frac{14}{15} = -\frac{9}{60} - \frac{56}{60}$ Write an equivalent fraction for each fraction.

$= \frac{-9 - 56}{60}$ To subtract $\frac{56}{60}$ from $-\frac{9}{60}$, subtract 56 from -9 and keep the same denominator.

$= -\frac{65}{60}$

$= -1\frac{5}{60}$ Write the improper fraction as a mixed number.

$= -1\frac{1}{12}$ Write the fraction part in lowest terms to simplify. ∎

Application: Carpentry

Example 5

A sheet of plywood is $\frac{4}{3}$ feet wide and $\frac{59}{8}$ feet long. Write each dimension as a mixed number.

Solution

$$\begin{array}{r} 1 \text{ R } 1 \\ 3\overline{)4} \end{array} \longrightarrow 1\frac{1}{3} \qquad \begin{array}{r} 7 \text{ R } 3 \\ 8\overline{)59} \end{array} \longrightarrow 7\frac{3}{8}$$

The sheet of plywood is $1\frac{1}{3}$ feet wide and $7\frac{3}{8}$ feet long. ∎

Problem Set

Find each sum or difference. Write the answer in simplest form.

1. $\dfrac{4}{9} + \dfrac{3}{9}$

2. $\dfrac{1}{8} + \dfrac{3}{8}$

3. $\dfrac{9}{10} - \dfrac{3}{10}$

4. $-\dfrac{3}{4} + \dfrac{1}{4}$

5. $-\dfrac{7}{20} - \left(-\dfrac{3}{20}\right)$

6. $-\dfrac{7}{18} - \dfrac{13}{18}$

7. $\dfrac{1}{2} + \dfrac{1}{4}$

8. $-\dfrac{1}{6} + \dfrac{2}{3}$

9. $\dfrac{3}{8} - \left(-\dfrac{1}{4}\right)$

10. $-\dfrac{3}{10} - \left(-\dfrac{17}{20}\right)$

11. $-\dfrac{3}{40} - \left(-\dfrac{2}{10}\right)$

12. $-\dfrac{7}{16} - \dfrac{7}{8}$

13. $\dfrac{7}{30} + \dfrac{9}{20}$

14. $\dfrac{7}{8} - \dfrac{1}{6}$

15. $-\dfrac{7}{30} - \left(-\dfrac{1}{25}\right)$

16. $\dfrac{15}{16} - \left(-\dfrac{1}{10}\right)$

17. $\dfrac{4}{9} + \dfrac{3}{7}$

18. $\dfrac{4}{5} + \dfrac{2}{9}$

19. $-\dfrac{2}{9} - \left(-\dfrac{2}{3}\right)$

20. $-\dfrac{7}{12} - \dfrac{3}{4}$

Convert each improper fraction to a mixed number.

21. $\dfrac{9}{4}$

22. $\dfrac{5}{3}$

23. $\dfrac{4}{3}$

24. $-\dfrac{5}{5}$

25. $\dfrac{7}{6}$

26. $\dfrac{7}{2}$

27. $\dfrac{25}{5}$

28. $-\dfrac{8}{7}$

29. $-\dfrac{16}{5}$

30. $\dfrac{13}{9}$

31. $\dfrac{42}{10}$

32. $\dfrac{35}{12}$

33. $-\dfrac{54}{8}$

34. $\dfrac{100}{9}$

35. $\dfrac{75}{20}$

Select the best answer.

36. Which fraction is not an improper fraction?

   A. $\dfrac{4}{3}$ **C.** $\dfrac{7}{7}$

   B. $\dfrac{5}{6}$ **D.** $\dfrac{9}{2}$

37. Which fraction is equivalent to a whole number?

   A. $\dfrac{3}{6}$ **C.** $\dfrac{8}{6}$

   B. $\dfrac{4}{5}$ **D.** $\dfrac{10}{5}$

Find the difference. Write the answer as a mixed number in simplest form.

38. $-\dfrac{1}{10} - \dfrac{14}{15}$

39. $-\dfrac{1}{5} - \dfrac{11}{12}$

40. $-\dfrac{4}{9} - \dfrac{8}{11}$

41. $-\dfrac{3}{8} - \dfrac{9}{10}$

Solve each problem. Write answers in complete sentences with fractions and mixed numbers in simplest form.

42. One piece of wood measures $\dfrac{11}{16}$ feet and another piece of wood measures $\dfrac{5}{16}$ feet. What is the combined length of the two pieces of wood?

43. Ebenezer spent $\dfrac{3}{8}$ of his allowance on Saturday and $\dfrac{1}{5}$ on Sunday. What fraction of his allowance did he spend?

44. Kia had $\dfrac{8}{9}$ yard of ribbon. She used $\dfrac{2}{3}$ yard for a bow. How much ribbon does Kia have left?

*45. **Challenge** Roscoe drank $\dfrac{1}{4}$ quart of juice for breakfast, $\dfrac{1}{2}$ quart of water for lunch, and $\dfrac{1}{2}$ quart of milk for dinner. Between meals, he drank $\dfrac{5}{8}$ quart of water. How much more water did Roscoe drink than milk and juice combined?

*46. **Challenge** Darlene played a video game for 15 minutes in the morning, $\dfrac{1}{2}$ hour in the afternoon, and 10 minutes in the evening. What was the total time she spent playing the video game, expressed in hours as a fraction in simplest form?

Working with Improper Fractions and Mixed Numbers

Sometimes it is easier to work with a value as a mixed number, but other times it is better to work with an equivalent improper fraction.

If you keep in mind that a mixed number is the sum of a whole number and a fraction, you can express the mixed number as an improper fraction.

To convert a mixed number to an improper fraction, just use common denominators to add the whole part of the mixed number to the fraction part. If you do the same thing with variables as you work with a specific example, you can see how the general strategy works.

THINK ABOUT IT

The number $5\frac{1}{2}$ is not the same as $5 \cdot \frac{1}{2}$. It is the same as $5 + \frac{1}{2}$.

With Numbers	With Variables	
$5\frac{1}{2} = 5 + \frac{1}{2}$	$x\frac{a}{b} = x + \frac{a}{b}$	
$= \frac{5}{1} + \frac{1}{2}$	$= \frac{x}{1} + \frac{a}{b}$	Write the whole as a fraction with denominator 1.
$= \frac{5}{1} \cdot \frac{2}{2} + \frac{1}{2}$	$= \frac{x}{1} \cdot \frac{b}{b} + \frac{a}{b}$	Multiply to get common denominators.
$= \frac{5 \cdot 2}{1 \cdot 2} + \frac{1}{2}$	$= \frac{x \cdot b}{1 \cdot b} + \frac{a}{b}$	Simplify.
$= \frac{5 \cdot 2}{2} + \frac{1}{2}$	$= \frac{x \cdot b}{b} + \frac{a}{b}$	Simplify.
$= \frac{5 \cdot 2 + 1}{2}$	$= \frac{x \cdot b + a}{b}$	Add fractions.
$= \frac{10 + 1}{2} = \frac{11}{2}$		Simplify the number problem.

Converting Mixed Numbers to Improper Fractions

CONVERTING MIXED NUMBERS TO IMPROPER FRACTIONS

Step 1 Multiply the whole part by the denominator of the fraction part.
Step 2 Add the result to the numerator. Use this as the numerator of the improper fraction.
Step 3 Keep the original denominator.

(continued)

Example 1 Convert each improper fraction to a mixed number.

Ⓐ $2\frac{3}{5}$

Solution

$$2\frac{3}{5} = \frac{2 \cdot 5 + 3}{5}$$ Multiply the whole part by the denominator. Add the result to the numerator.

$$= \frac{13}{5}$$ Simplify. ∎

Ⓑ $-6\frac{7}{8}$

Solution Follow the steps for $6\frac{7}{8}$. Keep the negative sign in front.

$$-\left(6\frac{7}{8}\right) = -\left(\frac{6 \cdot 8 + 7}{8}\right)$$ Multiply the whole part by the denominator. Add the result to the numerator.

$$= -\frac{55}{8}$$ Simplify. ∎

Adding and Subtracting Mixed Numbers

A mixed number has an integer part and a fraction part.

$$3 \text{ is the integer part, } \rightarrow 3\frac{2}{5} \leftarrow \frac{2}{5} \text{ is the fraction part}$$

ADDING AND SUBTRACTING WITH MIXED NUMBERS

Method 1
Add or subtract the integer parts and fraction parts separately.
Simplify if possible.

Method 2
Write integers and mixed numbers as improper fractions.
Add or subtract the fractions.
Simplify if possible.

Example 2

Find the value of each expression. Write the answer in simplest form.

Ⓐ $2\frac{3}{4} + 3\frac{1}{12}$

Solution Use Method 1.

$$2\frac{3}{4} = 2\frac{9}{12}$$ Write $\frac{3}{4}$ as the equivalent fraction $\frac{9}{12}$.

Add the integer parts: $2 + 3 = 5$.

$$+ \ 3\frac{1}{12} = 3\frac{1}{12}$$ Add the fraction parts: $\frac{9}{12} + \frac{1}{12} = \frac{10}{12}$.

$$5\frac{10}{12} = 5\frac{5}{6}$$ Simplify. ∎

B $\frac{1}{8} - 1\frac{3}{10}$

Solution   Use Method 2.

$\frac{1}{8} - 1\frac{3}{10} = \frac{1}{8} - \frac{13}{10}$ Write the mixed number as an improper fraction.

$= \frac{5}{40} - \frac{52}{40}$ Write each fraction as an equivalent fraction, using the least common denominator 40.

$= -\frac{47}{40}$ Subtract the fractions.

$= -1\frac{7}{40}$ Simplify by writing the improper fraction as a mixed number. ∎

C $4 - 2\frac{2}{5} + \frac{1}{2}$

Solution   Use Method 2.

$4 - 2\frac{2}{5} + \frac{1}{2} = \frac{4}{1} - \frac{12}{5} + \frac{1}{2}$ Write the integer and mixed number as improper fractions.

$= \frac{40}{10} - \frac{24}{10} + \frac{5}{10}$ Write each fraction as an equivalent fraction, using the least common denominator 10.

$= \frac{40 - 24 + 5}{10}$

$= \frac{21}{10}$ Subtract and add to simplify the expression in the numerator.

$= 2\frac{1}{10}$ Write the improper fraction as a mixed number to simplify. ∎

Application: Carpentry

Example 3

A carpenter cuts a board $10\frac{3}{4}$ inches long from a board $33\frac{1}{4}$ inches long. The saw cut is $\frac{1}{8}$ inch wide. What is the length of the remaining piece?

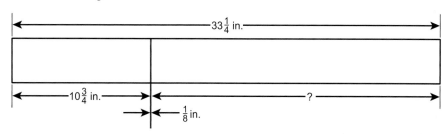

(continued)

Solution Subtract $10\frac{3}{4}$ and $\frac{1}{8}$ from $33\frac{1}{4}$. Use Method 2.

$$33\frac{1}{4} - 10\frac{3}{4} - \frac{1}{8} = \frac{133}{4} - \frac{43}{4} - \frac{1}{8}$$

$$= \frac{266}{8} - \frac{86}{8} - \frac{1}{8}$$

$$= \frac{179}{8}$$

$$= 22\frac{3}{8}$$

The remaining piece is $22\frac{3}{8}$ inches long. ∎

TIP

The expression $33\frac{1}{4} - \left(10\frac{3}{4} + \frac{1}{8}\right)$ can be used in this application. Find the sum $10\frac{3}{4} + \frac{1}{8}$ and then subtract that result from $33\frac{1}{4}$.

Problem Set

Find the value of each expression. Write the answer in simplest form.

1. $6\frac{1}{8} + 1\frac{3}{8}$

2. $6\frac{7}{20} - 2\frac{1}{20}$

3. $-\frac{2}{3} - 3\frac{2}{3}$

4. $1\frac{2}{5} - \left(-\frac{1}{5}\right)$

5. $1\frac{1}{4} + 4\frac{5}{12}$

6. $\frac{11}{12} - 2\frac{5}{6}$

7. $1\frac{5}{6} - \left(-\frac{2}{3}\right)$

8. $5\frac{1}{2} - 3\frac{5}{6}$

9. $4\frac{3}{8} - 2\frac{9}{16}$

10. $-1\frac{9}{10} - \frac{3}{4}$

11. $1\frac{5}{6} - \left(-1\frac{3}{10}\right)$

12. $8 - 3\frac{1}{4} + \frac{7}{8}$

13. $\frac{1}{3} + 3\frac{1}{6} + 3$

14. $-\frac{1}{3} - 2\frac{1}{4} - 1\frac{1}{6}$

15. $4\frac{1}{2} - 1\frac{1}{10} + 6\frac{2}{5}$

16. $\frac{1}{40} - 1\frac{1}{25} - \frac{11}{100}$

Convert each mixed number to an improper fraction.

17. $1\frac{1}{4}$

18. $3\frac{1}{2}$

19. $4\frac{1}{5}$

20. $2\frac{3}{4}$

21. $-1\frac{5}{6}$

22. $6\frac{1}{4}$

23. $-2\frac{3}{5}$

24. $7\frac{1}{3}$

25. $9\frac{7}{8}$

26. $8\frac{3}{10}$

27. $5\frac{8}{9}$

28. $-8\frac{2}{5}$

29. $9\frac{12}{13}$

30. $25\frac{1}{4}$

31. $3\frac{a}{b}$

Solve each problem.

A. Write an expression or equation to model the problem.

B. Answer the question using a mixed number in simplest form.

32. Ed wrote a book report in $1\frac{1}{2}$ hours. He spent $\frac{3}{4}$ hours studying for a math quiz. How much more time did he spend on the book report?

33. A cafeteria served $5\frac{1}{4}$ pounds of beef, $2\frac{5}{8}$ pounds of ham, and $4\frac{1}{2}$ pounds of turkey one day. What was the total amount of meat served that day?

34. A punch recipe calls for $1\frac{1}{3}$ cups of orange juice, $\frac{3}{4}$ cup of grape juice, and $2\frac{1}{2}$ cups of apple juice. How much fruit juice does the recipe call for?

35. A group hiked $2\frac{7}{10}$ miles from their campground to a scenic overlook and then $3\frac{1}{2}$ miles from the overlook to a lake, where they ate lunch. After lunch they hiked $4\frac{3}{4}$ miles directly back to the campground. How much farther did the group hike before lunch than after lunch?

36. The diagram represents a set of stairs. All angles in the diagram are right angles. Two of the treads are each $11\frac{3}{4}$ inches long. What is the length of the bottom tread, labeled x in.?

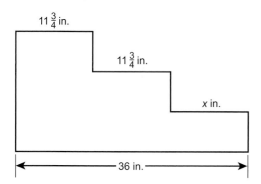

*37. **Challenge** A pool manager told three new employees to report the amount of time they worked on their first day of employment. The reported times were $5\frac{1}{2}$ hours, 6.75 hours, and 5 hours 48 minutes. What was the total time, expressed in hours as a mixed number?

*38. **Challenge** Kristen had a board 8 feet long. She cut these lengths from the board: 1 foot $2\frac{3}{8}$ inches, $10\frac{5}{8}$ inches, and 2 feet $6\frac{1}{4}$ inches. Allowing $\frac{1}{8}$ inch for each saw cut, what was the length of the remaining piece?

*39. **Challenge** Write the fifth term in the sequence below. Then find the sum of all five terms.

$$3, \frac{3}{2}, \frac{3}{4}, \frac{3}{8}, ?$$

Multiplying and Dividing Mixed Numbers

You will use your skills of multiplying and dividing fractions to multiply and divide mixed numbers.

To multiply mixed numbers, change each mixed number to an improper fraction. Then, multiply the numerators, multiply the denominators, and write the product in lowest terms.

Multiplying Mixed Numbers

Example 1 Multiply. Write each product as either a whole number or a mixed number in lowest terms.

Ⓐ $3 \cdot 2\frac{1}{2}$

Solution

$3 \cdot 2\frac{1}{2} = \frac{3}{1} \cdot \frac{5}{2}$ Write each factor as an improper fraction.

$= \frac{15}{2}$ Multiply.

$= 7\frac{1}{2}$ Convert the answer to a mixed number. ∎

> **THINK ABOUT IT**
>
> Since $3 \geq 1$, $\frac{3}{1}$ is an improper fraction

Ⓑ $2\frac{2}{3} \cdot 4\frac{4}{5}$

Solution Write each mixed number as an improper fraction.

$2\frac{2}{3} \cdot 4\frac{4}{5} = \frac{8}{\cancel{3}_{1}} \cdot \frac{\overset{8}{\cancel{24}}}{5}$ Write each factor as an improper fraction and divide out the common factor of 3.

$= \frac{64}{5}$ Multiply.

$= 12\frac{4}{5}$ Convert the answer to a mixed number. ∎

C $6\frac{1}{7} \cdot (-7)$

Solution Write each factor as an improper fraction.

$$6\frac{1}{7} \cdot (-7) = \frac{43}{\overset{1}{\cancel{7}}} \cdot \left(-\frac{\overset{1}{\cancel{7}}}{1}\right) \quad \text{Divide out the common factor of 7.}$$

$$= -\frac{43}{1} \qquad \text{Multiply.}$$

$$= -43 \qquad \text{Simplify.} \quad \blacksquare$$

Dividing Mixed Numbers

Dividing mixed numbers is like multiplying. Start by changing the mixed numbers to improper fractions. Next, change division to multiplying by the reciprocal.

Example 2   Divide. Write each quotient as either a whole number or a mixed number in lowest terms.

A $-5\frac{2}{3} \div \left(-2\frac{1}{2}\right)$

Solution Write each mixed number as an improper fraction.

$$-5\frac{2}{3} \div \left(-2\frac{1}{2}\right) = -\frac{17}{3} \div \left(-\frac{5}{2}\right) \quad \begin{array}{l}\text{Write each factor as an improper}\\ \text{fraction.}\end{array}$$

$$= -\frac{17}{3} \cdot \left(-\frac{2}{5}\right) \quad \text{Multiply by the reciprocal of } -\frac{5}{2}.$$

$$= \frac{34}{15} \quad \begin{array}{l}\text{Multiply. Both factors are negative, so}\\ \text{the product is positive.}\end{array}$$

$$= 2\frac{4}{15} \quad \begin{array}{l}\text{Convert the answer to a mixed}\\ \text{number.} \quad \blacksquare\end{array}$$

B $6\frac{1}{2} \div 2$

Solution Write each factor as an improper fraction.

$$6\frac{1}{2} \div 2 = \frac{13}{2} \div \frac{2}{1} \quad \text{Write each factor as an improper fraction.}$$

$$= \frac{13}{2} \cdot \frac{1}{2} \quad \text{Multiply by the reciprocal of } \frac{2}{1}.$$

$$= \frac{13}{4} \quad \text{Multiply.}$$

$$= 3\frac{1}{4} \quad \text{Convert the answer to a mixed number.} \quad \blacksquare$$

> **TIP**
>
> **Estimate to check your answer for reasonableness. In Example 2B, $6 \div 2 = 3$ and $7 \div 2 = 3\frac{1}{2}$.**

(continued)

C $\frac{a}{b} \div 3\frac{3}{4}$

Solution Write the mixed number as an improper fraction.

$$\frac{a}{b} \div 3\frac{3}{4} = \frac{a}{b} \div \frac{15}{4} \qquad \text{Write the mixed number as an improper fraction.}$$

$$= \frac{a}{b} \cdot \frac{4}{15} \qquad \text{Multiply by the reciprocal of } \frac{15}{4}.$$

$$= \frac{4a}{15b} \qquad \text{Commutative Property of Multiplication} \quad \blacksquare$$

Application: Catering

Example 3

A A recipe serves six people. Carla needs to serve 18 people. If the recipe calls for $1\frac{3}{4}$ cups of flour, how much flour will Carla need?

Solution Carla needs to triple every ingredient because 18 people is 3 times the number of people her recipe will serve.

$$1\frac{3}{4} \cdot 3 = \frac{7}{4} \cdot \frac{3}{1} \qquad \text{Write the factors as improper fractions.}$$

$$= \frac{21}{4} \qquad \text{Multiply.}$$

$$= 5\frac{1}{4} \qquad \text{Convert the improper fraction to a mixed number.} \quad \blacksquare$$

She needs $5\frac{1}{4}$ cups of flour. $\blacksquare$

B A recipe that serves four people calls for $1\frac{1}{3}$ cups of flour. Carla has $9\frac{1}{3}$ cups of flour. How many people can Carla serve?

Solution Divide to find by how much she can multiply the recipe.

$$9\frac{1}{3} \div 1\frac{1}{3} = \frac{28}{3} \div \frac{4}{3} \qquad \text{Write the mixed numbers as improper fractions.}$$

$$= \frac{\overset{7}{\cancel{28}}}{\underset{1}{\cancel{3}}} \cdot \frac{\overset{1}{\cancel{3}}}{\underset{1}{\cancel{4}}} \qquad \text{Multiply by the reciprocal of } \frac{4}{3}.$$

$$= \frac{7}{1} \qquad \text{Multiply.}$$

$$= 7 \qquad \text{Simplify.} \quad \blacksquare$$

Carla can multiply the recipe by 7. Multiply to find the maximum number of people Carla can serve.

$$7 \cdot 4 = 28$$

Carla can serve 28 people. $\blacksquare$

Problem Set

Multiply. Write each product as either a whole number or a mixed number in lowest terms.

1. $1\frac{1}{2} \cdot 8$

2. $6 \cdot 4\frac{2}{3}$

3. $10 \cdot 3\frac{1}{4}$

4. $-5 \cdot 2\frac{5}{6}$

5. $3\frac{1}{3} \cdot 2\frac{1}{6}$

6. $4\frac{1}{2} \cdot 4\frac{1}{2}$

7. $-5\frac{2}{3} \cdot 3\frac{3}{4}$

8. $2\frac{3}{7} \cdot 1\frac{3}{4}$

9. $8\frac{1}{3} \cdot (-24)$

10. $4\frac{2}{5} \cdot 3\frac{4}{7}$

11. $3\frac{5}{6} \cdot 4\frac{1}{2} \cdot \left(-\frac{3}{4}\right)$

12. $1\frac{2}{10} \cdot \left(-2\frac{1}{12}\right) \cdot 1\frac{1}{2}$

13. $\frac{x}{2} \cdot 2\frac{4}{5}$

14. $5 \cdot y \cdot \left(-2\frac{4}{13}\right)$

Divide. Write each quotient as either a whole number or a mixed number in lowest terms.

15. $7\frac{1}{2} \div 2\frac{1}{2}$

16. $10 \div 4\frac{1}{4}$

17. $3\frac{1}{2} \div \frac{1}{2}$

18. $5 \div 1\frac{1}{8}$

19. $4\frac{2}{5} \div 1\frac{1}{3}$

20. $6\frac{5}{6} \div 3\frac{2}{3}$

21. $4\frac{4}{5} \div \frac{3}{10}$

22. $2\frac{1}{7} \div 4\frac{2}{7}$

23. $6\frac{2}{3} \div 2\frac{2}{15}$

24. $10\frac{5}{8} \div 3\frac{1}{4}$

25. $\frac{x}{7} \div 1\frac{3}{7}$

26. $-2\frac{1}{2} \div c$

27. $3\frac{2}{5} \cdot 1\frac{1}{2} \div 2\frac{3}{4}$

*28. Challenge $24\frac{3}{4} \div 2\frac{1}{6} \div 1\frac{2}{3}$

Solve each problem.

29. A carpenter is cutting a board that is $8\frac{1}{2}$ feet long into 6 sections of equal length. What will be the length of each section?

30. A carpenter is cutting a board that is $10\frac{1}{2}$ feet long into as many sections that are $1\frac{7}{8}$ feet long as he can.
   A. How many complete sections will he have?
   B. How much will be left over?

31. A recipe serves four people. Andy needs to serve 12 people. If the recipe calls for $1\frac{1}{3}$ cups of sugar, how much sugar will Andy need?

32. A recipe that serves four people calls for $2\frac{3}{4}$ cups of nuts. Antonya has $16\frac{1}{2}$ cups of nuts. How many people can Antonya serve?

33. A book weighs $4\frac{7}{16}$ pounds. How much does a crate containing two dozen of these books weigh if the crate itself weighs $3\frac{1}{4}$ pounds?

Equations with Fractions and Mixed Numbers

Use the properties of equality to solve equations with fractions and mixed numbers.

Using Addition and Subtraction to Solve Equations with Fractions

Fractions and mixed numbers are just types of numbers. So addition and subtraction properties of equality that you use to solve equations with integers also work with fractions and mixed numbers.

Example 1 Solve.

Ⓐ $t + \dfrac{2}{3} = 6$

Solution

$t + \dfrac{2}{3} - \dfrac{2}{3} = 6 - \dfrac{2}{3}$ Subtraction Property of Equality

$t = 6 - \dfrac{2}{3}$ Simplify on the left.

$t = \dfrac{18}{3} - \dfrac{2}{3}$ Rename 6 with a denominator of 3.

$t = \dfrac{16}{3} = 5\dfrac{1}{3}$ Subtract and write the answer as a mixed number.

Check $5\dfrac{1}{3} + \dfrac{2}{3} = 5 + \dfrac{3}{3} = 5 + 1 = 6$ ∎

Ⓑ $1\dfrac{4}{5} = x - \dfrac{3}{10}$

Solution

$1\dfrac{4}{5} = x - \dfrac{3}{10}$

$1\dfrac{4}{5} + \dfrac{3}{10} = x - \dfrac{3}{10} + \dfrac{3}{10}$ Addition Property of Equality

$1\dfrac{4}{5} + \dfrac{3}{10} = x$ Simplify on the right.

$1\dfrac{8}{10} + \dfrac{3}{10} = x$ Rename $\dfrac{4}{5}$ with a denominator of 10.

$$1\frac{11}{10} = x \qquad \text{Add.}$$

$$1 + 1\frac{1}{10} = x \qquad \text{Write } \frac{11}{10} \text{ as a mixed number.}$$

$$2\frac{1}{10} = x \qquad \text{Add.} \blacksquare$$

TIP

If the fraction part is an improper fraction, rewrite the fraction part as a mixed number, and then combine the whole parts.

Using Multiplication and Division to Solve Equations with Fractions

Multiplication and division properties of equality that you use to solve equations with integers also work with fractions and mixed numbers.

Example 2 Solve.

A $\frac{1}{3}h = \frac{5}{8}$

Solution Use division to isolate the variable h.

$$\frac{1}{3}h = \frac{5}{8}$$

$$\frac{1}{3} \div \frac{1}{3} \cdot h = \frac{5}{8} \div \frac{1}{3} \qquad \text{Divide each side by } \frac{1}{3}.$$

$$\frac{1}{3} \cdot \frac{3}{1} \cdot h = \frac{5}{8} \cdot \frac{3}{1} \qquad \text{Write each division as multiplication by the reciprocal.}$$

$$h = \frac{15}{8} = 1\frac{7}{8} \qquad \text{Multiply and simplfy.} \blacksquare$$

B $6 = \frac{2}{3}p$

Solution Multiply by the reciprocal to isolate the variable p.

$$6 = \frac{2}{3}p$$

$$6 \cdot \frac{3}{2} = \frac{2}{3} \cdot \frac{3}{2} \cdot p \qquad \text{Multiply each side by the reciprocal of } \frac{2}{3}.$$

$$6 \cdot \frac{3}{2} = p \qquad \text{Simplify on the right.}$$

$$\frac{18}{2} = p \qquad \text{Multiply.}$$

$$9 = p \qquad \text{Simplify.} \blacksquare$$

(continued)

REMEMBER

Division Property of Equality
For any real numbers a, b, and n (where $n \neq 0$), if $a = b$, then
$$\frac{a}{n} = \frac{b}{n}.$$

Multiplication Property of Equality
For any real numbers a, b, and n, if $a = b$, then $an = bn$.

TIP

Often, the division step is skipped and the first step is to multiply each side by the reciprocal. That method will be shown from now on.

C $3\frac{5}{7}a = 4$

Solution   Convert the mixed number to an improper fraction, and then multiply by the reciprocal to isolate a.

$$3\frac{5}{7}a = 4$$

$$\frac{26}{7}a = 4 \qquad \text{Write } 3\frac{5}{7} \text{ as an improper fraction.}$$

$$\frac{26}{7} \cdot \frac{7}{26} \cdot a = 4 \cdot \frac{7}{26} \qquad \text{Multiply each side by the reciprocal of } \frac{26}{7}.$$

$$a = 4 \cdot \frac{7}{26} \qquad \text{Simplify on the left.}$$

$$a = \frac{28}{26} = 1\frac{2}{26} = 1\frac{1}{13} \qquad \text{Multiply and simplify.} \quad \blacksquare$$

Application: Growth

Example 3

In June, Richard measured the height of a tree as $2\frac{3}{4}$ feet tall. When he measured it again in October, it was $5\frac{1}{2}$ feet tall. Write and solve an equation to find how much the tree grew between June and October.

Solution

$$2\frac{3}{4} - 2\frac{3}{4} + g = 5\frac{1}{2} - 2\frac{3}{4} \qquad \text{Subtraction Property of Equality}$$

$$g = 5\frac{1}{2} - 2\frac{3}{4} \qquad \text{Simplify on the left.}$$

$$g = 5\frac{2}{4} - 2\frac{3}{4} \qquad \text{Use the LCD of 4 to rename } 5\frac{1}{2}.$$

$$g = 4\frac{6}{4} - 2\frac{3}{4} \qquad \text{Rename 5 as } 4\frac{4}{4}. \text{ Add } \frac{4}{4} \text{ to } \frac{2}{4}.$$

$$g = 2\frac{3}{4} \qquad \text{Subtract.}$$

The tree grew $2\frac{3}{4}$ feet between June and October. $\quad \blacksquare$

> **TIP**
> Renaming $5\frac{2}{4}$ as $4\frac{6}{4}$ is not really necessary, but is one strategy. Instead, we could just break apart the mixed numbers and subtract whole parts from whole parts and fraction parts from fraction parts, and then simplify.

Problem Set

Solve.

1. $x + \dfrac{5}{6} = 3$

2. $\dfrac{1}{3} + g = 4\dfrac{1}{2}$

3. $\dfrac{1}{6}c = 12$

4. $-5\dfrac{4}{5} + h = 10\dfrac{1}{5}$

5. $-\dfrac{7}{10} = k - 6\dfrac{1}{10}$

6. $2\dfrac{3}{4} + a = 3\dfrac{3}{8}$

7. $-\dfrac{1}{2} + m = -5\dfrac{3}{7}$

8. $\dfrac{1}{2} + x + \dfrac{3}{4} = 5$

9. $\dfrac{3}{4}a = \dfrac{2}{5}$

10. $9 = \dfrac{1}{5}x$

11. $\dfrac{4}{9} = 2y$

12. $y + 4\dfrac{1}{3} = -2\dfrac{1}{2}$

13. $1\dfrac{1}{5} + d = -6\dfrac{1}{3}$

14. $-\dfrac{1}{2}n = 15$

15. $\dfrac{5}{8}q = -20$

16. $10 = q - 2\dfrac{1}{8}$

17. $-1\dfrac{1}{6}b = 5$

18. $21 = 3\dfrac{1}{2}w$

19. $-2 = -\dfrac{m}{2}$

20. $t - 4\dfrac{7}{9} = 16 - \dfrac{1}{2}$

21. $\dfrac{1}{8}g + \dfrac{1}{8}g = 7$

22. $3\dfrac{1}{8} + p - 1\dfrac{3}{4} = 10\dfrac{3}{5}$

23. $3\dfrac{3}{4} - 2b = 15\dfrac{7}{8}$

24. $-1\dfrac{1}{2}f + \dfrac{7}{10} = 5f$

Solve each problem.

A. Write an expression or equation.

B. Simplify or solve.

C. State the answer as a complete sentence with a mixed number in simplest form.

25. Gary ran $5\dfrac{1}{2}$ miles. This is $2\dfrac{3}{4}$ miles longer than Finn ran. Write and solve an equation to find how far Finn ran.

26. The perimeter of the triangle is $8\dfrac{5}{8}$ inches. Write and solve an equation to find the value of x.

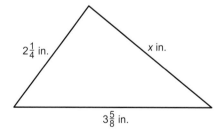

27. A team of runners ran a relay race. Each runner ran $7\dfrac{1}{2}$ kilometers. The total length of the race was 45 kilometers. Write and solve an equation to find how many runners were on the team.

28. The sum of twice a number and $6\dfrac{1}{10}$ is $9\dfrac{2}{5}$. Write and solve an equation to find the number.

*29. Challenge The mean of a set of values is the quotient of the sum of the values and the number of values. Write and solve an equation to find the value of x in the data set below if the mean of the data set is $4\dfrac{1}{8}$.

$$6\dfrac{1}{2},\ 2\dfrac{1}{4},\ x,\ 4\dfrac{3}{4}$$

*30. Challenge To find the median of a set of values, first arrange the data in order. Then choose the middle values if the number of values is odd, or find the mean of the two middle values if the number of values is even. Write and solve an equation to find the value of y in the data set below if the median of the data set is $3\dfrac{13}{15}$.

(Assume the data are already listed in order.)

$$2\dfrac{1}{2},\ 2\dfrac{3}{4},\ 3\dfrac{5}{6},\ y,\ 4\dfrac{5}{8},\ 4\dfrac{3}{4}$$

UNIT 5   Combined Operations

This yacht is propelled by a sail, a motor, or both.

Many yachts can be powered by the wind, by a gas engine, or both. A hybrid automobile can run on gasoline or electric power. These combinations are very powerful. Combining addition or subtraction with multiplication or division is powerful as well. You can use equations and expressions with mixed operations to solve many complex problems.

Big Ideas

▶ You can use the laws of arithmetic to solve algebraic equations and inequalities.

▶ Solving an equation or inequality means finding values for the variable or variables that make the equation or inequality a true statement.

Unit Topics

▶ The Distributive Property

▶ Like Terms

▶ Expressions with Mixed Operations

▶ Equations with Mixed Operations

▶ Error Analysis

▶ Inequalities

The Distributive Property

When you simplify an expression involving parentheses, the order of operations tells you to begin inside parentheses and work your way out. There is another way to simplify expressions that have parentheses.

The distributive property combines multiplication with either addition or subtraction.

DISTRIBUTIVE PROPERTY

For all numbers *a*, *b*, and *c*:   **Examples**

$$a(b + c) = ab + ac$$ $$3(5 + 2) = 3 \cdot 5 + 3 \cdot 2$$

and

$$a(b - c) = ab - ac$$ $$6(4 - 10) = 6 \cdot 4 - 6 \cdot 10$$

Verifying the Distributive Property

You can use the order of operations to verify the distributive property.

Example 1   Verify the distributive property in each case.

A $3(5 + 2) = 3 \cdot 5 + 3 \cdot 2$

Solution

$$3(5 + 2) = 3 \cdot 5 + 3 \cdot 2$$
$$3(7) = 15 + 6$$
$$21 = 21 \ \blacksquare$$

On the left side, add inside parentheses first. On the right side, use the distributive property to multiply first.

> **TIP**
>
> When you use the distributive property, you have *distributed* the factor through the terms.

B $6(4 - 10) = 6 \cdot 4 - 6 \cdot 10$

Solution

$$6(4 - 10) = 6 \cdot 4 - 6 \cdot 10$$
$$6(-6) = 24 - 60$$
$$-36 = -36 \ \blacksquare$$

On the left side, subtract inside parentheses first. On the right side, use the distributive property to multiply first.

Using the Distributive Property to Rewrite Expressions

You can use the distributive property to change an addition expression without parentheses to one with parentheses (and vice versa).

Example 2 Rewrite each expression without grouping symbols.

Ⓐ $2(5 + 7)$

Solution

$2(5 + 7) = 2 \cdot 5 + 2 \cdot 7$ ∎

Ⓑ $-3(4 + x)$

Solution

$-3(4 + x) = -3 \cdot 4 + (-3) \cdot x$ ∎

Example 3 Rewrite each expression with grouping symbols.

Ⓐ $2 \cdot 3 + 2 \cdot 11$

Solution

$2 \cdot 3 + 2 \cdot 11 = 2(3 + 11)$ ∎

Ⓑ $8 \cdot 1 + 8 \cdot (-7)$

Solution

$$8 \cdot 1 + 8 \cdot (-7) = 8(1 + (-7))$$
$$= 8(1 - 7) \qquad \text{Simplify } 1 + (-7) \text{ by writing } 1 - 7. \ ∎$$

Ⓒ $5r - 5 \cdot 12$

Solution

$5r - 5 \cdot 12 = 5(r - 12)$ ∎

Using the Distributive Property to Evaluate Expressions

Using the distributive property to combine multiplication with either addition or subtraction gives you a powerful tool for evaluating certain types of expressions.

Example 4 Use properties and mental math to evaluate each expression.

Ⓐ $6 \cdot 74$

Solution

$$\begin{aligned} 6 \cdot 74 &= 6(70 + 4) && \text{Write 74 as a sum.} \\ &= 6 \cdot 70 + 6 \cdot 4 && \text{Apply the distributive property.} \\ &= 420 + 24 && \text{Evaluate the expression.} \\ &= 444 \ ∎ \end{aligned}$$

B $8 \cdot 99$

Solution

$$8 \cdot 99 = 8(100 - 1) \qquad \text{Write 99 as a difference.}$$
$$= 8 \cdot 100 - 8 \cdot 1 \qquad \text{Apply the distributive property.}$$
$$= 800 - 8 \qquad \text{Evaluate the expression.}$$
$$= 792 \ \blacksquare$$

C $7 \cdot 67 + 7 \cdot 3$

Solution

$$7 \cdot 67 + 7 \cdot 3 = 7(67 + 3) \qquad \text{Apply the distributive property.}$$
$$= 7(70) \qquad \text{The sum 70 is easier to multiply.}$$
$$= 490 \ \blacksquare$$

TIP

Use the methods shown in Example 4 to do mental math. In Example 4B, writing 99 as 100 − 1 gives you numbers that are easy to work with.

Solving Equations by Recognizing the Distributive Property

Example 5 Solve each equation.

A $3 \cdot 5 + 3 \cdot a = 3(5 + 7)$

Solution By the distributive property, you know that $3 \cdot 5 + 3 \cdot 7 = 3(5 + 7)$, so $a = 7$. $\blacksquare$

B $b(1.2 + 5.4) = 8 \cdot 1.2 + 8 \cdot 5.4$

Solution By the distributive property, you know that $8(1.2 + 5.4) = 8 \cdot 1.2 + 8 \cdot 5.4$, so $b = 8$. $\blacksquare$

Application: Perimeter

Example 6 Find the perimeter of the rectangle.

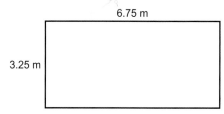

6.75 m

3.25 m

Solution

$$P = 2l + 2w \qquad \text{Write the formula for perimeter of a rectangle.}$$
$$= 2 \cdot 6.75 + 2 \cdot 3.25 \qquad \text{Substitute 6.75 for length } l \text{ and 3.25 for width } w.$$
$$= 2(6.75 + 3.25) \qquad \text{Apply the distributive property and then add the}$$
$$= 2(10) \qquad \qquad \text{decimals to get 10, which is easy to multiply.}$$
$$= 20$$

The perimeter is 20 meters. $\blacksquare$

Problem Set

. . . .

Verify the distributive property in each case.

1. $2(3 + 6) = 2 \cdot 3 + 2 \cdot 6$

2. $10(5 + 1) = 10 \cdot 5 + 10 \cdot 1$

3. $-1(-3 + 2) = -1 \cdot (-3) + (-1) \cdot 2$

4. $4(6 - 1) = 4 \cdot 6 - 4 \cdot 1$

5. $2(8 - 9) = 2 \cdot 8 - 2 \cdot 9$

6. $-6(1 - 3) = -6 \cdot 1 - (-6) \cdot 3$

Rewrite each expression without grouping symbols.

7. $5(5 + 1)$

8. $2(6 + 6)$

9. $4(v + 7)$

10. $-20(2 + 8)$

11. $-9(1 + y)$

12. $4(-8 + w)$

Rewrite each expression with grouping symbols.

13. $3 \cdot 6 + 3 \cdot 9$

14. $7 \cdot 5 + 7 \cdot (-6)$

15. $4 \cdot 2 - 4 \cdot 11$

16. $3x - 3 \cdot 7$

17. $5 \cdot 8 - 5s$

18. $6n - 6d$

19. $-2x - 2y$

20. $10a - 10 \cdot 1$

Use properties and mental math to evaluate each expression.

21. $2 \cdot 65$

22. $5 \cdot 37$

23. $6 \cdot 99$

24. $5 \cdot 98$

25. $8 \cdot 102$

26. $9 \cdot 34 + 9 \cdot 6$

27. $8 \cdot 87 + 8 \cdot 13$

28. $7 \cdot 248 - 7 \cdot 48$

*29. Challenge $4.58 \cdot 101$

*30. Challenge $12.05 \cdot 86 - 12.05 \cdot 75$

Use the distributive property to solve each equation.

31. $2 \cdot 6 + 2 \cdot x = 2(6 + 3)$

32. $5 \cdot a + 5 \cdot 7 = 5(-1 + 7)$

33. $n(4 + 16) = 7 \cdot 4 + 7 \cdot 16$

34. $-2(x + 1) = -2 \cdot 4 + (-2) \cdot 1$

35. $10(-5 + s) = 10 \cdot (-5) + 10 \cdot (-1)$

36. $a(1.5 + 1.5) = -3 \cdot 1.5 + (-3) \cdot 1.5$

Use the distributive property to solve each problem. Show your work.

37. Find the perimeter of the rectangle.

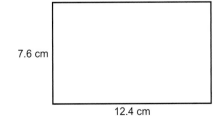

7.6 cm

12.4 cm

38. Find the perimeter of the equilateral hexagon.

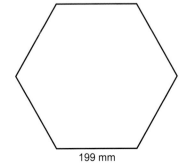

199 mm

39. The diagram represents a parcel of land formed by two rectangular regions. Find the total area.

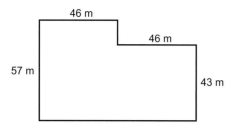

40. Find the total cost of each set of purchases.

   A. 5 gallons of milk at $3.95 per gallon

   B. 9 square yards of carpet at $29.99 per square yard

   C. 6 boxes of popcorn at $1.85 per box

   D. 4 bars of soap at $1.67 each and 4 tubes of toothpaste at $2.33 each

   E. 15 towels at $11.25 each and 15 washcloths at $3.75 each

*41. Challenge Find the total cost of each set of purchases. Round each answer to the nearest cent.

   A. 8 gallons of gasoline at $2.999 per gallon

   B. 20 ounces of cereal at $0.241 per ounce

Like Terms

To simplify some variable expressions, you need to identify and combine like terms.

Identifying Like Terms

A sum or difference expression is made up of *terms*. **Like terms** have the same variable part or parts. Numbers are considered to be like terms; they can be called *numerical terms*. Terms are made up of factors that are multiplied together.

THINK ABOUT IT

Like terms can have exponents. For example, the like terms $3x^2$ and $5x^2$ have the exponent 2.

Example 1   Identify the like terms.

A $5x, 5y, -2x, 5, -11$

Solution

$\{5x, -2x\}, \{5, -11\}, 5y$ The terms $5x$ and $-2x$ have the same variable. The terms 5 and -11 are numerical terms.

The terms $5x$ and $-2x$ form one pair of like terms; and the terms 5 and -11 form another pair of like terms. ■

B $-3a, 2b, 6ab, 1, a$

Solution   The term $6ab$ is the only term that has both variables a and b, so it is not like any of the other terms.

$\{-3a, a\}, 2b, 6ab, 1$ The terms $-3a$ and a have the same variable.

The terms $-3a$ and a are like terms. ■

C $6, 4p, 6p^2, -p, 3pq$

Solution

$6, \{4p, -p\}, 6p^2, 3pq$ The terms $4p$ and $-p$ have the same variables.

The terms $4p$ and $-p$ are like terms. ■

Using the Distributive Property to Combine Like Terms

The distributive property states that $a(b + c) = ab + ac$, which can also be written $ba + ca = (b + c)a$. So, if you have an expression like $5x - 2x$, you can use the distributive property to write it as $(5 - 2)x$ and simplify it to $3x$. This is how you combine like terms.

Example 2 Combine like terms.

Ⓐ $5x + 2x$

Solution

$$5x + 2x = (5 + 2)x \qquad \text{Apply the distributive property } ba + ca = (b + c)a.$$
$$= 7x \qquad \text{Add inside the parentheses.} \blacksquare$$

Ⓑ $3y - y + 6y$

Solution

$$3y - y + 6y = 3y - 1y + 6y \qquad \text{Write } -y \text{ as } -1y \text{ so that it has a numerical factor.}$$
$$= (3 - 1 + 6)y \qquad \text{Apply the distributive property.}$$
$$= 8y \qquad \text{Simplify inside the parentheses.} \blacksquare$$

Identifying and Combining Like Terms

The numerical factor in a term is called a **coefficient**. To combine like terms, you only need to add or subtract the coefficients.

COMBINING LIKE TERMS

To combine like terms, combine their coefficients. Keep the variable part the same.

Examples

$4x + 5x = 9x$

$3ab + 2ab - 1ab = 4ab$

REMEMBER

Combining like terms is based on the distributive property.

$4x + 5x = (4 + 5)x = 9x$

Example 3 Combine the like terms in each expression.

Ⓐ $2a + 3 - 5a + 8b + 3ab$

Solution

$$2a + 3 - 5a + 8b + 3ab = 2a - 5a + 3 + 8b + 3ab \qquad \text{Rewrite so that like terms are together.}$$
$$= -3a + 3 + 8b + 3ab \qquad \text{Combine like terms.} \blacksquare$$

Ⓑ $3s + rs - 4r - 6rs - 8rs$

Solution

$$3s + rs - 4r - 6rs - 8rs = 3s - 4r + 1rs - 6rs - 8rs \qquad \text{Rewrite } rs \text{ as } 1rs. \text{ Write like terms together.}$$
$$= 3s - 4r - 13rs \qquad \text{Combine like terms.} \blacksquare$$

Application: Sales Tax

Example 4 The sales tax rate in a certain state is 5%. Write a simplified expression for the total cost of an item that has a price of x dollars.

(continued)

Solution   The decimal equivalent of 5% is 0.05. When you pay 5% of x dollars in sales tax, you pay $0.05x$ dollars in sales tax.

Total cost = price of item + sales tax

$$= x + 0.05x$$

$$= 1.00x + 0.05x \qquad \text{Write } x \text{ as } 1.00x.$$

$$= 1.05x \qquad \text{Combine like terms.}$$

The total amount paid is $1.05x$ dollars. ∎

Problem Set

Identify the like terms.

1. $4x, 4y, 3y, 5x, -11$

2. $4a, -2b, a, 1, -1$

3. $3c, 3d, 6c, 6, 4a$

4. $-x, y, 6x, -8x, -8, -8z$

5. $4ab, -2b, 4a, 7, -5ab, -5$

6. $12c, d, c, -c, 12, 4d$

7. $-5u, 9v, 6uv, 2v, -uv, -5$

8. $7b, -8ab, 6, 4a, 7, 6bc, -5$

9. $3, 3rs, 3r, 3s, 8rs, 1, -9$

10. $-10, 4xy, 4y, 3y, 5y, -10y$

11. $4w, -9x, 4w, 2wxy, -wy, -wxy$

12. $\frac{1}{2}x, -3x, \frac{1}{2}, 2, -xy, \frac{1}{3}$

13. $1.5s, 1.5w, 2s, 2w, 10sw, 2$

14. $2ab, -2ab, 1.01ab, -b, -a$

Combine like terms.

15. $4a + 3a$

16. $7x + 7x$

17. $-3c + 5c$

18. $\frac{1}{4}x - \frac{1}{8}x$

19. $-5x - 2.2x + x$

20. $6t - \frac{1}{2}t + 8t - \frac{1}{2}t$

21. $5u - 5u + u - u$

22. $x + x + x - 10x$

* 23. **Challenge** $\frac{2}{3}a - \frac{1}{4}a + \frac{a}{12}$

* 24. **Challenge** $\frac{2}{5}x + 0.7x + \frac{1}{25}x$

Combine the like terms in each expression.

25. $8a + 5b - 2a$

26. $x + 4x - 6y + 5$

27. $3t + 4t - t + 5$

28. $5xy - 3x + 6y - xy + y$

29. $a - a + 6b - b - 5b + 6$

30. $3ax + 3x - 5ax - x - 5a + 10ax$

31. $z + 4w - (-3w) + 12z - z$

32. $3.5x + 4x - y + 2.5y - 1$

33. $r + rs - 5rs - 5rs + 2r - 6$

34. $4 - cd - 2cd - 3cd + 4 - c + d$

35. $5(x + 3) - 2x$

36. $a + 3(a - 1) - 5a$

37. $-6x + 2.5(x - 1) - 5x$

38. $x + \frac{3}{4}x - y + 5y + 3$

39. $5b + 3(2b + 1) - 5ab - 3$

* 40. **Challenge** $2.4(2x - 5r) + 3(1.1s + r) - 2x$

Solve each problem.

41. Write a simplified expression for the total cost of each purchase described. Show how you combine like terms to obtain your simplified expression.

   A. The price of an item is *d* dollars and the sales tax rate is 6%.

   B. The price of a meal is *m* dollars and an 18% tip is added.

   C. The price of a hotel room is *r* dollars and there is a hotel tax of 4.5%.

42. Write a simplified expression for the perimeter of each polygon.

   A. Rectangle

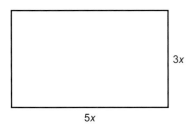

   $3x$

   $5x$

   B. Regular pentagon

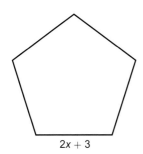

   $2x + 3$

   C. Two rectangles combined

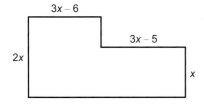

   $3x - 6$

   $3x - 5$

   $2x$

   x

*43. **Challenge** Coach Dixon is ordering T-shirts for his players. Each T-shirt costs $8.85. There is a $35 setup fee for silk-screening and a screening charge of $2.15 per shirt.

   A. Write a simplified expression for the total cost of *x* T-shirts. Show how you combine like terms to obtain your simplified expression.

   B. Find the total cost of 12 T-shirts. Show how you evaluate your expression to obtain your answer.

   C. The T-shirt company offers a 10% discount per shirt for orders of at least 20 shirts. (The discount is applied to both the cost of the shirt and the screening charge.) Explain why 20 shirts cost less than 19 shirts.

*44. **Challenge** The diagram consists of a circle with radius *r* and a square. The circle is *tangent* to each side of the square, which means that the circle touches each side of the square in exactly one point. Write a simplified expression for the sum of the circumference of the circle and perimeter of the square. (Hint: The formula for the circumference of a circle is $C = 2\pi r$.)

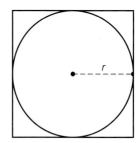

   r

Expressions with Mixed Operations

To simplify an expression that contains negative numbers, fractions, or decimals, use the **order of operations**.

> ### ORDER OF OPERATIONS
> **Step 1** Perform operations within grouping symbols.
> **Step 2** Multiply and divide from left to right.
> **Step 3** Add and subtract from left to right.

Simplifying Numerical Expressions

Example 1 Simplify.

Ⓐ $5 \cdot 2 - 6(-2)$

Solution

$$
\begin{aligned}
5 \cdot 2 - 6(-2) &= 10 - 6(-2) && \text{Multiply.} \\
&= 10 - (-12) && \text{Multiply.} \\
&= 10 + 12 && \text{To subtract } -12, \text{ add } 12. \\
&= 22 \ \blacksquare
\end{aligned}
$$

Ⓑ $-5 + 60 \div 5 - 2(-3)$

Solution

$$
\begin{aligned}
-5 + 60 \div 5 - 2(-3) &= -5 + 12 - 2(-3) && \text{Divide.} \\
&= -5 + 12 - (-6) && \text{Multiply.} \\
&= -5 + 12 + 6 && \text{To subtract } -6, \text{ add } 6. \\
&= 7 + 6 && \text{Add from left to right.} \\
&= 13 \ \blacksquare
\end{aligned}
$$

Ⓒ $-3 - 28 \div (3 + 1)$

Solution

$$
\begin{aligned}
-3 - 28 \div (3 + 1) &= -3 - 28 \div 4 && \text{Add inside the grouping symbols.} \\
&= -3 - 7 && \text{Divide.} \\
&= -10 && \text{Subtract from left to right.} \ \blacksquare
\end{aligned}
$$

D $\dfrac{2 \cdot (7 - 15)}{5 - 10 + 3}$

REMEMBER

A fraction bar represents division. It is also a grouping symbol.

Solution

$\dfrac{2 \cdot (7 - 15)}{5 - 10 + 3} = \dfrac{2 \cdot (-8)}{5 - 10 + 3}$ In the numerator, subtract inside the parentheses.

$\phantom{\dfrac{2 \cdot (7 - 15)}{5 - 10 + 3}} = \dfrac{-16}{-2}$ In the numerator, multiply. In the denominator, subtract and add from left to right.

$\phantom{\dfrac{2 \cdot (7 - 15)}{5 - 10 + 3}} = 8$ Divide. ■

Evaluating Algebraic Expressions

Variables in an algebraic expression can stand for any values. When you need a specific value for the expression, you just need to replace the variables with specific values. To evaluate an algebraic expression, substitute values for the variables and then simplify the resulting numerical expression.

Example 2

A Evaluate $7n + 5$ when $n = -8$.

Solution

$7n + 5 = 7 \cdot (-8) + 5$ Substitute -8 for n.

$ = -56 + 5$ Multiply.

$ = -51$ Add. ■

B Evaluate $\dfrac{c - 5d}{10(2d + 1)}$ when $c = 195$ and $d = -1$.

Solution

$\dfrac{c - 5d}{10(2d + 1)} = \dfrac{195 - 5 \cdot (-1)}{10(2 \cdot (-1) + 1)}$ Substitute 195 for c and -1 for d.

$\phantom{\dfrac{c - 5d}{10(2d + 1)}} = \dfrac{195 - (-5)}{10(-2 + 1)}$ Multiply $5 \cdot (-1)$ in the numerator. and $2 \cdot (-1)$ in the denominator.

$\phantom{\dfrac{c - 5d}{10(2d + 1)}} = \dfrac{195 + 5}{10(-1)}$ To subtract -5, add 5 in the numerator. Add $-2 + 1$ in the denominator.

$\phantom{\dfrac{c - 5d}{10(2d + 1)}} = \dfrac{200}{-10}$ Add in the numerator. Multiply in the denominator.

$\phantom{\dfrac{c - 5d}{10(2d + 1)}} = -20$ Divide. ■

Simplifying Expressions with Decimals and Fractions

Example 3 Simplify.

Ⓐ $\dfrac{-2 \cdot 1.5 + 3 \cdot (-2.15)}{0.5}$

Solution

$$\dfrac{-2 \cdot 1.5 + 3 \cdot (-2.15)}{0.5} = \dfrac{-3.0 + (-6.45)}{0.5} \qquad \text{Multiply in the numerator.}$$

$$= \dfrac{-9.45}{0.5} \qquad \text{Add in the numerator.}$$

$$= -18.9 \qquad \text{Divide.} \quad \blacksquare$$

Ⓑ $-3 \cdot \dfrac{2}{5} + \dfrac{1}{2} \cdot (-6)$

Solution

$$-3 \cdot \dfrac{2}{5} + \dfrac{1}{2} \cdot (-6) = -\dfrac{3}{1} \cdot \dfrac{2}{5} + \left(\dfrac{1}{2}\right) \cdot \left(-\dfrac{6}{1}\right) \qquad \text{Write the integers as fractions.}$$

$$= -\dfrac{6}{5} + (-3) \qquad \text{Multiply the fractions.}$$

$$= -\dfrac{6}{5} + \left(-\dfrac{15}{5}\right) \qquad \text{Write } -3 \text{ as a fraction with the denominator 5.}$$

$$= -\dfrac{21}{5} \qquad \text{Add.} \quad \blacksquare$$

> **REMEMBER**
>
> You can write an improper fraction as a mixed number.
> $$-\dfrac{21}{5} = -4\dfrac{1}{5}$$

Application: Temperature

Example 4 The formula to convert a temperature from degrees Celsius to Fahrenheit is $F = \dfrac{9}{5}C + 32$. What is the Fahrenheit equivalent of -12 degrees Celsius?

Solution Use the formula to convert degrees Celsius to degrees Fahrenheit.

$$F = \dfrac{9}{5}C + 32 \qquad \text{Write the formula.}$$

$$= \dfrac{9}{5} \cdot (-12) + 32 \qquad \text{Substitute } -12 \text{ for } C.$$

$$= \dfrac{9}{5} \cdot \left(-\dfrac{12}{1}\right) + 32 \qquad \text{Write } -12 \text{ as a fraction.}$$

$$= -\dfrac{108}{5} + 32 \qquad \text{Multiply the fractions.}$$

$$= -21.6 + 32 \qquad \text{Divide.}$$

$$= 10.4 \qquad \text{Add.}$$

$-12°C$ is equivalent to $10.4°F$. ■

Problem Set

Simplify.

1. $3 \cdot 5 + 6 \cdot (-1)$

2. $-6 \cdot 5 - 8 \cdot 10$

3. $10 \cdot (-3) - 3 \cdot (-4)$

4. $-6 \cdot (-1) + 6 \cdot 1 - 6 \cdot 2$

5. $-3 + 80 \div 8 - 5 \cdot (-1)$

6. $1 - 6 \cdot 3 + 5 \cdot 2$

7. $12 \div 6 - 10 \cdot 5 - 10 \cdot (-3)$

8. $7 + 2(3 + 7) - 5 \cdot (-3)$

9. $\dfrac{8}{3 \cdot 4} + 10 \cdot 2$

10. $-5 - (-24) \div 3 + 11$

11. $20 - (-24 - 3) + 16 \div 4$

12. $-1 + 5(100 - 95) + 4 \cdot (-2)$

13. $\dfrac{(62 - 12) - (4 \cdot 6)}{23 + 5 \cdot (8 - 10)}$

14. $\dfrac{15 \cdot (12 - 10)}{2 - 3 - 5}$

15. $\dfrac{2 - 8 \cdot 2 + 20 \div 4}{120 \div 40}$

*16. **Challenge** $2 \cdot 12 + 5 \cdot 2 - (1 + 20) + 40 \div (-2)$

*17. **Challenge** $\dfrac{8 - 13}{2 + 3 \cdot (8 - 7)} - 2 + 16 \cdot (14 - 19)$

*18. **Challenge** $16 - \dfrac{18}{9 \cdot 3} \cdot 5$

Evaluate the expression, using the given value(s) of the variable(s).

19. $5a + 10$ when $a = -3$

20. $-2c - 4$ when $c = 5$

21. $22 - 5x - 3x$ when $x = 6$

22. $-6a + a - 3b$ when $a = -5$ and $b = -1$

23. $r \div 3 - 10r + 3(r + 2)$ when $r = 9$

24. $10 + 4(x - 6) - 5(x + 2)$ when $x = 0$

25. $\dfrac{n}{2} + \dfrac{6n}{2} + n$ when $n = 10$

26. $\dfrac{x - 2y}{5(3y + 5)}$ when $x = 1$ and $y = -2$

27. $\dfrac{-3 \cdot (a - b)}{2 - a + 6}$ when $a = -4$ and $b = -2$

28. $\dfrac{xy - 2x}{3 + 3(x + y)}$ when $x = 5$ and $y = 4$

29. $\dfrac{(a - b)(a + b)}{-5 + 3a}$ when $a = 5$ and $b = 7$

30. $\dfrac{x + 2}{x - 2} \cdot \dfrac{y + 3}{y - 3}$ when $x = -1$ and $y = 12$

*31. **Challenge** $10 - \dfrac{n}{2} \cdot \dfrac{n}{4} + n$ when $n = 2.4$

*32. **Challenge** $\dfrac{-4a + b}{a - b} + b$ when $a = 2.5$ and $b = 5$

Simplify.

33. $12 \cdot 1.2 + 3 \cdot (-0.6)$

34. $-4 \cdot \dfrac{1}{8} + 6 \cdot \dfrac{2}{3}$

35. $\dfrac{16.2 - 16}{16}$

36. $\dfrac{0.25 + 1.75}{40 \cdot 0.2}$

37. $5.6 + 1.05 \; 4.4 \div 2$

38. $\dfrac{1}{4} \cdot \dfrac{8}{9} + \dfrac{3}{4} \cdot \dfrac{4}{9}$

39. $\dfrac{0.25 \cdot (-4) \cdot (-0.6)}{-6 \cdot 0.02}$

*40. **Challenge** $\dfrac{-6 \cdot 2.5 + 2 \cdot (-1.4)}{0.4}$

Solve each problem. Show your work.

41. The formula to convert degrees Celsius to degrees Fahrenheit is $F = \frac{9}{5}C + 32$. The formula to convert degrees Fahrenheit to degrees Celsius is $C = \frac{5}{9}(F - 32)$.

A. What is the Fahrenheit equivalent of 5 degrees Celsius?

B. What is the Celsius equivalent of 5 degrees Fahrenheit?

C. What is the Celsius equivalent of −40 degrees Fahrenheit?

*42. Challenge The formula for the area A of a trapezoid is $A = \frac{1}{2}(b_1 + b_2)h$, where b_1 and b_2 represent the lengths of the parallel bases and h represents the height. Find the area of the trapezoid.

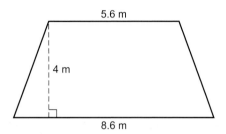

5.6 m

4 m

8.6 m

Equations with Mixed Operations

To solve equations with mixed operations, you need to understand *variable terms* and *indicated operations*.

In the equation $5 + 2x = 21$, the variable term is $2x$ and the indicated operations are as follows: The variable is multiplied by 2 and then 5 is added.

In the equation $\frac{t}{3} - 2 = 1$, the variable term is $\frac{t}{3}$ and the indicated operations are as follows: The variable is divided by 3 and then 2 is subtracted.

Solving Simple Equations

To solve an equation, you need to isolate the variable on one side. In $5 + 2x = 21$, subtract 5 from both sides to isolate the terms. The result is $2x = 16$. Similarly, in $\frac{t}{3} - 2 = 1$, add 2 to both sides. The result is then $\frac{t}{3} = 3$. If an equation has only one variable term and at most one numerical term on each side, use the method described below to isolate the variable. The idea is to peel back the layers one at a time.

SOLVING SIMPLE EQUATIONS IN ONE VARIABLE

Undo indicated operations in reverse order.

Example 1 Solve and check. $3x - 18 = 39$

Solution *Think:* The variable is multiplied by 3, and then 18 is subtracted. To isolate the variable, add 18 and then divide by 3.

$$3x - 18 = 39$$

$$3x - 18 + 18 = 39 + 18 \qquad \text{Add 18 to both sides to undo the subtraction.}$$

$$3x = 57$$

$$\frac{3x}{3} = \frac{57}{3} \qquad \text{Divide both sides by 3 to undo the multiplication.}$$

$$x = 19$$

(continued)

> **TIP**
>
> You can show your addition step in this format:
>
> $$3x - 18 = \quad 39$$
> $$\underline{+18 \quad +18}$$
> $$3x \quad = \quad 57$$

Check

$$3x - 18 = 39$$ Start with the original equation.

$$3 \cdot 19 - 18 \stackrel{?}{=} 39$$ Substitute 19 for x.

$$57 - 18 \stackrel{?}{=} 39$$ Multiply.

$$39 = 39 \checkmark \blacksquare$$

REMEMBER

The solution in Example 1 is 19, not 39.

Example 2 Solve.

Ⓐ $10 + \dfrac{a}{2} = 2$

TIP

In Example 2A, you could start by multiplying by 2, and then you would subtract 20 from each side.

Solution *Think:* The variable is divided by 2, and then 10 is added. To isolate the variable, subtract 10 and then multiply by 2.

$$10 + \dfrac{a}{2} = 2$$

$$10 - 10 + \dfrac{a}{2} = 2 - 10$$ Subtract 10 from both sides to undo the addition.

$$\dfrac{a}{2} = -8$$

$$2 \cdot \dfrac{a}{2} = 2 \cdot (-8)$$ Multiply both sides by 2 to undo the division.

$$a = -16 \blacksquare$$

TIP

Check all solutions. Substitute the solution into the original equation and verify that it makes a true statement.

Ⓑ $-6 = \dfrac{2}{3}c + 1$

Solution *Think:* The variable is multiplied by $\dfrac{2}{3}$, and then 1 is added. To isolate the variable, subtract 1 and then multiply by $\dfrac{3}{2}$, which is the reciprocal of $\dfrac{2}{3}$.

$$-6 = \dfrac{2}{3}c + 1$$

$$-6 - 1 = \dfrac{2}{3}c + 1 - 1$$ Subtract 1 from both sides to undo the addition.

$$-7 = \dfrac{2}{3}c$$

$$\dfrac{3}{2} \cdot (-7) = \dfrac{3}{2} \cdot \dfrac{2}{3}c$$ Multiply both sides by $\dfrac{3}{2}$ to undo the multiplication.

$$-\dfrac{21}{2} = 1 \cdot c$$

$$-\dfrac{21}{2} = c \blacksquare$$

TIP

In Example 2B, you could start by multiplying by $\dfrac{3}{2}$, and then you would subtract $\dfrac{3}{2}$ from each side. In general, undoing subtraction or addition first makes the numbers neater.

C $\dfrac{x+1}{3} = -5$

Solution *Think:* First 1 is added to the variable, and then the result is divided by 3. To isolate the variable, multiply by 3, and then subtract 1.

$$\dfrac{x+1}{3} = -5$$

$$3 \cdot \dfrac{x+1}{3} = 3 \cdot (-5) \qquad \text{Multiply both sides by 3 to undo the division.}$$

$$x + 1 = -15$$

$$x + 1 - 1 = -15 - 1 \qquad \text{Subtract 1 from both sides to undo the addition.}$$

$$x = -16 \ \blacksquare$$

> **THINK ABOUT IT**
>
> The equation in Example 2C can be written $\frac{1}{3}(x+1) = -5$. You could solve it the same way as shown here.

Combining Like Terms to Solve Equations

To solve some equations, it helps to simplify expressions by combining like terms. You don't absolutely have to simplify first, but a simpler equation reduces your risk of making mistakes.

Example 3 Solve.

A $5x + 5 - 8x - 4 = -29$

Solution

$$5x + 5 - 8x - 4 = -29$$

$$-3x + 1 = -29 \qquad \text{Combine like terms on the left side.}$$

$$-3x + 1 - 1 = -29 - 1 \qquad \text{Subtract 1 from both sides to undo the addition.}$$

$$-3x = -30$$

$$\dfrac{-3x}{-3} = \dfrac{-30}{-3} \qquad \text{Divide both sides by } -3 \text{ to undo the multiplication.}$$

$$x = 10 \ \blacksquare$$

B $5(n - 2) - n = 14.8$

Solution

$$5(n - 2) - n = 14.8$$

$$5n - 10 - n = 14.8 \qquad \text{Apply the distributive property to remove parentheses.}$$

$$4n - 10 = 14.8 \qquad \text{Combine like terms.}$$

$$4n - 10 + 10 = 14.8 + 10 \qquad \text{Add 10 to both sides to undo the subtraction.}$$

$$4n = 24.8$$

$$\dfrac{4n}{4} = \dfrac{24.8}{4} \qquad \text{Divide both sides by 4 to undo the multiplication.}$$

$$n = 6.2 \ \blacksquare$$

Solving Equations that Have the Variable on Both Sides

If the variable appears on both sides of the equation, add or subtract a variable term so that the variable appears on only one side.

Example 4 Solve. $3x + 1 = 5x - 7$

Solution

$$3x + 1 = 5x - 7$$

$3x - 3x + 1 = 5x - 3x - 7$ Subtract $3x$ from both sides so that the variable appears on only one side.

$$1 = 2x - 7$$

$1 + 7 = 2x - 7 + 7$ Add 7 to both sides to undo the subtraction.

$$8 = 2x$$

$\dfrac{8}{2} = \dfrac{2x}{2}$ Divide both sides by 2 to undo the multiplication.

$$4 = x \ \blacksquare$$

> **THINK ABOUT IT**
>
> You could begin solving the equation in Example 4 by subtracting $5x$ from both sides, but that would result in a negative coefficient for x. Using positive coefficients helps you avoid mistakes.

Application: Number Problem

Example 5 Three more than twice a number is 31. What is the number?

Solution Let n represent the number.

Three more than twice the number is 31.

3	+	$2n$	$= 31$	Write the equation.
		$2n$	$= 28$	Subtract 3 from both sides.
		n	$= 14$	Divide by 2.

The number is 14. ■

Application: Simple Interest

Example 6 Andy deposited some money to open a bank account that paid 8% simple interest. He made no other deposits or withdrawals. At the end of one year, the balance was $270. How much did Andy deposit?

Solution Let x represent the amount Andy deposited.

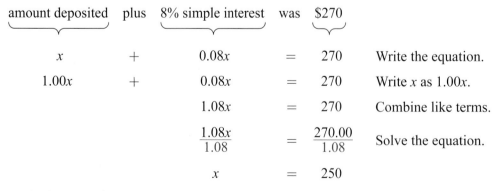

amount deposited   plus   8% simple interest   was $270

x	+	$0.08x$	$=$	270	Write the equation.
$1.00x$	+	$0.08x$	$=$	270	Write x as $1.00x$.
		$1.08x$	$=$	270	Combine like terms.
		$\dfrac{1.08x}{1.08}$	$=$	$\dfrac{270.00}{1.08}$	Solve the equation.
		x	$=$	250	

Andy deposited $250. ■

Problem Set

Solve and check.

1. $2x - 12 = 14$

2. $5x + 16 = 56$

3. $12.5 + 3x = 20$

4. $18 - 6.3x = 49.5$

5. $-1 + 12x = 29$

6. $10 - 1.4x = 10.84$

7. $-12x + 14 = -34$

8. $-24x - 15 = -27$

Solve.

9. $6 + \dfrac{x}{3} = 1$

10. $-4 + \dfrac{a}{5} = 8$

11. $-1 = \dfrac{x}{9} - 2$

12. $-3 = \dfrac{3}{4}r + 2$

13. $\dfrac{2}{9}x - 7 = 9$

14. $6 = \dfrac{9}{10}a - 1$

15. $\dfrac{x + 3}{5} = -1$

16. $44 = \dfrac{n - 6}{2}$

17. $-1 = -\dfrac{x + 1}{5}$

*18. Challenge $\dfrac{3 - x}{9} = \dfrac{1}{4}$

Solve.

19. $2x + 6 - 7x - 10 = 16$

20. $-x + 11 - 2x - 4x = -24$

21. $0 = 14 - n + 4n - 10$

22. $-15 = 13 - 6c + c + 14.5$

23. $6(x - 1) - 2x = 38$

24. $-9(r - 1) + r = 20$

25. $4(a - 6) - a = 42.3$

*26. Challenge $4(a - 11) - 7(2a + 1) = -2.28$

Solve.

27. $6b + 27 = -4b - 3$

28. $6x + 2 = 10x - 7$

29. $4(x + 5) = 3(x + 1) - 6$

*30. Challenge $-2(5 - t) - t = 4(2t + 1) - 6$

*31. Challenge
$s - 0.5(2 - s) - 7.3 = 4.5(2s + 10) - s$

*32. Challenge $\dfrac{1}{2}(8 - x) = \dfrac{1}{5}(x + 10) - x$

Solve each problem. Write and solve an equation to answer each question. State what your variable represents.

33. Write and solve equations for each word sentence.

   A. Five more than 3 times a number is 38.

   B. Seven less than one-third of a number is 5.

   C. The product of 5 and a number is 18 more than twice the number.

34. At the end of a year, a bank account balance is $1319.17. The account had earned 6% simple interest during the year, and there had been no deposits or withdrawals. What was the balance at the beginning of the year?

35. Tia paid $46.28 for a sweater. That amount included a 4% sales tax. What was the price of the sweater?

*36. **Challenge** In one week, Ed spent $12.25 more on entertainment than on all other items combined. During that week, he spent a total of $34.75. How much did Ed spend on entertainment?

*37. **Challenge** There are four employees on a building crew: a laborer, two carpenters who each earn 50% more than the laborer, and a supervisor who earns 80% more than the laborer. The total payroll for the crew one week was $4205. How much did each employee earn that week?

*38. **Challenge** The rectangle and triangle have the same perimeter. What is the value of n?

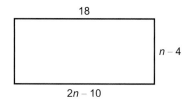

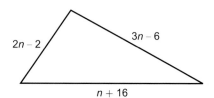

Error Analysis

It is important to be able to identify errors in solving equations and in solving application problems.

Identifying Errors in Equation Solutions

Example 1   Identify the student's error and write a correct solution.

$$2x - 8 = 20$$
$$2x = 12$$
$$x = 6$$

Solution   The student's error is subtracting 8 from 20 on the right side. The correct step is to add 8 to both sides.

Correct solution:

$$2x - 8 = 20$$
$$2x = 28$$
$$x = 14 \ \blacksquare$$

(continued)

> **TIP**
>
> Check your solutions. A check for Example 1A shows that $x = 6$ is incorrect:
>
> $$2x - 8 = 20$$
> $$2 \cdot 6 - 8 \overset{?}{=} 20$$
> $$12 - 8 \overset{?}{=} 20$$
> $$4 \neq 20$$

B

$$6 + \frac{n}{5} = 26$$
$$\frac{n}{5} = 20$$
$$n = 4$$

Solution   The student's error is dividing 20 by 5 on the right side. The correct step is to multiply both sides by 5.

Correct solution:

$$6 + \frac{n}{5} = 26$$
$$\frac{n}{5} = 20$$
$$n = 100 \ \blacksquare$$

C

$$-7x - 9 = -30$$
$$-7x = -21$$
$$x = -3$$

Solution   The student made a sign error when dividing -21 by -3. The correct solution is $x = 3$. $\blacksquare$

D

$$3(r - 5) = 13$$
$$3r - 5 = 13$$
$$3r = 18$$
$$r = 6$$

Solution   The student's error is forgetting to distribute 3 on the left side. The correct step is to distribute 3; that is, multiply both r and -5 by 3.

One correct solution: Another correct solution:

$$3(r - 5) = 13$$
$$3r - 15 = 13$$
$$3r = 28$$
$$r = \frac{28}{3}$$

$$3(r - 5) = 13$$
$$\frac{3(r - 5)}{3} = \frac{13}{3}$$
$$r - 5 = \frac{13}{3}$$
$$r - 5 + 5 = \frac{13}{3} + 5$$
$$r = \frac{28}{3} \ \blacksquare$$

E

$$2x + 1 = 5x - 13$$
$$7x + 1 = -13$$
$$7x = -14$$
$$x = -2$$

Solution   The student's error is combining like terms that are on different sides of the equation. Like terms must be on the same side of the equation to be combined. The correct step is to subtract either $2x$ or $5x$ from both sides of the equation.

One correct solution: Another correct solution:

$$2x + 1 = 5x - 13$$
$$2x + 1 - 2x = 5x - 13 - 2x$$
$$1 = 3x - 13$$
$$14 = 3x$$
$$\frac{14}{3} = x$$

$$2x + 1 = 5x - 13$$
$$2x + 1 - 5x = 5x - 13 - 5x$$
$$-3x + 1 = -13$$
$$-3x = -14$$
$$x = \frac{14}{3} \ \blacksquare$$

Identifying Errors in Solutions to Application Problems

In solving application problems, students sometimes solve equations correctly, but make errors of other types, especially not writing the correct equations in problem solving.

Example 2 Identify the student's error in the incorrect solution of each application problem. Find the correct solution.

Ⓐ Application: Perimeter The perimeter of a rectangle is 60 feet, and its length is 20 feet. Find the width of the rectangle.

Incorrect solution:

$$20w = 60$$
$$w = 3$$
The width of the rectangle is 3 feet.

Solution The student's error is using the area formula instead of the perimeter formula. The correct formula for the perimeter of a rectangle is $P = 2l + 2w$.

Correct solution:

$$P = 2l + 2w$$
$$60 = 2 \cdot 20 + 2w$$
$$60 = 40 + 2w$$
$$20 = 2w$$
$$10 = w$$
The width of the rectangle is 10 feet. ■

Ⓑ Application: Number Problem Six less than 3 times a number is 33. What is the number?

Incorrect solution:

$$6 - 3n = 33$$
$$-3n = 27$$
$$n = -9$$
The number is -9.

Solution   The student's error is incorrectly translating *Six less than three times a number*. The correct translation is $3n - 6$, not $6 - 3n$.

Correct solution:

$$3n - 6 = 33$$
$$3n = 39$$
$$n = 13$$

The number is 13. ∎

C **Application: Distance, Rate, and Time**   Mr. Vance drove 190 miles to visit a friend. First, he drove for $1\frac{1}{2}$ hours at an average rate of 60 miles per hour. Then he drove the rest of the way at an average rate of 40 miles per hour. What was Mr. Vance's total driving time?

Incorrect solution:

$$60 \cdot 1\frac{1}{2} + 40t = 190$$
$$90 + 40t = 190$$
$$40t = 100$$
$$t = 2\frac{1}{2}$$

Mr. Vance's total driving time was $2\frac{1}{2}$ hours.

Solution   The student's error is using the solution to the equation as the answer to the question. The variable t represents the number of hours driving at 40 miles per hour. The correct total driving time in hours was: $1\frac{1}{2} + 2\frac{1}{2} = 4$.

Correct answer:

Mr. Vance's total driving time was 4 hours. ∎

Problem Set

Identify the student's error and write a correct solution.

1.

$4x - 10 = 14$

$4x = 14$

$x = 1$

2.

$-(n - 5) = 6$

$-n - 5 = 6$

$-n = 11$

$n = -11$

3.

$6(x - 1) = -48$

$6x - 6 = -48$

$6x = -54$

$x = -9$

4.

$8 = -8(p - 3)$

$8 = -8p + 24$

$-16 = -8p$

$-2 = p$

5.

$-13 = 2a - 8$

$-5 = 2a$

$-10 = a$

6.

$1 = 35 - 5(x + 3)$

$1 = 35 - 5x + 3$

$1 = 38 - 5x$

$-37 = -5x$

$\frac{37}{5} = x$

7.

$5a + 5 = -10$

$5a = -15$

$a = -75$

8.

$2 + \frac{s}{3} = 11$

$\frac{s}{3} = 13$

$s = 39$

9.

$$2 - \frac{x}{7} = -2$$

$$-\frac{x}{7} = -4$$

$$x = -28$$

10.

$$7 - 2x = 6x + 14$$

$$7 = 4x + 14$$

$$-7 = 4x$$

$$-\frac{7}{4} = x$$

11.

$$3 - \frac{x+4}{9} = -2$$

$$-\frac{x+4}{9} = -5$$

$$-x + 4 = -45$$

$$x = -49$$

12.

$$7 - 2(5s - 4) + s = 6s + 14$$

$$7 - 10s + 8 + s = 6s + 14$$

$$-9s + 15 = 6s + 14$$

$$-3s + 15 = 14$$

$$-3s = -1$$

$$s = \frac{1}{3}$$

13.

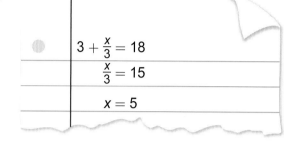

$$-12a - 1 = -49$$

$$-12a = -48$$

$$a = -4$$

14.

$$3 + \frac{x}{3} = 18$$

$$\frac{x}{3} = 15$$

$$x = 5$$

15.

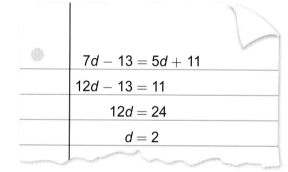

$$7d - 13 = 5d + 11$$

$$12d - 13 = 11$$

$$12d = 24$$

$$d = 2$$

16.

$$-2 = 5x - 4(x + 7)$$

$$-2 = 5x - 4x - 28$$

$$-2 = x - 28$$

$$-30 = x$$

17.

$$r + 6(r - 2) + 3r = 9$$
$$r + 6r - 2 + 3r = 9$$
$$10r - 2 = 9$$
$$10r = 11$$
$$r = \frac{11}{10}$$

18.

$$5(v + 4) = 3(v + 2) + 25$$
$$5v + 20 = 3v + 6 + 25$$
$$5v + 20 = 3v + 31$$
$$8v + 20 = 31$$
$$8v = 11$$
$$v = \frac{11}{8}$$

Identify the student's error in the incorrect solution of each application problem. Find the correct solution.

19. The area of a rectangle is 100 square feet, and its length is 40 feet. Find the width of the rectangle.

Incorrect solution:

$$A = 2l + 2w$$
$$100 = 2 \cdot 40 + 2w$$
$$100 = 80 + 2w$$
$$20 = 2w$$
$$10 = w$$

The width of the rectangle is

10 feet.

20. The product of 4 and a number is 12 more than 92. What is the number?

Incorrect solution:

$$4n + 12 = 92$$
$$4n = 80$$
$$n = 20$$

The number is 20.

21. The sum of three consecutive integers is 90. What is the greatest of the three integers?

Incorrect solution:

$$x + (x + 1) + (x + 2) = 90$$
$$x + x + 1 + x + 2 = 90$$
$$3x + 3 = 90$$
$$3x = 87$$
$$x = 29$$

The greatest of the three integers is 29.

22. Margo and Nicole went shopping. Margo spent 50% more than Nicole. Together they spent a total of $90. How much did Nicole spend?

Incorrect solution:

Let x represent the amount Nicole spent.

$$x + 0.50x = 90$$
$$1.00x + 0.50x = 90$$
$$1.50x = 90$$
$$x = \frac{90}{1.50}$$
$$x = 60$$

Nicole spent $60.

Inequalities

Working with inequalities is similar to working with equations.

Identifying Solutions of Inequalities

An **inequality** is a mathematical sentence that compares numbers or expressions using one of the symbols $<$, $>$, $\leq$, or $\geq$.

A **solution** of a one-variable inequality is a value for the variable that makes the inequality true.

The set of all solutions of an inequality is the **solution set** of the inequality.

Example 1   Identify the solution set of the inequality $x > -3$, using the replacement set $\{-5, -3.5, -3, -2, 0, 1\}$.

Solution   Determine which of the numbers are to the right of -3 on a number line.

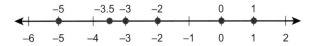

Using the replacement set, only the numbers -2, 0, and 1 are to the right of -3. The solution set is $\{-2, 0, 1\}$. ∎

These statements are all false:

$-5 > -3$, $-3.5 > -3$, and $-3 > -3$.

These statements are all true:

$-2 > -3$, $0 > -3$, and $1 > -3$.

Graphing Simple Inequalities

Most inequalities that have a solution have an infinite number of solutions.

The **graph of a one-variable inequality** is the set of points on a number line that represents all the solutions of the inequality.

When graphing a one-variable inequality, draw an open dot if the endpoint is not a solution, and draw a solid dot if the endpoint is a solution. Draw a shaded arrow on one side of the endpoint to show the solutions. The following table shows some simple one-variable inequalities and their graphs.

Inequality	Words	Graph
$x < 2$	x is less than 2.	A number line from −2 to 6 with an open circle at 2 and shading to the left.
$n > -1$	n is greater than −1.	A number line from −3 to 5 with an open circle at −1 and shading to the right.
$s \leq 0$	s is less than or equal to 0.	A number line from −4 to 4 with a closed circle at 0 and shading to the left.
$a \geq 4.35$	a is greater than or equal to 4.35.	A number line from −2 to 6 with a closed dot at 4.35 and shading to the right.

Solving and Graphing Inequalities

Equivalent inequalities are inequalities that have the same solution set. The properties of order tell you how to obtain equivalent inequalities by adding, subtracting, multiplying, and dividing.

PROPERTIES OF ORDER

Property	Symbols	Examples
Addition and Subtraction Properties of Order Adding or subtracting the same number on both sides of an inequality produces an equivalent inequality.	If $a > b$, then $a + c > b + c$. If $a < b$, then $a + c < b + c$. If $a \geq b$, then $a + c \geq b + c$. If $a \leq b$, then $a + c \leq b + c$. If $a > b$, then $a - c > b - c$. If $a < b$, then $a - c < b - c$. If $a \geq b$, then $a - c \geq b - c$. If $a \leq b$, then $a - c \leq b - c$.	If $5 > 2$, then $5 + 6 > 2 + 6$. If $x > 3$, then $x + 4 > 3 + 4$. If $u + 5 \leq 11$, then $u + 5 - 5 \leq 11 - 5$.
Multiplication and Division Properties of Order Multiplying or dividing both sides of an inequality by a *positive* number produces an equivalent inequality.	For any $c > 0$, If $a > b$, then $a \cdot c > b \cdot c$. If $a < b$, then $a \cdot c < b \cdot c$. If $a \geq b$, then $a \cdot c \geq b \cdot c$. If $a \leq b$, then $a \cdot c \leq b \cdot c$. If $a > b$, then $\frac{a}{c} > \frac{b}{c}$. If $a < b$, then $\frac{a}{c} < \frac{b}{c}$. If $a \geq b$, then $\frac{a}{c} \geq \frac{b}{c}$. If $a \leq b$, then $\frac{a}{c} \leq \frac{b}{c}$.	If $2 < 3$, then $4 \cdot 2 < 4 \cdot 3$. If $2x \geq 6$, then $\frac{2x}{2} \geq \frac{6}{2}$.

(continued)

Property	Symbols	Examples
Multiplication and Division Properties of Order Multiplying or dividing both sides of an inequality by a *negative* number and *reversing the direction of the inequality symbol* produces an equivalent inequality.	For any $c < 0$, If $a > b$, then $a \cdot c < b \cdot c$. If $a < b$, then $a \cdot c > b \cdot c$. If $a \geq b$, then $a \cdot c \leq b \cdot c$. If $a \leq b$, then $a \cdot c \geq b \cdot c$. If $a > b$, then $\frac{a}{c} < \frac{b}{c}$. If $a < b$, then $\frac{a}{c} > \frac{b}{c}$. If $a \geq b$, then $\frac{a}{c} \leq \frac{b}{c}$. If $a \leq b$, then $\frac{a}{c} \geq \frac{b}{c}$.	If $\frac{a}{-3} < 5$, then $-3\left(\frac{a}{-3}\right) > -3 \cdot 5$. If $12 > 8$, then $\frac{12}{-4} < \frac{8}{-4}$.

Multiply both sides by -2 and see what happens.

$$5 > 2$$
$$5 \cdot (-2) \overset{?}{>} 2 \cdot (-2)$$
$$-10 < -4$$

The method of solving an inequality is similar to the method of solving an equation. Use inverse operations along with the properties of order to obtain simpler inequalities that are equivalent. When you have the simplest equivalent inequality, you have the statement that best describes the solution set. When you have that statement, graph it.

Example 2 Solve and graph each inequality.

A $5x - 10 < 60$

Solution

$$5x - 10 < 60$$
$$5x - 10 + 10 < 60 + 10 \qquad \text{Add 10 to both sides.}$$
$$5x < 70$$
$$\frac{5x}{5} < \frac{70}{5} \qquad \text{Divide both sides by 5.}$$
$$x < 14$$

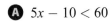

6   8   10   12   14   16   18   20   22

B $\dfrac{-t}{3} \geq 2$

Solution

$$\dfrac{-t}{3} \geq 2$$

$$-3 \cdot \left(\dfrac{-t}{3}\right) \leq -3 \cdot 2 \qquad \text{Multiply both sides by } -3. \text{ Reverse the inequality symbol.}$$

$$t \leq -6$$

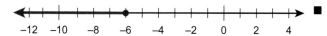

C $2(a + 2) - a > 0$

Solution

$$2(a + 2) - a > 0$$

$$2a + 4 - a > 0 \qquad \text{Apply the distributive property.}$$

$$a + 4 > 0 \qquad \text{Combine like terms.}$$

$$a + 4 - 4 > 0 - 4 \qquad \text{Subtract 4 from both sides.}$$

$$a > -4$$

D $3 > -\dfrac{5x + 1}{2}$

Solution

$$3 > -\dfrac{5x + 1}{2}$$

$$3 > -\dfrac{1}{2}(5x + 1) \qquad \text{Write } -\dfrac{5x + 1}{2} \text{ as } -\dfrac{1}{2}(5x + 1).$$

$$-2 \cdot 3 < -2 \cdot \left(-\dfrac{1}{2}\right)(5x + 1) \qquad \text{Multiply both sides by } -2. \text{ Reverse the inequality symbol.}$$

$$-6 < 5x + 1$$

$$-6 - 1 < 5x + 1 - 1 \qquad \text{Subtract 1 from both sides.}$$

$$-7 < 5x$$

$$\dfrac{-7}{5} < \dfrac{5x}{5} \qquad \text{Divide both sides by 5.}$$

$$-\dfrac{7}{5} < x$$

Application: Comparing Membership Fees

Example 3   Eli is deciding whether to join gym A or gym B. Gym A costs $50 to join and $31.50 per month. Gym B costs $170 to join and $24 per month. For what length of time will it cost less to belong to gym A?

Solution   Let x represent the number of months Eli belongs to a gym.

Cost of gym A < Cost of gym B

$50 + 31.50x < 170 + 24x$	Write an inequality to represent the situation.
$50 + 31.50x - 24x < 170 + 24x - 24x$ $50 + 7.50x < 170$	Subtract $24x$ from both sides so that the variable appears on only one side.
$50 - 50 + 7.50x < 170 - 50$ $7.50x < 120$	Subtract 50 from both sides.
$\dfrac{7.50x}{7.50} < \dfrac{120}{7.50}$ $x < 16$	Divide both sides by 7.50.

It will cost less to belong to gym A for any number of months less than 16 months. ■

Problem Set

Identify the solution set of the inequality, using the given replacement set.

1. $x > -5$; $\{-8, -5.01, -5, -4.8, 0, 4\}$

2. $x < -1$; $\{-2, -1.6, -1, 0, 0.5\}$

3. $x \geq 4$; $\{-4, -3, 0, 3.8, 4, 4.2, 5\}$

4. $x \leq -3.5$; $\{-3.55, -3.5, -3.4, -3, 0, 1, 5\}$

5. $x > -1$; $\left\{-4, -1.5, -1\frac{1}{4}, -\frac{3}{5}, 0, \frac{1}{10}\right\}$

*6. **Challenge** $x < -3.2$; $\left\{-4, -3\frac{1}{4}; -3.21, -3\frac{3}{20}, -3\frac{1}{8}, -3, 0\right\}$

Solve and graph each inequality.

7. $4x - 15 < 17$

8. $\dfrac{b}{2} \le 4$

9. $-8 < 2x + 4$

10. $7x + 9 \ge 2$

11. $-\dfrac{v}{6} \ge -2$

12. $-5x - 25 > 30$

13. $1 - x \le -6$

14. $6 - 3r - 25 > r + 1$

15. $\dfrac{x}{4} - 5 < -1$

16. $1 - \dfrac{t}{2} < -1$

17. $3(d + 5) > 30$

18. $2(x + 3) - 1 > 3$

19. $1 < \dfrac{4k + 3}{2}$

20. $-\dfrac{x + 3}{2} \le -9$

21. $1 < -\dfrac{x - 1}{5}$

22. $x - 3(x + 1) - 7 > -x$

*23. Challenge $4(a - 4) - 5(2a + 3) > 1 + a$

*24. Challenge $\dfrac{1}{2}(w + 6) - 1 < \dfrac{1}{3}w$

*25. Challenge $-10 < 3 + \dfrac{2x - 7}{2}$

*26. Challenge $r - 5 > 3 - \dfrac{4r - 1}{3}$

Solve each problem. Write and solve an inequality to answer each question. State what your variable represents.

27. Carlos wants to send a gift basket to his grand-mother. Deliver Quick charges $4.15 plus $0.85 per pound. Ship Fast charges $2.75 plus $1.05 per pound.

   A. For what weights will it cost less to use Ship Fast than Deliver Quick?

   B. For what weight do the two companies charge the same amount? What is that charge?

28. Kathleen is a sales associate in a jewelry store. She earns $560 per week plus an 8% commission on sales. How much does she need to sell in a week to earn at least $700 that week?

29. The cost to ride a Sedan Service taxicab is $2.90 plus $1.80 per mile. The cost to ride a Green taxicab is $2.15 plus $1.95 per mile.

   A. For what distances does it cost less to ride a Green taxicab than a Sedan Service taxicab?

   B. For what distance is the cost the same? What is that cost?

*30. Challenge The Golden Rectangle has been used in art and architecture since ancient times. It is a rectangle whose length is approximately 1.618 times its width. An artist has 1000 centimeters of framing material. He wants to frame a painting in the shape of a Golden Rectangle. Describe the dimensions he can use for the painting. Round dimensions to the nearest centimeter.

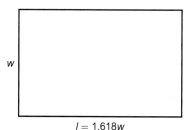

$l = 1.618w$

UNIT 6 Number Properties

The Horsehead Nebula is 14,181,382,433,000,000 kilometers away.

Astronomers study things that are very, very far away. For example, the Horsehead Nebula is about 14,000 trillion kilometers away. On the other extreme, molecular geneticists study things that are very, very small. A double helix of DNA has a diameter of about one nanometer (a billionth of a meter.) With exponents, you can describe very great or very small distances.

Big Ideas

· ·

▶ A number is any entity that obeys the laws of arithmetic; all numbers obey the laws of arithmetic. The laws of arithmetic can be used to simplify algebraic expressions.

▶ Expressions, equations, and inequalities express relationships between different entities.

▶ If you can create a mathematical model for a situation, you can use the model to solve other problems that you might not be able to solve otherwise. Algebraic equations can capture key relationships among quantities in the world.

Unit Topics

· ·

▶ Positive Exponents

▶ Factors and Primes

▶ GCF and Relative Primes

▶ Negative Exponents

▶ Powers of Ten

▶ Scientific Notation

Positive Exponents

A **power** is a special kind of product.

A power has a **base** and an **exponent.** In the power a^n, a is the base and n is the exponent. Read a^n as "a to the nth power." You can read a^2 as "a squared" and a^3 as "a cubed."

Simplify a power by multiplying. The exponent tells how many times to use the base as a factor.

> **TIP**
>
> Exponents are normally written above and to the right of the base.

POSITIVE EXPONENTS

For any real number a and natural number n:

$$a^n = \underbrace{a \cdot a \cdot a \cdot a \cdot \ldots \cdot a}_{n \text{ factors}}$$

Simplifying Powers

Example 1   Simplify.

A 2^4

Solution

$2^4 = 2 \cdot 2 \cdot 2 \cdot 2$ Use 2 as a factor 4 times.

$\quad = 16$ Multiply. ∎

B $(-4)^2$

Solution

$(-4)^2 = (-4) \cdot (-4)$ Use -4 as a factor 2 times.

$\qquad = 16$ Multiply the factors. ∎

C $\left(\dfrac{1}{2}\right)^5$

Solution

$\left(\dfrac{1}{2}\right)^5 = \dfrac{1}{2} \cdot \dfrac{1}{2} \cdot \dfrac{1}{2} \cdot \dfrac{1}{2} \cdot \dfrac{1}{2}$ Use $\dfrac{1}{2}$ as a factor 5 times.

$\qquad = \dfrac{1}{32}$ Multiply. ∎

> **TIP**
>
> Writing a power as a product first will help you avoid mistakes. In Example 1B, write $(-4) \cdot (-4)$, then multiply.

Exponents 0 and 1

EXPONENTS 0 AND 1

For all nonzero a,

$$a^0 = 1$$

$$a^1 = a$$

To simplify an expression, always follow the order of operations.

1. Grouping Symbols
2. Exponents
3. Multiplication and Division
4. Addition and Subtraction

Use these rules to simplify expressions.

Example 2   Simplify.

A $4^0 \cdot 3^3$

Solution

$4^0 \cdot 3^3 = 1 \cdot 3^3$	Use $a^0 = 1$ to simplify 4^0.
$= 1 \cdot 3 \cdot 3 \cdot 3$	Use 3 as a factor 3 times.
$= 27$	Multiply. ■

B $(9 - 6)^2 + 2^1$

Solution

$(9 - 6)^2 + 2^1 = 3^2 + 2^1$	Subtract inside the parentheses.
$= 9 + 2^1$	Simplify 3^2.
$= 9 + 2$	Simplify 2^1.
$= 11$	Add. ■

C -4^2

Solution

$-4^2 = -(4 \cdot 4)$	Use 4 as a factor 2 times.
$= -(16)$	Multiply the factors.
$= -16$	Simplify. ■

> **TIP**
>
> Use the phrase "Please Excuse My Dear Aunt Sally" to remember the order of operations. (Parenthesis, Exponents, Multiply, and Divide from left to right, and finally, Add and Subtract from left to right.)

> **TIP**
>
> Notice that, unlike in Example 1B, the negative is not inside the parentheses, so the answer remains negative.

Writing a Number as a Power

When a number can be written in the form a^n (where n is an integer), the number is a **power** of a.

Example 3

Ⓐ Write 16 as a power of 2.

Solution

$$16 = 2 \cdot 2 \cdot 2 \cdot 2 \qquad \text{Use 2 as a factor 4 times.}$$
$$= 2^4 \qquad\qquad \text{Write using an exponent.} \quad \blacksquare$$

Ⓑ Write 125 as a power of 5.

Solution

$$125 = 5 \cdot 5 \cdot 5 \qquad \text{Use 5 as a factor 3 times.}$$
$$= 5^3 \qquad\qquad \text{Write using an exponent.} \quad \blacksquare$$

> **TIP**
>
> Divide the final product, 16, by the base, 2, and then divide the quotient by 2 again. Repeat until the final quotient is 1. The number of times the division is carried out is the exponent. This process is called repeated division.

Evaluating Expressions with Variables and Exponents

To evaluate an expression with variables, first substitute the given values. Then simplify using the order of operations.

Example 4 Evaluate.

Ⓐ $-6b^3$ when $b = 4$

Solution

$$-6b^3 = -6 \cdot 4^3 \qquad \text{Substitute 4 for } b.$$
$$= -6 \cdot 64 \qquad \text{Evaluate } 4^3.$$
$$= -384 \qquad \text{Multiply.} \quad \blacksquare$$

Ⓑ $4m^3n^2$ when $m = -2$ and $n = 5$

Solution

$$4m^3n^2 = 4 \cdot (-2)^3 \cdot 5^2 \qquad \text{Substitute } -2 \text{ for } m \text{ and 5 for } n.$$
$$= 4 \cdot (-8) \cdot 25 \qquad \text{Evaluate } (-2)^3 \text{ and } 5^2.$$
$$= -800 \qquad\qquad \text{Multiply.} \quad \blacksquare$$

Ⓒ $2x^3y^2$ when $x = 3$ and $y = -4$

Solution

$$2x^3y^2 = 2 \cdot 3^3 \cdot (-4)^2 \qquad \text{Substitute 3 for } x \text{ and } -4 \text{ for } y.$$
$$= 2 \cdot 27 \cdot 16 \qquad \text{Evaluate } 3^3 \text{ and } (-4)^2.$$
$$= 864 \qquad\qquad \text{Multiply.} \quad \blacksquare$$

> **THINK ABOUT IT**
>
> Unless it appears after parentheses, an exponent applies only to a single number or variable.
>
> $$-6b^3 = -6 \cdot b \cdot b \cdot b$$
>
> On the other hand,
>
> $$(-6b)^3 = (-6b) \cdot (-6b) \cdot (-6b)$$

> **TIP**
>
> A negative number raised to an even power is positive. A negative number raised to an odd power is negative.

Application: Genealogy

Example 5

You can use exponents to model the number of ancestors in each generation of a person's family tree.

In this family tree, *M* stands for *Mother* and *F* stands for *Father.*

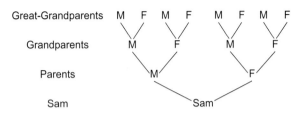

A How many people are 1 generation above Sam in the family tree? Write the number as a power of 2.

Solution

There are 2 people. Sam's 2 parents are 1 generation back. $2 = 2^1$

B How many people are 2 generations above Sam in the family tree? Write the number as a power of 2.

Solution

There are 4 people. Sam's 4 grandparents are 2 generations back. $4 = 2^2$

C Use the pattern to predict. How many people were in the *sixth* generation above Sam?

Solution

There are 2^n people in the generation that is *n* generations above Sam. So, there were 2^6 or 64 people in that generation. Sam has 64 great-great-great-great-grandparents. ∎

Problem Set

Simplify.

1. 2^3

2. 3^4

3. 1^3

4. 4^0

5. $\left(\dfrac{2}{3}\right)^2$

6. $(2.5)^3$

7. 5^5

8. 7^0

9. $(-6)^2$

10. $\left(-\dfrac{3}{2}\right)^3$

11. $(7.85)^1$

12. $(5)^0 \cdot 2^1$

13. $(-2)^4$

14. 7^4

15. $4^0 - 2^2$

16. $3^n = 27$

17. $4^n = 256$

18. $6^n = 1296$

19. $(2^6 \div 4^2)^3$

20. $[6^2 - (2^4 \cdot 3^0)] \cdot [(4 - (-3)^2]$

21. -6^2

Write as a power of the given number.

22. Write 32 as a power of 2.

23. Write 1000 as a power of 10.

24. Write 81 as a power of 3.

25. Write $\frac{1}{16}$ as a power of $\frac{1}{2}$.

Evaluate.

26. $5n^3$ when $n = -2$

27. $(-2a)^3$ when $a = 3$

28. $-4c^4$ when $c = -1$

29. $4t^2 - v^3$ when $t = 8$ and $v = 2$

***30.** **Challenge** x^2yz^3 when $x = -1$, $y = 4$, and $z = \frac{1}{2}$

***31.** **Challenge** $(jk)^3 + (hj)^2$ when $h = 1$, $j = \frac{1}{2}$, and $k = -4$

Solve.

32. Ron bought a full bag of dried fruit. On the first day, he ate $\frac{1}{2}$ the bag. On the second day, he ate $\frac{1}{2}$ of what was left. Each day, he eats half the fruit remaining in the bag. What fraction of a full bag will Ron eat on the fourth day?

33. Hal helped three friends. Each friend helped three other friends. Each of those people helped three more friends. If the pattern continues, how many people will receive help during the sixth round? Write your answer as a power. Then simplify.

Factors and Primes

Prime numbers are the building blocks of all counting numbers. Every counting number greater than 1 can be written as a product of primes.

When you multiply two or more whole numbers, each of those whole numbers is a **factor** of the product.

Finding Factors

Example 1   Find the factors of the given number.

A 24

Solution   Think of whole number pairs that have a product of 24.

Since $1 \times 24 = 24$, **1** and **24** are factors of 24.

Since $2 \times 12 = 24$, **2** and **12** are factors of 24.

Since $3 \times 8 = 24$, **3** and **8** are factors of 24.

Since $4 \times 6 = 24$, **4** and **6** are factors of 24.

The factors of 24 are 1, 2, 3, 4, 6, 8, 12, and 24. ■

B 49

Solution   Think of whole number pairs that have a product of 49.

Since $1 \times 49 = 49$, **1** and **49** are factors of 49.

Since $7 \times 7 = 49$, **7** is a factor of 49.

The factors of 49 are 1, 7, and 49. ■

C 17

Solution   The only whole number pair with a product of 17 is 1×17.

The factors of 17 are 1 and 17. ■

Prime and Composite Numbers

A natural number greater than 1 is **prime** if its only positive factors are 1 and itself. A natural number greater than 1 is **composite** if it has positive factors other than 1 and itself.

All natural numbers greater than 1 are either prime or composite. The number 1 is neither prime nor composite.

Example 2 Tell whether the number is prime or composite.

A 15

Solution

$15 = 5 \cdot 3$. So, 15 is composite. ∎

B 31

Solution

The only factors of 31 are 1 and 31. So, 31 is prime. ∎

C 58

Solution

$58 = 2 \cdot 29$. So, 58 is composite. ∎

Prime Factorization

The **prime factorization** of a number shows the number written as the product of prime factors. Every composite number can be written as the product of two or more prime numbers. A **factor tree** can help you find the prime factorization.

Example 3 Find the prime factorization of each number.

A 36

Solution

 Write 36 as the product of two whole numbers.

Continue factoring until all factors are prime.

The prime factorization of 36 is $2 \cdot 2 \cdot 3 \cdot 3$, or $2^2 \cdot 3^2$. ∎

B 68

Solution

 Write 68 as the product of two whole numbers.

Continue factoring until all factors are prime.

The prime factorization of 68 is $2 \cdot 2 \cdot 17$, or $2^2 \cdot 17$. ∎

Divisibility Rules

When factoring, it helps to know some rules for when one number is divisible by another.

Example 4 Use divisibility rules to help find the prime factorization of each number.

Ⓐ 230

Solution

230: The ones digit is 0. So, 230 is divisible by 10.

10: The ones digit is 0. So, 10 is divisible by 2.

The prime factorization of 230 is $2 \cdot 5 \cdot 23$. ∎

Ⓑ 468

Solution

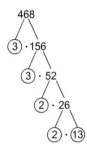

468: $4 + 6 + 8 = 18$. So, 468 is divisible by 3.

156: $1 + 5 + 6 = 12$. So, 156 is divisible by 3.

52: The ones digit is 2. So, 52 is divisible by 2.

26: The ones digit is 6. So, 26 is divisible by 2.

The prime factorization of 468 is $2^2 \cdot 3^2 \cdot 13$. ∎

Ⓒ 385

Solution

385: The ones digit is 5. So, 385 is divisible by 5.

77: $7 \cdot 11 = 77$. So 77 is divisible by 11.

The prime factorization of 385 is $5 \cdot 7 \cdot 11$. ∎

Problem Set

Find the factors of the given number.

1.	12	**3.**	32	**5.**	60	**7.**	99
2.	18	**4.**	55	**6.**	96	**8.**	125

Tell whether the number is prime or composite. If a number is composite, show one factorization not including the number 1. For example, for 50 you could show 5 × 10.

9.	49	**11.**	30	**13.**	27
10.	51	**12.**	19	**14.**	79

Find the prime factorization of each number.

15.	12	**18.**	65	**21.**	336
16.	30	**19.**	120	**22.**	450
17.	31	**20.**	124	**23.**	660

Determine whether the number is divisible by 2, 3, 5, and 10. Copy the table and record your answers by writing *yes* or *no* in the table.

24. 32

25. 50

26. 296

27. 308

28. 6600

2	3	5	10

Solve.

29. A marching band has 128 members. The band's director wants to arrange the band into rows with the same number of band members in each row. He wants between 3 and 15 members in each row. What are all the ways the director can arrange the band members?

30. Eggs are sold by the dozen. A standard egg carton contains 2 rows of 6 eggs. Draw or describe two other unique ways an egg carton could be designed using equal rows of eggs. Which design do you think is best? Explain.

GCF and Relative Primes

Just as people can be related to each other in a way that can be described with genes, numbers can be related to each other through factors.

> **DEFINITION**
>
> A number that is a factor of two different numbers is called a **common factor**. The greatest of the common factors is called the **greatest common factor** or **GCF**.

Finding the Greatest Common Factor

Example 1

Ⓐ Find the common factors of 16 and 28. Then find the GCF.

Solution

The factors of 16 are 1, 2, 4, 8, and 16.

The factors of 28 are 1, 2, 4, 7, 14, and 28.

The common factors are 1, 2, and 4.

The GCF is 4. ■

Ⓑ Find the common factors of 24, 30, and 36. Then find the GCF.

Solution

The factors of 24 are 1, 2, 3, 4, 6, 8, 12, and 24.

The factors of 30 are 1, 2, 3, 5, 6, 10, 15, and 30.

The factors of 36 are 1, 2, 3, 4, 6, 9, 12, 18, and 36.

The common factors are 1, 2, 3, and 6.

The GCF is 6. ■

> **THINK ABOUT IT**
>
> For any two numbers, the number 1 is always a common factor.

Using Prime Factorization to Find the GCF

You can find the GCF of two or more numbers by looking at their prime factorizations in exponential form. The GCF is the product of the least powers of all common bases.

Example 2 Find the GCF of 108 and 264.

Solution

The prime factorization of 108 is $2^2 \cdot 3^3$.

The prime factorization of 264 is $2^3 \cdot 3 \cdot 11$.

The common bases are 2 and 3. The least power of 2 is 2^2. The least power of 3 is 3^1.

The GCF is $2^2 \cdot 3^1$ or 12. ■

Relative Primes

Two numbers are **relatively prime** if they do not have common factors except 1. In other words, their GCF is 1.

Example 3 Determine whether the numbers are relatively prime or not.

Ⓐ 32 and 24

Solution

The factors of 32 are 1, 2, 4, 8, 16, and 32.
The factors of 24 are 1, 2, 3, 4, 6, 8, 12, and 24.

The numbers have common factors 1, 2, 4, and 8.
So, 32 and 24 are *not* relatively prime. ■

Ⓑ 42 and 55

Solution

The factors of 42 are 1, 2, 3, 6, 7, 14, 21, and 42.
The factors of 55 are 1, 5, 11, and 55.

The GCF of 42 and 55 is 1.
So, 42 and 55 are relatively prime. ■

Application: Packaging

Example 4 A store manager ordered 400 red bouncing balls, 216 green bouncing balls, and 180 yellow bouncing balls. She wants to package the bouncing balls into bags with an equal number of balls in each bag, without mixing the different colors. What is the greatest number of bouncing balls that can be packaged in a bag?

Solution Find the GCF of 400, 216, and 180.

$400 = 2^4 \cdot 5^2$ Find the prime factorization of each number.

$216 = 2^3 \cdot 3^3$

$180 = 2^2 \cdot 3^2 \cdot 5$

The only base common to every prime factorization is 2.
The least power of 2 is 2^2. The GCF is 4.
The greatest number of bouncing balls the store manager can package in a bag is 4. ■

Problem Set

Find all common factors of the numbers.

1. 10 and 12
2. 20 and 24
3. 21 and 28
4. 40 and 48
5. 40, 50, and 60
6. 48, 60, and 100

Find the GCF by listing common factors.

7. 10 and 25
8. 44 and 55
9. 32 and 48
10. 35 and 50
11. 36 and 42
12. 28, 35, and 63
13. 36, 54, and 90
14. 36, 80, and 100

Find the GCF by using prime factorization.

15. 8 and 12
16. 54 and 72
17. 121 and 143
18. 72 and 180
19. 90 and 252
20. 600 and 220
21. 232, 268, and 288
*22. **Challenge** 612, 756, and 1440

Determine whether the numbers are relatively prime or not. Write *relatively prime* **or** *not relatively prime.*

23. 20 and 36
24. 21 and 29
25. 30 and 49
26. 77 and 195
27. 63 and 64
28. 98 and 105

Solve.

29. A school principal is setting up chairs in equal rows for an assembly. Students from each of three grades will sit together, and each row will have students from one grade only. If there are 112 sixth graders, 84 seventh graders, and 98 eighth graders, what is the greatest number of chairs the principal can place in each row? How many rows are needed for each grade?

30. A florist is making balloon bouquets using a stock of 216 red balloons and 360 pink balloons. What is the greatest number of identical bouquets she can make? How many of each color balloon will be in each bouquet?

Negative Exponents

A positive exponent means repeated multiplication. A negative exponent means repeated division.

A power in which the exponent is a negative number can be simplified using the following rules.

PROPERTIES OF NEGATIVE EXPONENTS

For all nonzero a and integer n:

$$a^{-1} = \frac{1}{a} \qquad a^{-n} = \frac{1}{a^n} \qquad \frac{1}{a^{-n}} = a^n$$

Simplifying Negative Exponents

Example 1 Simplify.

A 10^{-1}

Solution

$10^{-1} = \frac{1}{10^1}$ Write the expression using a positive exponent.

$\phantom{10^{-1}} = \frac{1}{10}$ Simplify. ■

THINK ABOUT IT

When you simplify a power that has a negative exponent, the result can be a positive number.

B 4^{-2}

Solution

$4^{-2} = \frac{1}{4^2}$ Write the expression using a positive exponent.

$\phantom{4^{-2}} = \frac{1}{16}$ Simplify. ■

C $\frac{1}{2^{-3}}$

Solution

$\frac{1}{2^{-3}} = 2^3$ Write the expression using a positive exponent.

$\phantom{\frac{1}{2^{-3}}} = 8$ Simplify. ■

Simplifying Expressions with Negative Exponents

To simplify expressions with negative exponents, follow the order of operations.

Example 2 Simplify.

 $\dfrac{4}{3^{-2}}$

Solution

$\dfrac{4}{3^{-2}} = 4 \cdot \dfrac{1}{3^{-2}}$ Write the fraction as a product.

$= 4 \cdot 3^2$ Write the expression using a positive exponent.

$= 4 \cdot 9$ Evaluate the power.

$= 36$ Multiply. ∎

B $\dfrac{4^{-3}}{8^{-2}}$

Solution

$\dfrac{4^{-3}}{8^{-2}} = 4^{-3} \cdot \dfrac{1}{8^{-2}}$ Write the fraction as a product.

$= \dfrac{1}{4^3} \cdot 8^2$ Write the expression using positive exponents.

$= \dfrac{1}{64} \cdot 64$ Evaluate each power.

$= 1$ Multiply. ∎

C $\dfrac{(3-5)^{-2}}{3 \cdot 5^{-3}}$

Solution

$\dfrac{(3-5)^{-2}}{3 \cdot 5^{-3}} = \dfrac{(-2)^{-2}}{3 \cdot 5^{-3}}$ Subtract inside the parentheses.

$= \dfrac{5^3}{3(-2)^2}$ Write the expression using positive exponents.

$= \dfrac{125}{3 \cdot 4}$ Evaluate each power.

$= \dfrac{125}{12}$ Multiply. ∎

Solving Equations with Negative Exponents

You can use exponential properties to solve equations.

Example 3 Solve.

Ⓐ $6^n = \dfrac{1}{36}$

Solution

$6^n = \dfrac{1}{36}$

$\quad = \dfrac{1}{6^2}$ Write 36 as 6^2.

$\quad = 6^{-2}$ Write the positive exponent as a negative exponent.

Since $6^n = 6^{-2}$, $n = -2$. ■

Ⓑ $x^{-3} = \dfrac{1}{27}$

Solution

$x^{-3} = \dfrac{1}{27}$

$\quad = \dfrac{1}{3^3}$ Write 27 as 3^3.

$\quad = 3^{-3}$ Write the positive exponent as a negative exponent.

Since $x^{-3} = 3^{-3}$, $x = 3$. ■

> **REMEMBER**
>
> Solutions to an equation are those values for variables that make the equation true.

Problem Set

Simplify.

1. 3^{-2}

2. 4^{-2}

3. 2^{-1}

4. 2^{-4}

5. 6^{-3}

6. 3^{-4}

7. $\dfrac{1}{5^{-2}}$

8. $\dfrac{1}{3^{-4}}$

9. $\dfrac{1}{1^{-6}}$

10. $\dfrac{1}{8^{-2}}$

11. $\dfrac{2}{3^{-3}}$

12. $\dfrac{(-2)^3}{4^{-2}}$

13. $\dfrac{3^{-4}}{2^{-3}}$

14. $5 \cdot 10^{-2}$

15. $\dfrac{3^{-2}}{3^{-4}}$

16. $\dfrac{5^{-2}}{10^{-2}}$

17. $5^{-2} \cdot 2^{-3}$

18. $\dfrac{(6-4)^{-4}}{(-4+8)^3}$

19. $\dfrac{3^{-2}}{(-1)^3} \cdot 5^{-2}$

20. $9^{-2} \div 2^{-4}$

21. $(2^{-2})^3 \cdot \dfrac{1}{4^{-2}}$

Solve.

22. $t^{-1} = \dfrac{1}{4}$

23. $b^{-3} = \dfrac{1}{8}$

24. $4^k = \dfrac{1}{16}$

25. $3^k = \dfrac{1}{81}$

26. $\dfrac{2^{-2}}{3^{-3}} = s$

27. $\dfrac{1}{81} = 3^{-x}$

28. $3^{-2} \cdot p = 1$

29. $1 = 2^{-2} \cdot 2^w$

30. $9^b = 9^{-3} \cdot 9^3$

31. $\dfrac{2^{-4}}{3^{-3}} = \dfrac{27}{4^y}$

*32. Challenge If x is a nonzero real number, is x^{-2} always positive, always negative, or positive or negative depending on whether x is positive or negative? Explain.

*33. Challenge If x is a nonzero real number, is x^{-3} always positive, always negative, or positive or negative depending on whether x is positive or negative? Explain.

Powers of Ten

A **power of ten** is any number that can be written in the form 10^n, where n is an integer.

Some powers of ten are shown below.

$$10^3 = 1000$$
$$10^2 = 100$$
$$10^1 = 10$$
$$10^0 = 1$$
$$10^{-1} = 0.1$$
$$10^{-2} = 0.01$$
$$10^{-3} = 0.001$$

When you write a power of ten in standard form, you will use only the digits 0 and 1.

Converting a Power of Ten Between Exponential and Standard Form

To write 10^n in standard form, use the following rules.

POWERS OF TEN IN STANDARD FORM

To write 10^n in standard form, start with 1.0:
When **$n \geq 0$**, shift the decimal point n places to the right of 1.
When **$n < 0$**, shift the decimal place n places to the left of 1.

Example 1

A Write 10^7 and 10^{-5} in standard form.

Solution

$10^7 = 10{,}000{,}000$ Write a 1 followed by 7 zeros.

$10^{-5} = 0.00001$ Write a 1 in the fifth decimal place. ∎

(continued)

B Write 0.00000001 and 100,000 as powers of 10.

Solution

$0.00000001 = 10^{-8}$ The digit 1 is in the eighth decimal place. Write 10^{-8}.

$\quad\;\;100,000 = 10^5$ There are 5 zeros after 1. Write 10^5. ∎

THINK ABOUT IT

Negative powers of ten are between 0 and 1. Positive powers of ten are greater than 1.

Order of Magnitude

Order of magnitude is an estimate of a number using the nearest power of 10.

To use order of magnitude to compare distances or sizes, start by approximating each size with a power of ten. Then, find the difference in the powers of 10. For instance, if one object is 10^2 meters long while another is 10^5 meters long, you can say that the larger one is 3 orders of magnitude longer than the other because $5 - 2 = 3$.

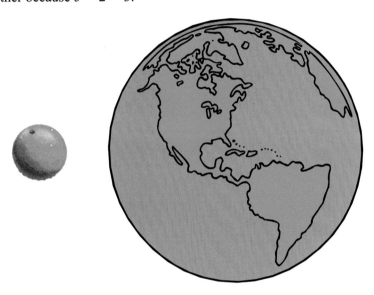

Example 2 The diameter of an orange is about 8 cm. The diameter of the earth is about 12,800 kilometers. How many orders of magnitude greater than an orange's diameter is the earth's diameter?

Solution

Orange	Earth	
0.08 m	12,800,000 m	Write each diameter in the same unit.
0.10	10,000,000	Round to the nearest power of ten.
10^{-1}	10^7	Write the power using an exponent.

Subtract to find the difference of the exponents. $7 - (-1) = 8$

The diameter of the earth is 8 orders of magnitude greater than the diameter of an orange. ∎

THINK ABOUT IT

When you simplify a power that has a negative exponent, the result can be a positive number.

Multiplying by Powers of Ten

To multiply a decimal number by a whole number power of ten, move the decimal point in the number one place to the right for each zero in the power of ten.

To multiply a decimal number by a decimal power of ten, move the decimal point in the number one place to the left for each decimal place in the power of ten.

Example 3   Multiply.

A 98.524×10^2

Solution

$98.524 \times 10^2 = 98.524$ Move the decimal point 2 places to the right. ■

$\qquad\qquad = 9852.4$

B 0.0065×10^6

Solution

$0.0065 \times 10^6 = 0.006500$ Move the decimal point 6 places to the right. ■

$\qquad\qquad = 6500$

C 305.48×10^{-6}

Solution

$305.48 \times 10^{-6} = 000305.48$ Move the decimal point 6 places to the left. ■

$\qquad\qquad = 0.00030548$

D 2156×10^{-3}

Solution

$2156 \times 10^{-3} = 2156$ Move the decimal point 3 places to the left. ■

$\qquad\qquad = 2.156$

TIP

Sometimes you need to add in extra zeros when you move a decimal point like Examples 3B and 3C.

Dividing by Powers of Ten

DIVIDING BY A POWER OF TEN

- To divide a decimal number by a whole number power of ten, move the decimal point in the number one place to the left for each zero in the power of ten.
- To divide a decimal number by a decimal power of ten, move the decimal point in the number one place to the right for each decimal place in the power of ten.

Example 4   Divide.

Ⓐ $65,215 \div 10^3$

Solution

$65,215 \div 10^3 = 65\underset{\smile\smile\smile}{2 1 5}$ Move the decimal point 3 places to the left. ■

$\qquad\qquad = 65.215$

Ⓑ $30.29 \div 10^5$

Solution

$30.29 \div 10^5 = \underset{\smile\smile\smile\smile\smile}{0 0 0 3 0}.29$ Move the decimal point 5 places to the left. ■

$\qquad\qquad = 0.0003029$

Ⓒ $6 \div 10^{-6}$

Solution

$6 \div 10^{-6} = 6.\underset{\smile\smile\smile\smile\smile\smile}{0 0 0 0 0 0}$ Move the decimal point 6 places to the right. ■

$\qquad\qquad = 6,000,000$

Ⓓ $0.00231 \div 10^{-4}$

Solution

$0.00231 \div 10^{-4} = 0.\underset{\smile\smile\smile\smile}{0 0 2 3 1}$ Move the decimal point 4 places to the right. ■

$\qquad\qquad = 23.1$

THINK ABOUT IT

A positive power of ten is greater than 1. When you divide a dividend by a number greater than 1, the quotient is less than the dividend. So, move the decimal point to the left.

Problem Set

Write in standard form.

1. 10^3

2. 10^8

3. 10^{-4}

4. 10^0

5. 10^{-5}

6. 10^{-9}

Write as a power of ten.

7. 1,000,000

8. 10

9. 10,000,000,000

10. 0.00001

11. 0.0000000001

12. 0.01

Multiply.

13. 3.65×10^3

14. 17×10^{-4}

15. 28.75×10^5

16. 5000×10^{-5}

17. 205×10^6

18. 0.005×10^7

19. 3.045×10^2

20. 438.15×10^{-2}

Divide.

21. $2400 \div 10^3$

22. $4 \div 10^5$

23. $64 \div 10^{-4}$

24. $31{,}300 \div 10^6$

25. $0.018 \div 10^{-3}$

26. $15 \div 10^{-8}$

27. $3148.215 \div 10^{-2}$

28. $61.19 \div 10^7$

Solve.

29. The population of the earth is about 6,650,000,000. The population of the state of Virginia is about 7,700,000. How many orders of magnitude greater than Virginia's population is earth's population?

30. Mars has a mass of 6.5×10^{23} kg and the sun has a mass of 1.99×10^{30} kg. How many orders of magnitude greater than Mars's mass is the sun's mass?

31. Jupiter has a mass of 1900×10^{24} kg and Mars has a mass of 6.5×10^{23} kg. How many orders of magnitude greater than Mars's mass is the Jupiter's mass?

*__32.__ **Challenge** The world's smallest mammal, the bumblebee bat, has a wingspan of about 15 cm. The world's largest aircraft, the Antonov An-255 has a wingspan of 88.4 meters. How many orders of magnitude greater than the wingspan of the bat is the wingspan of the aircraft?

Scientific Notation

You know that you can use standard form with digits and place value to show a number's value. When a number has lots of zeros, you can use scientific notation to represent very great or very small values.

A number is written in **scientific notation** when it is written as the product of a number that is greater than or equal to 1 but less than 10 and an integer power of ten.

Scientific notation is especially useful for writing very large or very small numbers that may have a great number of digits that are 0.

Scientific Notation and Standard Form

CONVERTING FROM SCIENTIFIC NOTATION TO STANDARD FORM

To convert scientific notation with an integer n power of ten, to standard form:
Move the decimal point n places to the right for positive n.
Move the decimal n places to the left for negative n.

Example 1 Write the number in standard form.

A 7.5×10^9

Solution

$7.5 \times 10^9 = 7.500000000$ Move the decimal point 9 places to the right and add zeros as needed. ■

$= 7,500,000,000$

B 3.95×10^{-6}

Solution

$3.95 \times 10^{-6} = 000003.95$ Move the decimal point 6 places to the left. Insert zeros as needed. ■

$= 0.00000395$

To convert standard form to scientific notation with an integer n power of ten:

Move the decimal point n places to the left until the number is greater than or equal to 1, and then write the positive n power of ten.

Move the decimal point n places to the right until the number is greater than or equal to 1, and then write the negative n power of ten.

Example 2   Write the number in scientific notation.

Ⓐ 35,000,000

Solution

$35{,}000{,}000 = 35{,}000{,}000.$ Move the decimal point 7 places to the left. ∎

$= 3.5 \times 10^7$

Ⓑ 0.0000024

Solution

$0.0000024 = 0.0000024$ Move the decimal point 6 places to the right. ∎

$= 2.4 \times 10^{-6}$

> **TIP**
>
> To remember whether to use a positive or negative power of ten, ask yourself if you want to make the first factor bigger or smaller. To make it bigger, use a positive exponent. To make it smaller, use a negative exponent.

Using Scientific Notation to Multiply Numbers

To multiply numbers with scientific notation,

1. use the commutative and associative properties to regroup the numbers and the powers of ten;
2. multiply the numbers.

Example 3   Multiply.

Ⓐ $(3.2 \times 10^2) \times (1.05 \times 10^3)$

Solution

$(3.2 \times 10^2) \times (1.05 \times 10^3) = 3.2 \times 1.05 \times 10^2 \times 10^3$ Commutative and Associative Properties of Multiplication

$= 3.36 \times 100 \times 1000$ Simplify exponents. Multiply.

$= 3.36 \times 100{,}000$ Multiply.

$= 3.36 \times 10^5$ Write in scientific notation. ∎

(continued)

B $(1.6 \times 10^2) \times (4.5 \times 10^{-3})$

Solution

$(1.6 \times 10^2) \times (4.5 \times 10^{-3}) = 1.6 \times 4.5 \times 10^2 \times 10^{-3}$	Commutative and Associative Properties of Multiplication
$= 7.2 \times 100 \times \dfrac{1}{10^3}$	Simplify exponents. Multiply.
$= 7.2 \times 100 \times \dfrac{1}{1000}$	Simplify exponents.
$= 7.2 \times \dfrac{1}{10}$	Multiply.
$= 7.2 \times 10^{-1}$	Write in scientific notation. ■

Application: Astronomy

Example 4

The speed of light is about 299,800 kilometers per second.

How many kilometers can light travel in one day? Write the answer in scientific notation.

Solution

$299{,}800 \times 60 = 17{,}988{,}000$	Find the kilometers light travels in 1 minute.
$17{,}988{,}000 \times 60 = 1{,}079{,}280{,}000$	Find the kilometers light travels in 1 hour.
$1{,}079{,}280{,}000 \times 24 = 25{,}902{,}720{,}000$	Find the kilometers light travels in 1 day.
$25{,}902{,}720{,}000 = 2.59 \times 10^{10}$	Write in scientific notation.

Light travels about 2.59×10^{10} kilometers in one day. ■

Problem Set

Write the number in standard form.

1. 5×10^3
2. 98×10^{-4}
3. 3×10^6
4. 15×10^{-1}
5. 2.36×10^6
6. 2.8×10^{-4}
7. 1.25×10^8
8. 8.4×10^2
9. 1.02×10^5
10. 9.215×10^{-7}
11. 5.148×10^8
12. 4.15×10^{-7}

Write the number in scientific notation.

13. 0.0056
14. 54,000
15. 0.006
16. 0.00000000078
17. 7200
18. 490,000,000
19. 0.00009
20. 3,050,000
21. 0.000068
22. 0.0000091
23. 9,304,000,000
24. 92,000

Multiply.

25. $(1.8 \times 10^3) \times (5 \times 10^2)$
26. $(2.1 \times 10^2) \times (3.5 \times 10^5)$
27. $(2 \times 10^{-3}) \times (3 \times 10^4)$
28. $(2.5 \times 10^4) \times (2.4 \times 10^3)$
29. $(3.6 \times 10^6) \times (2.2 \times 10^{-4})$
30. $(3.2 \times 10^3) \times (1.5 \times 10^{-5})$

Solve. Write your answer in scientific notation.

31. The state of Wyoming has roughly the shape of a rectangle that is 3.6×10^2 miles long and 2.8×10^2 miles high. What is the approximate area of Wyoming? Hint: The area of a rectangle is the product of its length and width.

32. It is estimated that the world population increases by about 8800 people each hour. At this rate, how much will the population increase in one decade?

33. The distance between the earth and the moon is about 384,000 kilometers. What is the distance between the earth and the moon in meters? Hint: There are 1000 meters in a kilometer.

UNIT 7   Geometry Basics

Architect Frank Lloyd Wright used geometric shapes to create the beautiful Solomon R. Guggenheim Museum in New York City.

Shapes such as polygons and circles provide us with shelter, art, and transportation. Some artists use geometric shapes in their art, but most painters and photographers use rectangular frames to surround their art. Look at any art museum, and you will see triangles, rectangles, and other polygons in the structure of the building and in the artwork inside.

Big Ideas

▶ Many problems can be solved by using the properties of angles, triangles, and circles.

▶ There are several useful aspects of every geometric figure that can be measured, calculated, or approximated.

Unit Topics

▶ Points, Lines, and Planes

▶ Rays and Angles

▶ Parallel Lines and Transversals

▶ Triangles

▶ Polygons

▶ Circles

▶ Transformations

▶ Congruence

Points, Lines, and Planes

Geometry is the study of points, lines, angles, shapes, and areas of surfaces and solids.

Points and Lines

As you begin to study geometry, you will learn the basics of points, lines, and planes.

> **DEFINITION**
>
> A **point** is a location in space with no length, width, or depth.

A point is named with a capital letter. Point *M*: •*M*

> **DEFINITION**
>
> A **line** is a collection of points arranged in a straight path.

THINK ABOUT IT

A dot is not a point. A dot just shows the location of a point.

Because points have no size, lines have no thickness. A line continues *infinitely,* or without end, in both directions. Therefore, arrows always appear on both ends of a line.

You can identify a line in two ways. Name any two points that are on the line (in any order), or use a lowercase letter that might appear near the line.

   line *GP*, line *PG*, $\overleftrightarrow{GP}$, $\overleftrightarrow{PG}$, or line *n*

TIP

When using the line symbol, such as in $\overleftrightarrow{GP}$, be sure to include the arrows on the small line above the letters.

Example 1

Ⓐ Name the points that are labeled in the figure.

Solution The figure is made up of more than four points, but only four points have been labeled. They are point *D*, point *H*, point *B*, and point *K*. ■

(continued)

B List all the ways the line can be named.

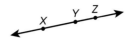

Solution There is no lowercase letter. You can only name it by using two points. It can be named: line *XY*, line *YX*, line *XZ*, line *ZX*, line *YZ* or line *ZY*. ∎

C List all the ways the line can be named.

Solution Because only one point on the line is named, the line cannot be named by using points. The only name possible is line *t*. ∎

TIP

In Example 1B, you can use the line symbol: $\overleftrightarrow{XY}$, $\overleftrightarrow{YX}$, and so on. The symbol should not be used for lowercase names; do not write $\overleftrightarrow{t}$ in Example 1C.

Planes

DEFINITION

A **plane** is a flat surface with infinite length and width but no thickness.

You're used to thinking of planes as horizontal surfaces, such as the plane that contains the top of your kitchen table. But planes can also be vertical, such as the planes that contain the walls of a room. Planes can even be slanted. Hold a stiff sheet of paper or cardboard and move it around to see some possible orientations. Remember that in geometry a plane extends infinitely in all directions while remaining completely flat. You can never actually draw an entire plane.

A plane is represented by a *parallelogram*. A parallelogram only represents a plane, because it would be impossible to draw an infinite flat surface with no sides. There are two ways to name a plane. Name any three points that are on the plane (in any order), or use the capital script letter that may appear near a corner of the parallelogram. When using three points, do not choose three points that are all on the same line, because many different planes can pass through a given line.

TIP

A parallelogram is a four-sided figure whose opposite sides, if extended, would never touch.

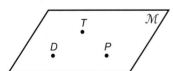 plane *DTP*, plane 𝓜

Other possible names for the plane can be made by changing the order of the points; two other names are plane *TPD* and plane *PDT*.

THINK ABOUT IT

An infinite number of different planes can pass through any given line.

Example 2

A Give three possible names for the plane.

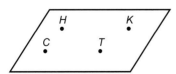

TIP

Plane *H* is not a valid name for the plane in Example 2A because *H* names a point.

Solution Choose any three points to name the plane. Three possible names are plane *CHT*, plane *TKH*, and plane *HCK*. No single capital script letter appears, so it cannot be named by using one letter. ∎

B Name the plane.

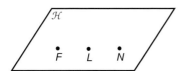

Solution   Although the line is not drawn, the three labeled points all lie on it, so the points cannot be used to name the plane. The only possible name is plane $\mathcal{H}$. ∎

Naming Points, Lines, and Planes in a Figure

Example 3   Refer to this figure for parts A, B, and C.

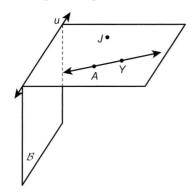

A Name the points drawn in the figure.

Solution   There are three points drawn in the figure: point J, point A, and point Y. ∎

B Name the lines drawn in the figure.

Solution   There are two lines drawn in the figure: $\overleftrightarrow{AY}$ and line u. ∎

C Name the planes in the figure.

Solution   There are two planes in the figure. One is plane JAY and the other is plane $\mathcal{B}$.

Notice that if point J were on line AY, you would not have enough information to name the plane that contains that line. ∎

> **THINK ABOUT IT**
>
> All planes contain an infinite number of points and an infinite number of lines.

Problem Set

List all the ways each line can be named.

1.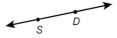

2.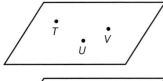

3.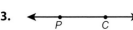

4.

5.

6.

Give three possible names for each plane.

7.

8.

9.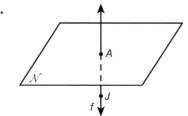

10.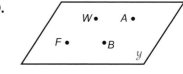

For problems 11 and 12,

A. Name the points drawn in the figure.
B. Name the lines drawn in the figure.

11.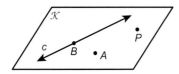

12.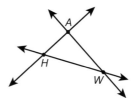

For problems 13 and 14,

A. Name the points drawn in the figure.
B. Name the lines drawn in the figure.
C. Name the plane drawn in the figure.

13.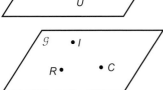

14.

Select the best answer.

15. Which best models a point?

   A. a floor

   B. a pebble

   C. a jump rope

   D. a stick

16. Which best models a plane?

   A. a floor

   B. a pebble

   C. a jump rope

   D. a stick

Draw a figure to match the given description.

17. $\overleftrightarrow{CM}$

18. plane *WXY*

19. lines *h* and *GH* are horizontal.

20. points *A* and *B* lie in plane $\mathcal{Z}$.

21. $\overleftrightarrow{AB}$, $\overleftrightarrow{AC}$, and $\overleftrightarrow{AD}$

*22. **Challenge** lines *CD* and *DM* in plane *MPD*

Write answers in complete sentences.

23. Lori said that when using three points to name a plane, you can choose any three points that form a triangle. Is she correct? Tell why or why not.

24. When points are used to name a line, why are two points used instead of just one?

*25. **Challenge** What are the possible figures formed by the intersection of three planes? Explain.

*26. **Challenge** What figure is formed by the intersection of two planes?

Rays and Angles

A ray in geometry is like a ray of sunshine.

THINK ABOUT IT

The term *endpoint* is used even though it is where the ray begins. A ray never ends.

Naming Rays

Name a ray by using two points. The first point must be the endpoint. The second point can be any other point on the ray.

ray HT or $\overrightarrow{HT}$

Example 1

Ⓐ Name the ray.

Solution The endpoint is point S. This is $\overrightarrow{SK}$. ∎

Ⓑ List all the ways the ray can be named.

Solution Point D is the endpoint.

There are two possible names for the ray: $\overrightarrow{DW}$ and $\overrightarrow{DP}$. ∎

THINK ABOUT IT

For Example 1B, notice that $\overrightarrow{PD}$ is not a correct answer because $\overrightarrow{PD}$ would be a ray that goes in the opposite direction of $\overrightarrow{DP}$.

Naming Angles

This angle is formed by ray FG and ray FH.
$\overrightarrow{FG}$ and $\overrightarrow{FH}$ are the sides and point F is the vertex.

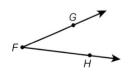

There are three ways to name an angle. You can use three points by naming a point on one side, the vertex, and then a point on the other side. You can use just the vertex point. Or you can use the number that may appear near the vertex of the angle, between the sides.

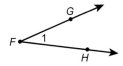

angle *GFH*, angle *HFG*, ∠*GFH*, ∠*HFG*
angle *F*, ∠*F*
angle 1, ∠1

TIP

When an angle name has three letters, the middle letter is always the name of the vertex point.

Example 2 List all the ways each angle can be named.

A

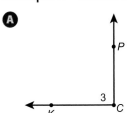

Solution The vertex is *C* so one possible name is ∠*C*. Other possible names are ∠*KCP*, ∠*PCK*, and ∠3. ■

B

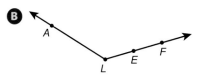

Solution The vertex is *L* so one possible name is ∠*L*. Other possible names are ∠*ALE*, ∠*ALF*, ∠*FLA*, and ∠*ELA*. ■

THINK ABOUT IT

In Example 2B, ∠ *FLE* is not a valid name because both *F* and *E* are on the same ray.

Measuring and Classifying Angles

Angles are measured in units called *degrees* (°). An angle that forms a corner or "L" shape measures 90°. These angles all measure 90°.

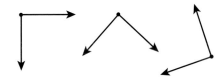

DEFINITIONS

A **right angle** is an angle that measures 90°.
An **acute angle** is an angle that measures less than 90°.
An **obtuse angle** is an angle that measures greater than 90° and less than 180°.

TIP

An angle that measures 180° is called a straight angle and looks like a line.

(continued)

Acute angles are narrower than right angles. Obtuse angles are wider than right angles.

Acute angles	Right angles	Obtuse angles
30°		120°
45°		150°

TIP

The box symbol indicates a measure of 90°.

Example 3   Determine if each angle appears to be acute, right, or obtuse.

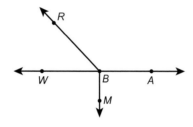

A ∠*RBA*

Solution   ∠*RBA* appears to be an obtuse angle. ■

B ∠*MBW*

Solution   ∠*MBW* appears to be a right angle. ■

C ∠*WBR*

Solution   ∠*WBR* appears to be an acute angle. ■

TIP

You can place a corner of a sheet of paper along one side of an angle to help determine its classification.

Example 4   Use the diagram to answer each question.

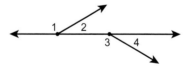

A   Which angles appear to be acute angles?

Solution   ∠2 and ∠4 appear to be acute. ■

B   Which angles appear to be obtuse angles?

Solution   ∠1 and ∠3 appear to be obtuse. ■

Application: Time

Example 5 For each time, tell if the angle formed by the minute and hour hands is acute, right, or obtuse.

A 1:30

Solution Obtuse angle ■

B 3:00

Solution Right angle ■

C 10:00

Solution Acute angle ■

D 8:15

Solution Obtuse angle ■

Problem Set

List all the ways each ray can be named.

1.

2.
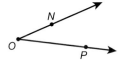

3.

4.

List all the ways each angle can be named.

5.

6.
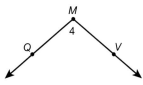

7.
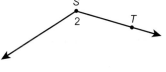

8.
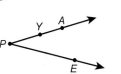

State whether each angle appears to be acute, right, or obtuse.

9.
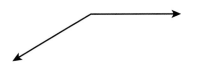

10.

11.
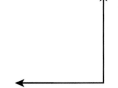

12.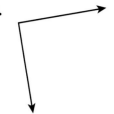

13.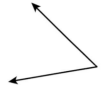

14.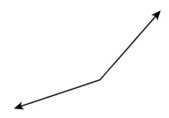

For problems 15 through 18,

A. Which angles, if any, appear to be acute?
B. Which angles, if any, appear to be right?
C. Which angles, if any, appear to be obtuse?
D. Which angles, if any, appear to be straight?

15.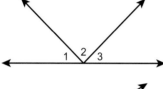

16.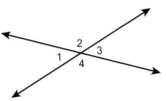

17.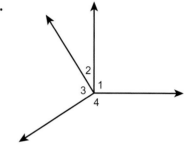

18.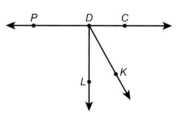

Answer each question.

19. What type of angle is made by the hands of a clock when it is 7 o'clock?

20. Why should ∠2 not be named as ∠D?

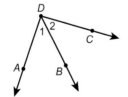

21. Name the sides of ∠1.

22. Name the sides of ∠ADC.

23. Classify the angles formed by the edges of a stop sign as acute, right, or obtuse.

24. Ralph looks up at the moon from point B on the ground as shown. Classify the angle of elevation, angle ABC, as acute, obtuse, or right.

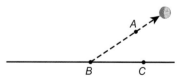

25. A gate is reinforced by adding a diagonal brace as shown. Classify angles 1 and 2 as acute, obtuse, or right.

Parallel Lines and Transversals

Two lines either intersect or do not intersect each other.

Parallel lines are lines on the same plane that never intersect. The symbol for parallel is ∥.

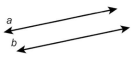

$a \parallel b$ is read "line a is parallel to line b."

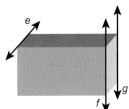

line $f \parallel$ line g

line $e \nparallel$ line f and line $e \nparallel g$ because they are not on the same plane.

A **transversal** is a line that intersects two or more lines in a plane.

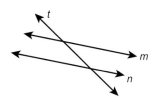

Line t is a transversal to lines m and n.

Pairs of Angles

Notice that eight angles are formed when a transversal crosses two lines.

Corresponding angles are angles that lie in the same position or "match up" with respect to the transversal when the transversal crosses two lines. Pairs of corresponding angles: $\angle 1$ and $\angle 5$, $\angle 2$ and $\angle 6$, $\angle 3$ and $\angle 7$, $\angle 4$ and $\angle 8$

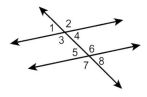

Alternate interior angles are the inside angles that do not share the same vertex and are on opposite sides of a transversal crossing two lines. Pairs of alternate interior angles: $\angle 3$ and $\angle 6$, $\angle 4$ and $\angle 5$

(continued)

Alternate exterior angles are the outside angles that do not share the same vertex and are on opposite sides of a transversal crossing two lines. Pairs of alternate exterior angles: ∠1 and ∠8, ∠2 and ∠7

Adjacent angles are two angles with a common side and a common vertex that do not overlap. There are several pairs of adjacent angles in the figure shown, including ∠1 and ∠2, ∠1 and ∠3, ∠3 and ∠4, ∠5 and ∠7, ∠5 and ∠6, and ∠7 and ∠8.

Example 1 Identify each pair of angles as corresponding, alternate interior, alternate exterior, adjacent, or none of these.

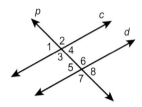

Ⓐ ∠3 and ∠6

Solution ∠3 and ∠6 are on opposite sides of the transversal, line *p*, and they do not share a vertex. They are inside, or in between, lines *c* and *d*, so they are alternate interior angles. ■

Ⓑ ∠2 and ∠7

Solution ∠2 and ∠7 are on opposite sides of the transversal, line *p*, and they do not share the same vertex. They are outside of lines *c* and *d*, so they are alternate exterior angles. ■

Ⓒ ∠5 and ∠6

Solution ∠5 and ∠6 share a common side and a common vertex. They are adjacent angles. ■

Ⓓ ∠4 and ∠8

Solution ∠4 and ∠8 are in the same position within their group of four angles. They are corresponding angles. ■

Ⓔ ∠2 and ∠8

Solution ∠2 and ∠8 have none of the names given. ■

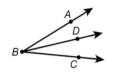

TIP

∠*ABD* and ∠*CBD* are adjacent angles.

common side: $\overrightarrow{BD}$

common vertex: *B*

TIP

interior = inside

exterior = outside

Finding Angle Measures

The letter *m* is used to represent the word *measure*. So, *m*∠1 is read as "the measure of angle 1."

The sum of the measures of two adjacent angles equals the measure of the angle formed by the sides that are not common.

In the figure, *m*∠*ABD* + *m*∠*DBC* = *m*∠*ABC*.

If *m*∠*ABD* = 20° and *m*∠*DBC* = 17°, then *m*∠*ABC* = 37°.

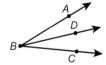

When two lines are crossed by a transversal, the sum of the measures of any two adjacent angles is 180°.

When the two lines crossed by the transversal are *parallel,* the following statements are also true:

The measures of any pair of corresponding angles are equal.
The measures of any pair of alternate interior angles are equal.
The measures of any pair of alternate exterior angles are equal.

Example 2   Find the measure of each angle if $j \parallel k$.

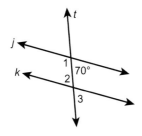

A $m\angle 1$

Solution $\angle 1$ is adjacent to the 70° angle. Because the sum of these angles is 180°, $m\angle 1 = 180° - 70° = 110°$. ∎

B $m\angle 2$

Solution $\angle 2$ and the 70° angle are alternate interior angles, so they have the same measure: $m\angle 2 = 70°$. ∎

C $m\angle 3$

Solution $\angle 3$ and the 70° angle are corresponding angles, so they have the same measure: $m\angle 3 = 70°$. ∎

Example 3   Find the measure of each angle if $m\angle 1 = 45°$ and $m \parallel n$.

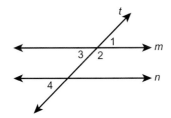

A $m\angle 2$

Solution $\angle 2$ is adjacent to $\angle 1$, so $m\angle 2 = 180° - 45° = 135°$. ∎

B $m\angle 3$

Solution $\angle 3$ is adjacent to $\angle 2$, so $m\angle 3 = 180° - 135° = 45°$. ∎

C $m\angle 4$

Solution $\angle 4$ and $\angle 1$ are alternate exterior angles, so they have the same measure: $m\angle 4 = 45°$. ∎

Problem Set

. . . .

Identify each pair of angles as corresponding, alternate interior, alternate exterior, adjacent, or none of these.

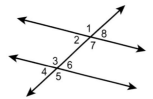

1. $\angle 3$ and $\angle 7$
2. $\angle 6$ and $\angle 7$
3. $\angle 3$ and $\angle 4$
4. $\angle 5$ and $\angle 7$
5. $\angle 4$ and $\angle 8$

6. $\angle 2$ and $\angle 6$
7. $\angle 2$ and $\angle 7$
8. $\angle 3$ and $\angle 8$
9. $\angle 2$ and $\angle 5$
10. $\angle 4$ and $\angle 6$

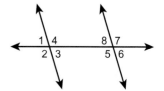

Find the measure of each angle if $c \parallel d$.

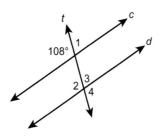

11. $m\angle 1$
12. $m\angle 2$
13. $m\angle 3$
14. $m\angle 4$

Find the measure of each angle if $g \parallel h$.

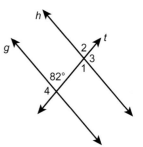

15. $m\angle 1$
16. $m\angle 2$
17. $m\angle 3$
18. $m\angle 4$

Find the measure of each angle if $m\angle 1 = 38°$ and $s \parallel t$.

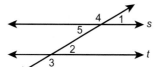

19. $m\angle 2$
20. $m\angle 3$
21. $m\angle 4$
22. $m\angle 5$

Find the measure of each angle if $m\angle 1 = 53°$ and $a \parallel b \parallel c$.

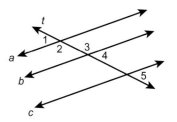

23. $m\angle 2$
24. $m\angle 3$
25. $m\angle 4$
26. $m\angle 5$

Answer each question.

27. Describe two ways to find $m\angle 1$ if $m \parallel n$.

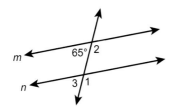

28. Two parallel lines are intersected by a transversal and one of the angles formed measures 27°. What are the measures of the other seven angles?

29. For each pair of angles, state whether they are alternate interior, alternate exterior, or corresponding. Then state which line is used as the transversal.

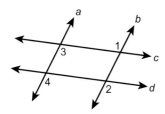

   A. $\angle 1$ and $\angle 2$

   B. $\angle 1$ and $\angle 3$

   C. $\angle 3$ and $\angle 4$

   D. $\angle 2$ and $\angle 4$

*30. **Challenge** For each pair of angles, state whether they are alternate interior, alternate exterior, or corresponding. Then state which line is used as the transversal.

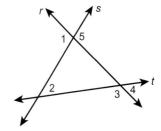

   A. $\angle 1$ and $\angle 2$

   B. $\angle 2$ and $\angle 3$

   C. $\angle 1$ and $\angle 4$

   D. $\angle 2$ and $\angle 5$

*31. **Challenge** *Vertical angles* are a pair of non-adjacent angles formed by two intersecting lines. They have a common vertex, but not a common side. Draw and label a pair of vertical angles.

*32. **Challenge** *Skew lines* are sometimes defined as lines that are not in the same plane and do not intersect. Or they may simply be defined as lines that are not in the same plane. Explain why the definitions are equivalent. Explain why any two lines can be classified in exactly one of the following ways: intersecting, parallel, or skew.

Triangles

Many figures can be formed when parts of lines, rather than lines, are used.

DEFINITION

A **line segment** is part of a line. It includes any two points on the line and all the points between those points.

A line segment is named by its endpoints. The points can be written in any order.

segment *ST*, segment *TS*, $\overline{ST}$, or $\overline{TS}$

TIP

A line segment is often more simply called a *segment*.

DEFINITION

A **triangle** is a figure made up of three segments joined at their endpoints. Each endpoint is a vertex.

To name a triangle, use all three vertices. They can be listed in any order.

One possible name is triangle *FGH* or △*FGH*.

TIP

The plural of *vertex* is *vertices*.

Classifying Triangles by Angle Measures

Every triangle can be classified according to its angle measures.

DEFINITIONS

An **acute triangle** is a triangle with three acute angles.
A **right triangle** is a triangle with a right angle.
An **obtuse triangle** is a triangle with an obtuse angle.

Example 1 Classify each triangle as acute, right, or obtuse.

Ⓐ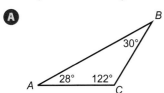

Ⓑ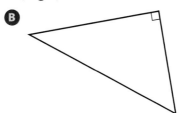

Solution Because angle *C* is an obtuse angle, the triangle is an obtuse triangle. ■

Solution Because one of the angles is a right angle, the triangle is a right triangle. ■

Triangle Angle Sum

TRIANGLE ANGLE SUM

The **triangle angle sum** property states: The sum of the measures of the angles of a triangle is 180°.

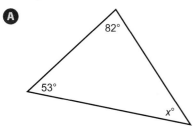

$$m\angle 1 + m\angle 2 + m\angle 3 = 180°$$

THINK ABOUT IT

It is not possible for a triangle to have more than one right angle or more than one obtuse angle.

Example 2 Find the value of *x* in each triangle.

Ⓐ

THINK ABOUT IT

In Example 2A, you can also solve the equation $x + 82 + 53 = 180$.

Solution Find the sum of the measures of the two known angles: $82° + 53° = 135°$. Subtract this sum from 180°: $180° - 135° = 45°$. Therefore, $x = 45$. ■

Ⓑ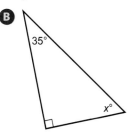

Solution Because the triangle is a right triangle, the sum of the measures of the two acute angles must be 90°.

$$x + 35 = 90$$

$$x + 35 - 35 = 90 - 35$$

$$x = 55 \quad ■$$

(continued)

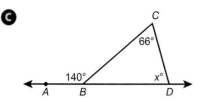

Solution ∠ABC and ∠CBD are adjacent angles and form a straight line, so $m\angle CBD = 180° - 140° = 40°$. Then, $40 + 66 + x = 180$.

$$40 + 66 + x = 180$$
$$106 + x = 180$$
$$x = 180 - 106$$
$$x = 74 \blacksquare$$

Classifying Triangles by Their Side Lengths

Triangles can also be classified according to their side lengths.

> **DEFINITIONS**
>
> In a **scalene triangle,** none of the side lengths are equal.
> In an **isosceles triangle,** at least two of the side lengths are equal.
> In an **equilateral triangle,** all three side lengths are equal.

> **THINK ABOUT IT**
>
> An equilateral triangle is also an isosceles triangle. An isosceles triangle may or may not be equilateral.

The two equal sides of an isosceles triangle are the *legs*. The remaining side is the *base*.

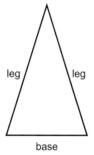

Application: Sports

Example 3 The sports pennant is shaped like an isosceles triangle. The perimeter is 45 inches. What are the lengths of the legs if the base is 9 inches long?

Solution   Let x represent the length of each leg. Then, $x + x + 9 = 45$.

$$x + x + 9 = 45$$

$2x + 9 = 45$	Combine like terms.
$2x = 36$	Subtract 9 from both sides.
$x = 18$	Divide both sides by 2.

The legs are each 18 inches long.

Check $18 + 18 + 9 = 45$ ∎

Application: Home Improvement

Example 4   A homeowner leans a ladder against her home so that the bottom of the ladder makes a 62° angle with the ground. What angle does the top of the ladder make with the building?

Solution   Draw a model. Assume that the ground is perpendicular to the building. The ladder, ground, and building form a right triangle.

$$x + 62 = 90$$
$$x = 90 - 62$$
$$x = 28$$

The top of the ladder makes a 28° angle with the building.

Check $28 + 62 + 90 = 180$ ∎

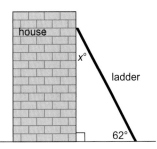

TIP

Two lines, or segments, that form right angles are *perpendicular* to each other.

Problem Set

Classify each triangle as acute, right, or obtuse.

1.
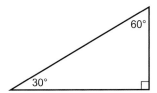
45°
110°   25°

2.
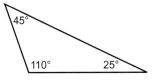
48°
72°   60°

3.
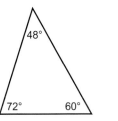
60°
30°

4.
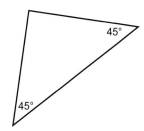
45°
45°

5.
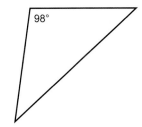
98°

6.
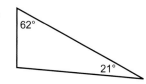
62°
21°

Find the value of x in each triangle.

7.

125°
38° $x°$

8.
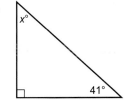
$x°$
41°

9.

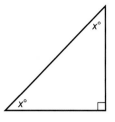

10.

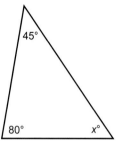

11.

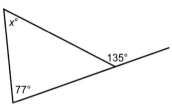

12.

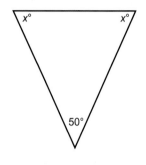

13.

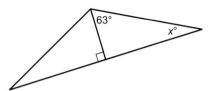

14.

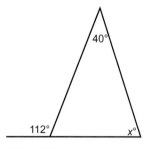

15. $\overline{AB} \parallel \overline{CD}$

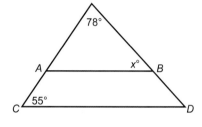

16. $r \parallel s \parallel t$

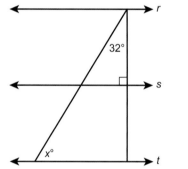

Find the value of each variable in the figure.

17. a

18. b

19. c

20. d

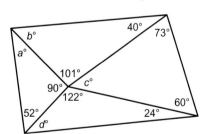

Name the triangle that appears to best fit each description. Name each triangle once.

21. right scalene

22. equilateral

23. obtuse isosceles

24. right isosceles

25. obtuse scalene

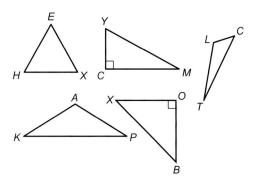

Answer each question.

26. $\overline{KA}$ and $\overline{AZ}$ are the legs of isosceles triangle *KAZ*. Find the value of *x*.

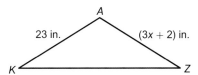

27. Explain why a triangle can have at most one obtuse angle or one right angle.

28. A homeowner leans a ladder against his house so that the top of the ladder makes a 31° angle with the house.

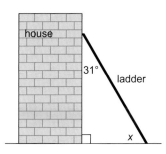

   A. What angle does the bottom of the ladder make with the ground?

   B. Classify the triangle formed by the ladder, the ground, and the building by side length and by angle measure.

29. The sports pennant is shaped like an isosceles triangle. The perimeter is 40 inches. What are the lengths of the legs if the base is 8 inches long?

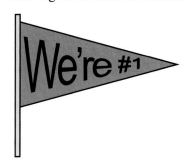

30. A billiards table has a wooden pool ball rack shaped like an equilateral triangle. The perimeter is 42 inches. What is the length of one leg of the triangle?

31. A sports team's logo is shaped like an equilateral triangle. The perimeter of the triangle is 10 inches. What is the length of a leg of the triangle?

*32. **Challenge** Explain why the measure of an exterior angle of a triangle equals the sum of the measures of the two nonadjacent interior angles of the triangle.

*33. **Challenge** Use these words to form as many two-word descriptions of a triangle as possible: *scalene, isosceles, equilateral, acute, right, obtuse.*

Polygons

Geometric figures can include segments or curves and can be open or closed.

Identifying Polygons

> **DEFINITION**
>
> A **polygon** is a closed figure formed by three or more line segments in a plane, such that each line segment intersects two other line segments at their endpoints only. The segments are called **sides** and the endpoints are called **vertices.**

Example 1   Classify each figure as a polygon or as not a polygon.

A

Solution   The figure is not a polygon because it is not closed. ■

B
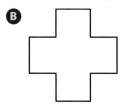

Solution   The figure is closed and made up of segments that meet at their endpoints. It is a polygon. ■

C

Solution   The figure is closed and made up of segments that meet at their endpoints. It is a polygon. ■

D

Solution   The figure is made up of two segments and a curve. It is not a polygon. ■

E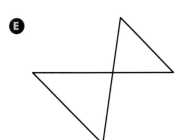

F _____

Solution The four segments do not intersect at their endpoints only. It is not a polygon. ■

Solution A polygon must contain at least three line segments. It is not a polygon. ■

Regular Polygons

An **equiangular polygon** is a polygon whose angle measures are all equal.
An **equilateral polygon** is a polygon whose side lengths are all equal.
A **regular polygon** is both equiangular and equilateral.

Example 2 Which polygons appear to be regular polygons?

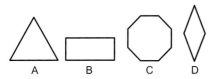

Solution Polygons A and C appear to be regular polygons because in both figures the sides appear to be the same length and the angles appear to be the same measure. However, polygons B and D do not appear to be regular polygons. Polygon B has equal angle measures (all 90°), but the side lengths are not all the same. Polygon D has equal side lengths, but not all the angle measures are the same. ■

THINK ABOUT IT

Polygon B is equiangular but not equilateral. Polygon D is equilateral but not equiangular.

Example 3 The angles formed by the sides of a regular hexagon (a polygon with six sides) have measures that sum to 720°. What is the degree measure of each angle?

Solution Let d represent the measure of an angle in the regular hexagon.

$6d = 720$ A regular hexagon has 6 congruent angles.

$\dfrac{6d}{6} = \dfrac{720}{6}$ Divide both sides by 6.

$d = 120$ Simplify.

Each angle measures 120°. ■

Classifying a Polygon by Its Number of Sides

Polygons can also be classified according to the number of sides that form the figure.

Number of Sides	Polygon Name
3	triangle
4	quadrilateral
5	pentagon
6	hexagon
7	heptagon
8	octagon
10	decagon
n	n-gon

THINK ABOUT IT

A triangle is the polygon with the fewest possible sides.

Example 4 Classify each polygon by its number of sides. Determine if the polygon appears to be regular or not regular.

A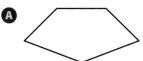

Solution pentagon, not regular ■

B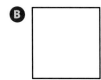

Solution quadrilateral, regular ■

THINK ABOUT IT

A square is always a regular quadrilateral.

C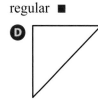

Solution hexagon, regular ■

D

Solution triangle, not regular ■

Application: Perimeter

Example 5

A A regular 15-gon has a perimeter of 450 centimeters. What is the length of each side of the polygon?

Solution A 15-gon is a polygon with 15 sides. Because the polygon is regular, all the sides are equal in length. You can use division to find the length of each side.

$450 \div 15 = 30$

The length of each side is 30 centimeters. ■

B Six sides of a decagon each measure 7 inches. The perimeter of the decagon is 78 inches. What is the length of each remaining side if each remaining side has the same length?

Solution A decagon has 10 sides. The lengths of six of the sides are known, so there are $10 - 6 = 4$ remaining sides of unknown length.

total length of 6 known sides: $6 \cdot 7 = 42$

total length of remaining sides: $78 - 42 = 36$

length of each remaining side: $36 \div 4 = 9$

Each of the four remaining sides has a length of 9 inches.

Check $6 \cdot 7 + 4 \cdot 9 = 42 + 36 = 78$ ∎

Problem Set

Classify each figure as a polygon or as not a polygon.

1.

2.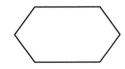

3.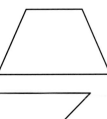

4.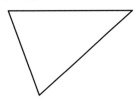

5.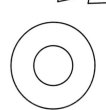

6.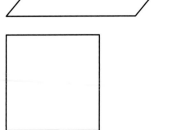

7.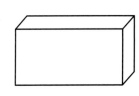

8.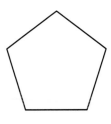

Does the polygon appear to be a regular polygon? Write *yes* or *no*.

9.

10.

11.

12.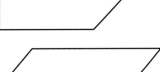

13.

14.

15.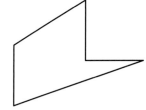

16.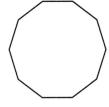

Classify each polygon by its number of sides. State whether the polygon appears to be regular or not regular.

17.

18.

19.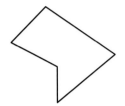

20.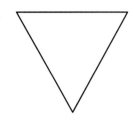

21.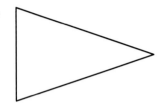

22.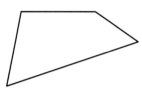

23.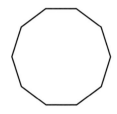

24.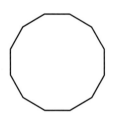

Answer each question.

25. A picture frame is shaped like a regular hexagon. One of the angles has a measure of 120°. What is the sum of the remaining angle measures?

26. What is the measure of each angle of an equiangular triangle?

27. A certain regular decagon has a perimeter of 352 feet. How long is each side?

28. The sum of the angle measures of a regular 20-gon is 3240°. What is the measure of each angle of a regular 20-gon?

29. A regular 12-gon (called a dodecagon) has a perimeter of 156 centimeters. What is the length of each side of the polygon?

30. Four sides of an octagon each measure 6 inches. The perimeter of the octagon is 52 inches. What is the length of each remaining side if each remaining side has the same length?

***31. Challenge** In a certain hexagon, the two shortest sides have the same length. The length of each remaining side is 2 inches more than the length of each shortest side. The perimeter of the hexagon is 38 inches. What are the lengths of the sides of the hexagon?

***32. Challenge** This 20-gon has 2 sides of one equal length, 8 sides of another equal length, and 9 sides of a third equal length. All angles in the diagram are right angles. $AB = 10$ cm, $BE = 33$ cm, and $AB = \frac{4}{3}CD$. Find the perimeter.

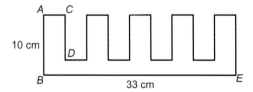

Circles

The circle is a common and useful shape.

When working with polygons, a side was defined as a line segment. A circle does not have any sides, so circles are not polygons.

The center of a circle is not part of the circle. It is used to determine which points form the circle. The center point is also used to name the circle.

circle *K*

Identifying Radii

radius

Example 1

A Name the radii shown in circle *P*.

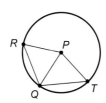

Solution The radii are $\overline{PR}$, $\overline{PQ}$, and $\overline{PT}$. ■

(continued)

B Name the radii shown in circle *A*.

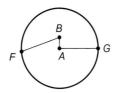

Solution   Because *A* is the center of the circle, $\overline{AG}$ is the only radius shown. ■

Identifying Chords and Diameters

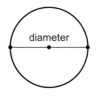

Example 2

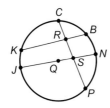

A Name the chords in circle *Q*.

Solution   Look for segments whose endpoints are on the circle. The chords are $\overline{KB}$, $\overline{JN}$, and $\overline{CP}$. ■

B Name the diameters in circle *Q*.

Solution   The only chord that passes through the center of the circle is $\overline{JN}$, so $\overline{JN}$ is a diameter of the circle. ■

Calculating a Radius or Diameter

Look again at circle *Q* in Example 2. Point *Q* separates the diameter $\overline{JN}$ into two segments of equal length: $\overline{QJ}$ and $\overline{QN}$, which are both radii.

Example 3

A What is the diameter of circle *M*?

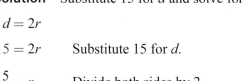

Solution The radius *r* is 18 inches.

$d = 2r$

$\quad = 2 \cdot 18 \qquad$ Substitute 18 for *r*.

$\quad = 36 \qquad\quad$ Multiply.

The diameter is 36 inches. ■

B Find the radius of a circle that has diameter 15 centimeters.

Solution Substitute 15 for *d* and solve for *r*.

$\quad d = 2r$

$15 = 2r \qquad$ Substitute 15 for *d*.

$\dfrac{15}{2} = r \qquad$ Divide both sides by 2.

$7.5 = r \qquad$ Simplify.

The radius is 7.5 centimeters. ■

Application: Boating

Example 4 A lake is approximately circular and has an average diameter of 3265 feet. A small island is located so the dock is at the center of the lake. A tour boat takes people to and from the island several times a day. If the boat travels about 26,120 feet every day, how many round trips does the boat make every day?

Solution The distance from the side of the lake to the island is the radius of the lake. Find the average radius of the lake.

$\quad d = 2r$

$3265 = 2r \qquad$ Substitute 3265 for *d*.

$\dfrac{3265}{2} = r \qquad$ Divide both sides by 2.

$1632.5 = r \qquad$ Simplify.

Divide the total distance the boat travels by the radius to determine how many one-way trips the boat makes.

$26{,}120 \div 1632.5 = 16$

$\qquad\qquad 16 \div 2 = 8 \qquad$ Divide to find the number of round trips.

The boat makes 8 round trips every day. ■

THINK ABOUT IT

A round trip is 2 times the radius, which equals the diameter. So, another way to find the number of round trips is to divide the total distance by the diameter.

$$\frac{26{,}120}{3265} = 8$$

Problem Set

For problems 1–6,

A. **Name all the radii.**
B. **Name all the chords.**
C. **Name all the diameters.**

1.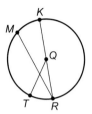

2.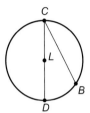

3.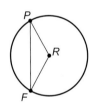

4.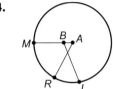

5.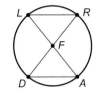

6.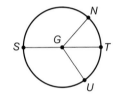

Write *true* or *false*.

7. All the radii of the same circle have the same length.

8. All the diameters of the same circle have the same length.

9. All the chords of the same circle have the same length.

10. A radius of a circle is shorter than any chord of the circle.

11. A diameter is the longest chord in a circle.

Answer each question.

12. What is the radius of circle S?

25.3 cm

13. What is the diameter of circle X?

$3\frac{1}{4}$ ft

14. Find the radius of a circle if its diameter is $2\frac{1}{2}$ meters.

15. Find the diameter of a circle if its radius is 34.5 centimeters.

16. Explain why a circle is not a polygon.

17. What must be true about $\overline{KR}$ if the circle is named circle E? Why?

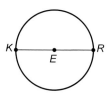

18. A circular swimming pool has a radius of 15 feet. What is the least number of times you can swim across the pool so that you swim one mile? (Hint: 1 mile = 5280 feet)

19. A town center has a circular lake with a diameter of 450 feet. A ferry boat takes visitors to and from the dock of a floating restaurant located in the center of the lake. If the boat travels about 3375 feet every day, how many one-way trips does the boat make every day?

*20. Challenge Ricardo is building a feeding station for his three cats. As the diagram illustrates, each cat will have its own bowl and all the bowls will be the same size. There will be 2 inches between the bowls as well as between the bowls and the edges of the feeder. Find the length and width of the feeding station.

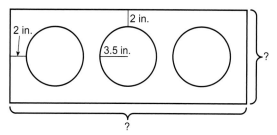

*21. Challenge In the diagram, points A, B, C, D, E, and F are on the circle.

A. Name all the chords.

B. Given that $\overline{AB} \parallel \overline{CD} \parallel \overline{EF}$, find $m\angle 1$, $m\angle 2$, $m\angle 3$. Justify your answers.

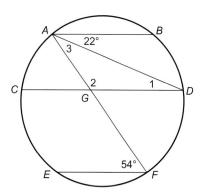

Transformations

A transformation is a change. With transformations, geometric figures can be moved around and altered.

TIP

A transformation can also be defined as a mapping between two sets of points.

A **transformation** is a change in the position, orientation, or size of a figure. There are three types of transformations that change the position, but not the size, of a figure.

Reflections

DEFINITION

A **reflection** is a transformation of a figure by flipping it across a line or line segment, creating a mirror image of the figure.

The line or line segment that the image is flipped across is called a **line of reflection**. It can also be called a *line of symmetry*.

Example 1 Draw the reflection over the given line.

A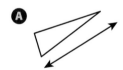

B

Solution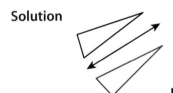

Solution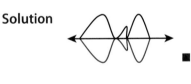

Example 2 Each figure was created by drawing the reflection of a figure over a given line. Draw the lines of reflection that could have been used.

A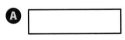

B

Solution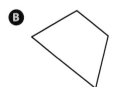

Solution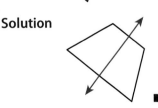

Rotations

A **rotation** is the turning of a figure around a given point.

The point the figure is rotated about is called the **center of rotation**. It can be located in, on, or outside the figure.

The number of degrees the figure is rotated is called the **angle of rotation**. It can be anywhere from 0° to 360° (a full circle). Figures can be rotated clockwise or counterclockwise.

Example 3 Draw the rotation about the given point.

A clockwise 90°

Solution

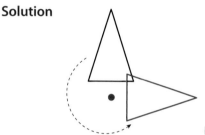

C clockwise 180°

Solution

B counterclockwise 270°

Solution

D counterclockwise 45°

Solution

TIP

Clockwise is the direction the hands of a clock move.

TIP

A quarter turn (15 minutes on a clock) is a 90° turn. A 180° turn is halfway around a circle.

THINK ABOUT IT

A 180° rotation clockwise and a 180° rotation counterclockwise produce the same result.

Describing Rotations

Example 4

A The figure in red was produced by rotating the figure in black about the given point. What angle of rotation and direction could have been used?

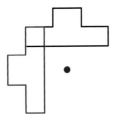

Solution The figure in red was produced by either rotating the figure in black 90° counterclockwise or 270° clockwise about the point. ■

B The figure in red was produced by rotating the figure in black 90° clockwise. Draw the point that was used as the center of rotation.

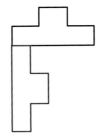

Solution Notice that the lower left point of the figure never moves.

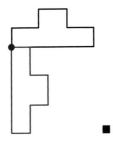

Translations

You can use a segment with an arrow (also called a **vector**) to indicate the direction and length of a translation.

Example 5   Draw the translation as the vector indicates.

A

B

Solution    ■

Solution 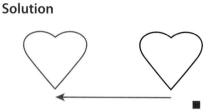   ■

Identifying Transformations

In a transformation, the original figure is the **preimage**. The new figure that results from the transformation is the **image**.

Example 6   Determine what type of transformation was done to the pre-image to result in the image shown. Write reflection, rotation, translation, or none of these.

A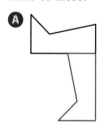

B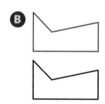

Solution   Rotation ■

Solution   Translation ■

C

D

Solution   None of these ■

Solution   Reflection ■

Application: Graphic Design

Example 7   A designer is working with logos on a grid. He is told to translate this logo 1 unit down and 3 units to the right, and then to perform a 90° clockwise rotation about the point that is at the center of the X. Draw the resulting figure.

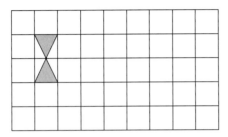

Solution   Slide 1 down and 3 right.   Then rotate 90° clockwise.

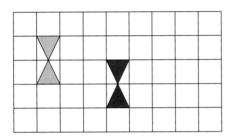   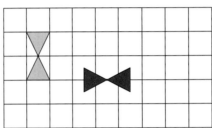

THINK ABOUT IT

A 90° counterclockwise rotation would have produced the same result.

Problem Set

Draw the reflection over the given line.

1.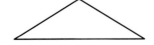

2.

3.

4.

Each figure was created by reflecting a figure over a line that passes through the figure. Draw all the lines of reflection that could have been used.

5.

6.

7.

Draw the rotation image about the given point.

8. counterclockwise 90°

9. clockwise 180°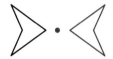

10. clockwise 90°

11. counterclockwise 270°

The red figure was produced by rotating the black figure about the given point. What angle of rotation and direction could have been used? (Use multiples of 90°.)

12.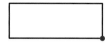

13.

14.

The red figure was produced by rotating the black figure as described. Draw the point that was used as the center of rotation.

15. 90° counterclockwise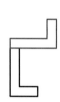

16. 180° clockwise

17. 180° clockwise

Draw the translation image as indicated by the vector.

18.

19.

20.

21.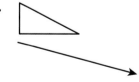

Determine what type of transformation was done to the black preimage to result in the red image shown. Write reflection, rotation, translation, or none of these.

22.

23.

24.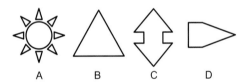

25.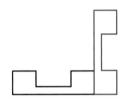

26.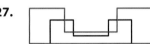

27.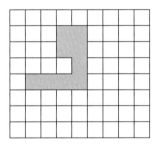

Answer each question.

28. A figure has *point symmetry* if its image coincides with its preimage after a rotation of 180° about its center. Which of the figures below have point symmetry?

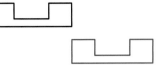

  A   B   C   D

*29. **Challenge** Which capital letters of the alphabet have a vertical line of symmetry? Which have a horizontal line of symmetry?

*30. **Challenge** Rotate this logo 90° clockwise about its bottom right point. Then translate it 2 units down and 1 unit left.

Congruence

Images that are the result of a reflection, rotation, or translation are congruent to their pre-images.

> **DEFINITION**
>
> **Congruent figures** are figures that have the same size and shape.

Tick marks indicate congruent sides and arcs indicate congruent angles. The triangles below are congruent. Notice that if one were reflected on top of the other, the sides and angles would match up exactly. The parts that match up are *corresponding parts*. These have the same number of tick marks or arcs.

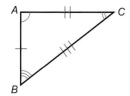 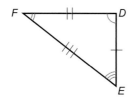

The symbol for congruence is ≅. You can use the congruence symbol to write a congruence statement to indicate that the two triangles are congruent. When doing so, be sure to name the triangles so that the corresponding vertices are in the same position in each name.

Two possible congruence statements for the triangles above are $\triangle ABC \cong \triangle DEF$ and $\triangle CAB \cong \triangle FDE$.

Identifying Congruent Parts

You can use the congruence symbol to name corresponding parts. For example, $\angle A \cong \angle D$ and $\overline{AB} \cong \overline{DE}$.

> **TIP**
>
> The expression $\angle A \cong \angle D$ is read as "Angle A is congruent to angle D."

Example 1

A $MNOP \cong ZWXY$

Identify the congruent segments and angles.

 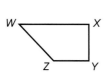

> **TIP**
>
> Names of polygons with more than three sides do not have a symbol before the name.

Solution The first vertex in the first name, *M*, corresponds with the first vertex in the second name, *Z*, and so on. *ZWXY* is a rotation of *MNOP*.

(continued)

If desired, you can redraw *ZWXY* so it is positioned like *MNOP*.

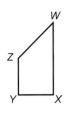

$$\angle M \cong \angle Z, \angle N \cong \angle W, \angle O \cong \angle X, \angle P \cong \angle Y$$
$$\overline{MN} \cong \overline{ZW}, \overline{NO} \cong \overline{WX}, \overline{OP} \cong \overline{XY}, \overline{PM} \cong \overline{YZ} \ \blacksquare$$

B *DFG* ≅ *HFG*

Identify the congruent segments and angles.

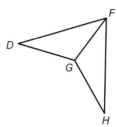

> **TIP**
>
> When angles are adjacent, name the angles using three vertices to avoid confusion.

Solution   Notice that if the triangles were pulled apart, both triangles would have segment *FG*.

$$\angle D \cong \angle H, \angle DFG \cong \angle HFG, \angle FGD \cong \angle FGH$$
$$\overline{DF} \cong \overline{HF}, \overline{FG} \cong \overline{FG}, \overline{GD} \cong \overline{GH} \ \blacksquare$$

Writing Congruence Statements

Example 2   Write a congruence statement for each pair of congruent polygons.

A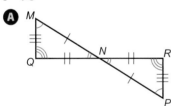

> **TIP**
>
> When naming a polygon, choose the vertices in consecutive order around the figure.

Solution   Name one of the triangles in any way. Then name the second triangle by matching corresponding vertices.

Possible answer: $\triangle MNQ \cong \triangle PNR$ ■

B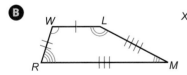

Solution   Possible answer: $WLMR \cong AFXP$ ■

Determining if Two Polygons Are Congruent

Example 3

Ⓐ Determine if $\triangle SLD \cong \triangle TLD$. Explain.

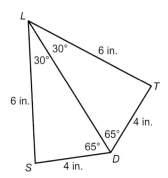

REMEMBER

When two polygons are congruent, all the corresponding sides and all the corresponding angles are congruent.

Solution Using the triangle angle sum property, $m\angle S = m\angle T = 180° - (30° + 65°) = 85°$, so $\angle S \cong \angle T$. The other corresponding angles are congruent. $\overline{LD} \cong \overline{LD}$ because it is a common side. The other corresponding sides have equal measures. All six corresponding parts are congruent, so the triangles are congruent. ■

Ⓑ Determine if $JRML \cong KVYN$. Explain.

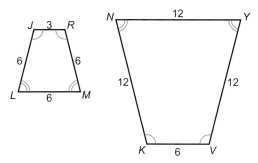

Solution All four pairs of corresponding angles are congruent, however, the corresponding sides are not congruent. For example, segment JR has a length of 3 units and segment KV has a length of 6 units. The polygons are not congruent. ■

Problem Set

Answer the following given that △*GEA* ≅ △*LCT*.

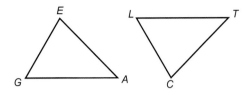

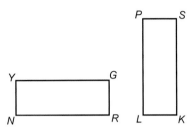

7. *GRNY* ≅ *KLPS*

Identify the congruent segments and angles.

1. What angle is congruent to ∠*L*?

2. What angle is congruent to ∠*E*?

3. What angle is congruent to ∠*T*?

4. What segment is congruent to $\overline{GE}$?

5. What segment is congruent to $\overline{GA}$?

6. What segment is congruent to $\overline{TC}$?

8. △*CNL* ≅ △*AML*

Identify the congruent segments and angles.

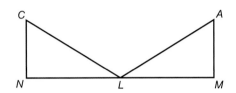

Each pair of polygons is congruent. Complete each congruence statement.

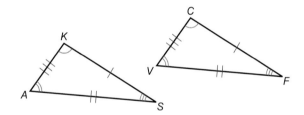

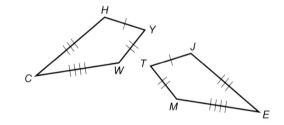

9. △*KAS* ≅ △_____

10. △_____ ≅ △*FVC*

11. △*ASK* ≅ △_____

12. △_____ ≅ △*VCF*

13. *CHYW* ≅ _____

14. _____ ≅ *JEMT*

15. *WYHC* ≅ _____

16. _____ ≅ *MTJE*

Write a congruence statement for each pair of congruent polygons.

17.

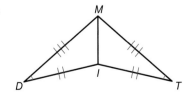

18.

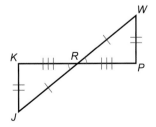

19.

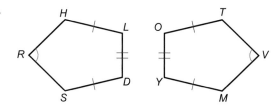

20.

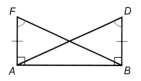

Answer each question.

21. Determine if $\triangle BAD \cong \triangle VBZ$. Explain.

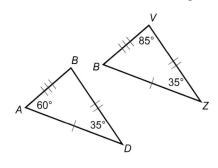

22. Determine if $ABCD \cong MNOP$. Explain.

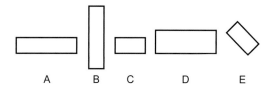

23. Which polygons appear to be congruent?

24. If $\triangle FRY \cong \triangle JAM$, $m\angle F = 40°$, and $m\angle Y = 70°$, what is $m\angle A$?

25. Given: $MTSK \cong BVNC$, $ST = 16$, $SK = 4y$, $VN = 3x + 1$, and $NC = y + 25$. Find the values of x and y.

26. Two triangles have the same perimeter. Must they be congruent? Explain.

27. All pairs of corresponding angles of two quadrilaterals are congruent. Must the quadrilaterals be congruent? Explain.

***28.** **Challenge** Draw and label a diagram to represent each set of conditions.

A. $\triangle ABC \cong \triangle DBC$ and $AB < AC$.

B. $\triangle ABC \cong \triangle CDB$ and $AB < AC$.

UNIT 8

Ratio, Proportion, and Percent

With proportional reasoning and some math, you can use building blocks to create a scale model of a car, a person, or even a town.

Model builders use ratios and percents to describe how their models compare to real objects. They can use proportions to figure out the length of every item in the model.

Big Ideas

· ·

▶ If you can create a mathematical model for a situation, you can use the model to solve other problems that you might not be able to solve otherwise. Algebraic equations can capture key relationships among quantities in the world.

▶ A number is any entity that obeys the laws of arithmetic; all numbers obey the laws of arithmetic. The laws of arithmetic can be used to simplify algebraic expressions.

Unit Topics

· ·

▶ Ratio

▶ Proportion

▶ Percents, Fractions, and Decimals

▶ Similarity and Scale

▶ Working with Percent

▶ Percent of Increase or Decrease

▶ Simple Interest

▶ Compound Interest

Ratio

A **ratio** is a comparison of two quantities by division.

A ratio can be written as a fraction, with a colon, or with the word "to."

$$\frac{2}{3} \qquad 2 : 3 \qquad 2 \text{ to } 3$$

TIP

All these ratios are read as "2 to 3."

Writing and Simplifying Ratios

To write a ratio in simplest form, write it as a fraction in simplest form.

Example 1 Simplify each ratio. Write your answer in all three forms.

A $\dfrac{8}{10}$

Solution Simplify the fraction.

$\dfrac{8 \div 2}{10 \div 2} = \dfrac{4}{5}$ Divide the numerator and the denominator by the greatest common factor.

$\dfrac{4}{5}$ or 4 : 5 or 4 to 5 ■

B 28 to 4

Solution Write the ratio as a fraction, and then simplify it.

$\dfrac{28}{4} = \dfrac{28 \div 4}{4 \div 4} = \dfrac{7}{1}$

$\dfrac{7}{1}$ or 7 : 1 or 7 to 1 ■

C 63 to 27

Solution Write the ratio as a fraction, and then simplify it.

$\dfrac{63}{27} = \dfrac{63 \div 9}{27 \div 9} = \dfrac{7}{3}$ Don't write a ratio as a mixed number.
Write the improper fraction $\dfrac{7}{3}$.

$\dfrac{7}{3}$ or 7 : 3 or 7 to 3 ■

Writing Rates to Represent Situations

A **rate** is a ratio of quantities that have different units. For example, 80 miles to 2 hours is a rate.

Example 2   Write a rate to represent each situation.

A It costs $3 for a 5-minute phone call.

Solution $\dfrac{3 \text{ dollars}}{5 \text{ minutes}}$ ∎

B A car travels 85 miles on 4 gallons of gasoline.

Solution $\dfrac{85 \text{ miles}}{4 \text{ gallons}}$ ∎

C Three T-shirts cost $17.50.

Solution $\dfrac{\$17.50}{3 \text{ shirts}}$ ∎

> **TIP**
>
> It is also correct, in some contexts, to use the reciprocal as the ratio as well. We could write the ratio $\dfrac{4 \text{ gallons}}{85 \text{ miles}}$ for Example 2B.

Finding Unit Rates

A **unit rate** is a rate that has a denominator of 1.

> **FINDING A UNIT RATE**
>
> **Step 1**   Separate the units from the number part of the fraction.
> **Step 2**   Simplify the number part of the fraction.

Example 3   Write a unit rate for each situation.

A Mr. Beck drives 120 miles in 3 hours.

Solution   Write a ratio. Divide the numerator and denominator by 3.

$$\frac{120}{3} \cdot \frac{\text{miles}}{\text{hours}} = \frac{120 \div 3}{3 \div 3} \cdot \frac{\text{miles}}{\text{hours}} = \frac{40}{1} \cdot \frac{\text{miles}}{\text{hours}}, \text{ or } 40 \text{ miles per hour} \quad ∎$$

B There are 36 servings in 4 bags.

Solution   Write a ratio. Divide the numerator and denominator by 4.

$$\frac{36}{4} \cdot \frac{\text{servings}}{\text{bags}} = \frac{36 \div 4}{4 \div 4} \cdot \frac{\text{servings}}{\text{bags}} = \frac{9}{1} \cdot \frac{\text{servings}}{\text{bags}}, \text{ or } 9 \text{ servings per bag} \quad ∎$$

C Ella types 474 words in 6 minutes.

Solution   Write a ratio. Divide the numerator and denominator by 6.

$$\frac{474}{6} \cdot \frac{\text{words}}{\text{minutes}} = \frac{474 \div 6}{6 \div 6} \cdot \frac{\text{words}}{\text{minutes}} = \frac{79}{1} \cdot \frac{\text{words}}{\text{minute}}, \text{ or }$$

79 words per minute   ∎

Comparing Parts and Wholes

You can use a ratio to compare a part to a part, a part to a whole, or a whole to a part.

Example 4 A jar contains 21 marbles: 8 white, 3 green, and 10 red. Write each described ratio in simplest form.

Ⓐ Number of white marbles to number of green marbles

Solution There are 8 white marbles and 3 green marbles.

The ratio is $\frac{8}{3}$, or 8 : 3, or 8 to 3. ■

Ⓑ Number of green marbles to total number of marbles

Solution There are 3 green marbles and 21 marbles in all.

$\frac{3}{21} = \frac{1}{7}$, so the ratio is $\frac{1}{7}$, or 1 : 7, or 1 to 7. ■

Ⓒ Total number of marbles to number of white marbles

Solution There are 21 marbles in all and 8 white marbles.

The ratio is $\frac{21}{8}$, or 21 : 8, or 21 to 8. ■

TIP

Example 4A compares a part to a part. Example 4B compares a part to a whole. Example 4C compares a whole to a part.

Application: Fuel Economy

Example 5 A car travels 255 miles and uses 8.5 gallons of gasoline. Write the unit rate that describes the car's fuel economy.

Solution Write a rate, and then convert it to a unit rate.

$$\frac{255}{8.5} \cdot \frac{\text{miles}}{\text{gallons}} = \frac{255 \div 8.5}{8.5 \div 8.5} \cdot \frac{\text{miles}}{\text{gallons}} = \frac{30}{1} \cdot \frac{\text{miles}}{\text{gallon}}$$

The car's fuel economy is described by the unit rate 30 miles per gallon. ■

Application: Win-Loss Ratio

Example 6 A softball team wins 12 of its 22 games, and loses the rest. What is the ratio of wins to losses in simplest form?

Solution $22 - 12 = 10$, so the team loses 10 games.

$$\frac{\text{number of wins}}{\text{number of losses}} = \frac{12}{10}$$

$\frac{12 \div 2}{10 \div 2} = \frac{6}{5}$ Divide by the greatest common factor to simplify the fraction.

The ratio of wins to losses is $\frac{6}{5}$, or 6 : 5, or 6 to 5. ■

REMEMBER

A ratio is not usually written as a mixed number or decimal, but a ratio can contain a mixed number or decimal.

Problem Set

. . . .

Simplify each ratio. Write your answer in all three forms.

1. $\frac{10}{12}$

2. 8 to 64

3. 20 : 30

4. $\frac{18}{9}$

5. 16 to 56

6. 32 : 72

7. $\frac{18}{54}$

8. 35 to 14

9. 30 : 42

10. $\frac{48}{16}$

11. 35 to 7

12. 88 : 11

13. $\frac{64}{24}$

14. 14 to 21

15. 30 : 18

16. $\frac{50}{140}$

Write a rate to represent each situation. Then write the unit rate.

17. Emile paid $3.96 for 4 songs.

18. The bakery set a price of $0.30 for 3 cookies.

19. It took a boy 20 minutes to walk 2 miles.

20. A car travels 120 miles on 6 gallons of gasoline.

21. The manager paid $37.50 for 5 movie tickets.

The table shows the number of students in each school club. Write a simplified ratio in all three forms for each situation.

22. number of drama students to number of chess students

23. number of music students to number of drama students

24. number of environmental students to number of drama and chess students

25. number of chess students to all students

Club	Students
Drama	20
Chess	10
Environmental	12
Music	18

Solve each problem.

A. Write a unit rate or a ratio.

B. Write your answer in a complete sentence.

26. A bike rider travels 68 miles in 5 hours. Write the unit rate that describes the bike rider's speed in miles per hour.

27. A type of bamboo grew 30 centimeters in 5 hours. Write the unit rate that describes the bamboo's rate of growth in centimeters per hour.

28. There are 42 students in the library. Fourteen of the students are boys. What is the ratio of boys to girls in simplest form?

29. There were 3 rainy days in one week. What is the ratio of rainy days to not rainy days in simplest form?

*30. **Challenge** A tortoise travels 0.875 miles in 0.25 hours.

   A. Write the unit rate that describes the tortoise's speed in miles per hour.

   B. Calculate the distance the tortoise will travel in 2.75 hours.

*31. **Challenge** Two restaurants are selling burgers at different prices. Burger Barn sells 5 burgers for $4.50. Bargain Burger sells 8 hamburgers for $6.00.

   A. What is the unit rate for Burger Barn?

   B. What is the unit rate for Bargain Burger?

   C. Which restaurant has the better deal? Explain.

Proportion

Ratios that describe the same numerical relationship are **equivalent ratios**.

Finding Equivalent Ratios

To multiply or divide the numerator and denominator of a fraction by the same value is the same as multiplying the fraction by a form of 1. Multiplying by 1 does not change the value, so it's a good way to find equivalent ratios.

Example 1 Find two ratios that are equivalent to the given ratio.

A 20 : 25

Solution Write the ratio as a fraction. Then multiply or divide the numerator and denominator by the same nonzero number.

$$\frac{20}{25} = \frac{20 \div 5}{25 \div 5} = \frac{4}{5}$$

$$\frac{20}{25} = \frac{20 \cdot 3}{25 \cdot 3} = \frac{60}{75} \quad \blacksquare$$

B 3 : 4

Solution This ratio is already in simplest form, so you can only multiply the numerator and denominator by the same nonzero number.

$$\frac{3}{4} = \frac{3 \cdot 2}{4 \cdot 2} = \frac{6}{8}$$

$$\frac{3}{4} = \frac{3 \cdot 10}{4 \cdot 10} = \frac{30}{40} \quad \blacksquare$$

THINK ABOUT IT

Saying that a ratio is $\frac{1.5}{2}$ is okay, but for convenience, we generally try to use integer values for the numerator and denominator and would write the ratio as $\frac{3}{4}$.

THINK ABOUT IT

Any given ratio has infinite equivalent ratios because there are infinite versions of 1 to multiply by.

Determining Whether Ratios Are Proportional

A **proportion** is an equation stating that two ratios are equal. In the proportion $\frac{a}{b} = \frac{c}{d}$, a and d are called the **extremes** and b and c are called the **means.** These definitions are easier to remember when you write the proportion with colons, because the extremes are on the exterior and the means are in the middle.

$$a : b = c : d$$

TIP

Read the proportion $\frac{a}{b} = \frac{c}{d}$, "a is to b as c is to d."

(continued)

Two ratios form a proportion if and only if the product of the means is equal to the product of the extremes.

MEANS-EXTREMES PRODUCT PROPERTY

For any *a* and *c* and nonzero *b* and *d*:

$$\frac{a}{b} = \frac{c}{d} \text{ if and only if } ad = bc.$$

Examples

$\frac{3}{5} = \frac{9}{15}$ because $3 \cdot 15 = 5 \cdot 9$

$\frac{7}{10} \neq \frac{2}{3}$ because $7 \cdot 3 \neq 10 \cdot 2$

If two ratios form a proportion, those ratios are called *proportional,* or *in proportion.*

When you write the product of the means and the product of the extremes, this is sometimes called **cross multiplying.**

ad is the product of the extremes.
bc is the product of the means.

ad and *bc* are called cross products.

> **TIP**
>
> These all mean the same thing:
>
> equal ratios
> equivalent ratios
> proportional ratios
> ratios in proportion

You could also simplify each ratio to determine if they are proportional, but cross multiplying is generally quicker.

Example 2 Determine whether the ratios are proportional.

Ⓐ $\frac{4}{6}$ and $\frac{10}{15}$

Solution

Method A Use the means-extremes product property.

$4 \cdot 15 \overset{?}{=} 6 \cdot 10$

$60 = 60$ ✓

The cross products are equal, so $\frac{4}{6}$ and $\frac{10}{15}$ are proportional.

Method B Simplify the ratios and then compare them.

$\frac{4}{6} = \frac{4 \div 2}{6 \div 2} = \frac{2}{3}$

$\frac{10}{15} = \frac{10 \div 5}{15 \div 5} = \frac{2}{3}$

The simplified ratios are identical, so $\frac{4}{6}$ and $\frac{10}{15}$ are proportional. ∎

B $\frac{8}{12}$ and $\frac{24}{30}$

Solution

Method A   Use the means-extremes product property.

$8 \cdot 30 \stackrel{?}{=} 12 \cdot 24$

$240 \neq 288$

The products are not equal, so $\frac{8}{12}$ and $\frac{24}{30}$ are not proportional.

Method B   Simplify the ratios and then compare them.

$\frac{8}{12} = \frac{8 \div 4}{12 \div 4} = \frac{2}{3}$

$\frac{24}{30} = \frac{24 \div 6}{30 \div 6} = \frac{4}{5}$

The simplified ratios are not identical, so $\frac{8}{12}$ and $\frac{24}{30}$ are not proportional. ∎

Solving Proportions

You can use the means-extremes product property to solve proportions.

Example 3   Solve each proportion.

A $\frac{n}{15} = \frac{6}{20}$

Solution

$\frac{n}{15} = \frac{6}{20}$

$20n = 90$ Multiply means and extremes. (Cross multiply.)

$\frac{20n}{20} = \frac{90}{20}$ Divide each side by 20.

$n = 4.5$ ∎

B $\frac{5.6}{14} = \frac{x}{8}$

Solution

$\frac{5.6}{14} = \frac{x}{8}$

$8 \cdot 5.6 = 14x$ Multiply means and extremes. (Cross multiply.)

$44.8 = 14x$

$\frac{44.8}{14} = \frac{14x}{14}$ Divide each side by 14.

$3.2 = x$ ∎

Application: Travel

You can apply proportions to many real-world situations.

Example 4 A train traveled 234 miles in 4 hours. If the train continues at the same rate, how many miles will it travel in 10 hours?

Solution Write and solve a proportion.

$$\frac{234 \text{ miles}}{4 \text{ hours}} = \frac{x \text{ miles}}{10 \text{ hours}}$$ The train continues at the same rate.
The rate for 4 hours equals the rate for 10 hours.

$$\frac{234}{4} = \frac{x}{10}$$ Write the proportion without units.

$$2340 = 4x$$ Cross multiply.

$$\frac{2340}{4} = \frac{4x}{4}$$ Divide both sides by 4.

$$585 = x$$ Simplify.

The train will travel 585 miles in 10 hours. ■

TIP

When you set up a proportion, include the units so that you can see if you have put everything in the right place.

THINK ABOUT IT

In Example 4, the proportion could have been set up as
$$\frac{4 \text{ hours}}{234 \text{ miles}} = \frac{10 \text{ hours}}{x \text{ miles}}.$$

Problem Set

Find two ratios that are equivalent to the given ratio.

1. $8 : 16$

2. $6 : 10$

3. $7 : 3$

4. $50 : 75$

5. $8 : 24$

6. $72 : 36$

7. $1 : 5$

8. $45 : 63$

9. $12 : 4$

10. $10 : 8$

Determine whether the ratios are proportional.

11. $\frac{6}{36}$ and $\frac{1}{6}$

12. $\frac{3}{18}$ and $\frac{2}{9}$

13. $\frac{10}{22}$ and $\frac{5}{11}$

14. $\frac{2}{4}$ and $\frac{20}{36}$

15. $\frac{15}{18}$ and $\frac{5}{6}$

16. $\frac{7}{35}$ and $\frac{35}{70}$

17. $\frac{11.9}{42}$ and $\frac{1.7}{6}$

18. $\frac{3.4}{8}$ and $\frac{34}{80}$

Solve each proportion.

19. $\dfrac{6}{18} = \dfrac{m}{3}$

20. $\dfrac{x}{8} = \dfrac{1}{2}$

21. $\dfrac{3}{b} = \dfrac{15}{20}$

22. $\dfrac{2.5}{8} = \dfrac{t}{12}$

23. $\dfrac{3.2}{y} = \dfrac{6}{12}$

24. $\dfrac{x}{4.8} = \dfrac{10}{15}$

25. $\dfrac{32.5}{50} = \dfrac{x}{20}$

26. $\dfrac{25}{75} = \dfrac{8.2}{a}$

27. $\dfrac{17}{b} = \dfrac{25.5}{33}$

28. $\dfrac{9.5}{6} = \dfrac{g}{18}$

29. $\dfrac{16}{5} = \dfrac{3}{n}$

*__30.__ **Challenge** $\dfrac{x}{16} = \dfrac{4}{x}$

*__31.__ **Challenge** $\dfrac{2}{a} = \dfrac{a}{50}$

*__32.__ **Challenge** $\dfrac{x+1}{32} = \dfrac{3}{4}$

Solve each problem.

A. Write a proportion.
B. Solve the proportion.
C. Write your answer in a complete sentence.

33. A car traveled 93 miles in $1\frac{1}{2}$ hours. If the car continues at the same rate, how many miles will it travel in $3\frac{1}{2}$ hours?

34. A machine is wrapping 18 boxes in 5 minutes. If the machine continues at the same rate, how many boxes will it wrap in 1 hour?

35. An employee made $27 in 3 hours. If the employee continues to earn at the same rate, how much will the employee make in 8 hours?

36. A grocery store is selling 5 pounds of oranges for $4.45. How much will 12 pounds of oranges cost?

37. A student reads 40 pages of a book in 60 minutes. If the student continues to read at the same rate, how long will it take to read 220 pages?

38. A printer can print 30 pages in 2.8 minutes. If the printer prints at the same rate, how long will it take to print 120 pages?

*__39.__ **Challenge** A swimming pool is filling at the rate of 40 gallons every 2 minutes.

    A. If the pool continues to fill at the same rate, how many gallons will be in the pool after 3 hours?

    B. The pool will hold about 88,000 gallons of water. How long will it take to fill the pool?

Percents, Fractions, and Decimals

Every fraction can be written as an equivalent decimal and as a percent.

A **percent** is a ratio that compares a number to 100. Every percent can be written as a fraction and as a decimal. The table shows a few examples.

Fraction	Decimal	Percent
$\frac{1}{10}$	0.1	10%
$\frac{1}{4}$	0.25	25%
$\frac{1}{2}$	0.5	50%

Converting Fractions to Decimals

A fraction bar can be thought of as a division symbol.

CONVERTING A FRACTION TO A DECIMAL

For any *b* and nonzero *a*:

$\frac{b}{a}$ is equivalent to $b \div a$.

Example

$\frac{1}{5} = 1 \div 5 = 0.2$

$$\begin{array}{r} 0.2 \\ 5\overline{)1.0} \\ \underline{1\,0} \\ 0 \end{array}$$

Example 1   Convert each fraction to a decimal.

A $\frac{3}{8}$

Solution

$\frac{3}{8} = 3 \div 8 = 0.375$

$$\begin{array}{r} 0.375 \\ 8\overline{)3.000} \\ \underline{2\,4} \\ 60 \\ \underline{56} \\ 40 \\ \underline{40} \\ 0 \end{array}$$ ■

B $\frac{2}{3}$

Solution   Divide.

$\frac{2}{3} = 2 \div 3 = 0.\overline{6}$

Place a bar over a digit or group of digits to indicate a repeating pattern.

$$
\begin{array}{r}
0.666\ldots \\
3\overline{)2.000} \\
\underline{18} \\
20 \\
\underline{18} \\
20 \\
\underline{18} \\
\vdots
\end{array}
$$

■

THINK ABOUT IT

You could go on forever with this division problem and always end up with another 6 above the bar.

Converting Decimals to Fractions

Every decimal represents a fraction or mixed number whose denominator is 10, 100, 1000, or some other power of 10.

CONVERTING A DECIMAL TO A SIMPLIFIED FRACTION

Write the decimal as a fraction or mixed number, and then simplify.

Example:

$0.36 = \dfrac{36}{100} = \dfrac{36 \div 4}{100 \div 4} = \dfrac{9}{25}$

Example 2   Convert each decimal to a fraction or mixed number. Simplify.

A 0.8

Solution

$0.8 = \dfrac{8}{10} = \dfrac{8 \div 2}{10 \div 2} = \dfrac{4}{5}$ ■

B 7.405

Solution

$7.405 = 7\dfrac{405}{1000} = 7\dfrac{405 \div 5}{1000 \div 5} = 7\dfrac{81}{200}$ ■

Converting Decimals to Percents

To write a decimal as a percent, write a fraction with a denominator of 100. The numerator is the percent. For example, $0.35 = \dfrac{35}{100} = 35\%$. Notice that you can obtain the answer by just moving the decimal point two places to the right.

CONVERTING A DECIMAL TO A PERCENT

Move the decimal point two places to the right and write a percent sign, %

Example:

$0.35 = 0.35.\%$

$0.35 = 35\%$

THINK ABOUT IT

You can write any decimal as a fraction with a denominator of 100 and then a percent.

$0.625 = \dfrac{625}{1000}$

$= \dfrac{625 \div 10}{1000 \div 10}$

$= \dfrac{62.5}{100}$

$= 62.5\%$

Example 3

A Convert 0.72 to a percent.

Solution $0.72 = 0.72\%$

$0.72 = 72\%$ ■

(continued)

B Convert 5.43 to a percent.

Solution $5.43 = 5.43.\%$

$5.43 = 543\%$ ∎

C Convert 0.0005 to a percent.

Solution $0.0005 = 0.00.05\%$

$0.0005 = 0.05\%$ ∎

Converting Percents to Decimals

Because a percent is a ratio with 100 in the denominator, converting a percent to a decimal is the same as dividing by 100.

> **CONVERTING A PERCENT TO A DECIMAL**
>
> Move the decimal point two places to the left and remove the % sign.
>
> **Example:**
>
> $68\% = 0.68.$
>
> $68\% = 0.68$

Example 4   Convert each percent to a decimal.

A 4%

Solution $4\% = 0.04.$

$4\% = 0.04$ ∎

B 127%

Solution $127\% = 1.27.$

$127\% = 1.27$ ∎

C 0.6%

Solution $0.6\% = 0.00.6$

$0.6\% = 0.006$ ∎

Converting Fractions to Percents

CONVERTING A FRACTION TO A PERCENT

Convert the fraction to a decimal, and then convert the decimal to a percent.

Example:

$$\frac{4}{5} = 4 \div 5 = 0.8 = 80\%$$

Example 5 Convert each fraction or mixed number to a percent. Round your answer to the nearest percent if rounding is necessary.

Ⓐ $\frac{3}{40}$

Solution $\frac{3}{40} = 3 \div 40 = 0.075 = 7.5\%$ ■

Ⓑ $2\frac{4}{13}$

Solution $2\frac{4}{13} = \frac{30}{13} = 30 \div 13 \approx 2.308 = 230.8\% \approx 231\%$ ■

THINK ABOUT IT

You can convert a fraction to a percent by solving a proportion.

$$\frac{3}{40} = \frac{n}{100\%}$$

$$300\% = 40n$$

$$\frac{300}{40}\% = n$$

$$7.5\% = n$$

So $\frac{3}{40} = 7.5\%$.

Converting Percents to Fractions

CONVERTING A PERCENT TO A SIMPLIFIED FRACTION

Write the percent as a fraction with a denominator of 100, and then simplify.

Example:

$$45\% = \frac{45}{100} = \frac{45 \div 5}{100 \div 5} = \frac{9}{20}$$

Example 6 Convert each percent to a fraction or mixed number. Simplify.

Ⓐ 320%

Solution $320\% = \frac{320}{100} = \frac{320 \div 20}{100 \div 20} = \frac{16}{5} = 3\frac{1}{5}$ ■

Ⓑ 8.7%

Solution $8.7\% = \frac{8.7}{100} = \frac{8.7 \times 10}{100 \times 10} = \frac{87}{1000}$ ■

TIP

In Example 6B you must multiply to eliminate the decimal in the numerator.

Application: Marketing

Example 7 A marketing survey indicates that 18 out of 64 people plan to purchase a video game in the next year. To the nearest tenth of a percent, what percent of those surveyed plan to purchase the video game?

Solution $\frac{18}{64} = 18 \div 64 = 0.28125 = 28.125\%$

About 28.1% of those surveyed plan to purchase the video game. ■

Problem Set

Convert each fraction to a decimal.

1. $\frac{7}{10}$

3. $\frac{3}{5}$

5. $\frac{19}{25}$

2. $\frac{4}{12}$

4. $\frac{11}{20}$

6. $\frac{3}{8}$

Convert each decimal to a fraction or mixed number. Simplify.

7. 0.75

9. 1.5

11. 0.34

8. 0.6

10. 6.05

12. 10.8

Convert each decimal to a percent.

13. 7.21

15. 0.03

17. 1.004

14. 6

16. 65.4

18. 62.01

Convert each percent to a decimal.

19. 7.8%

21. 0.5%

23. 10.85%

20. 23%

22. 0.007%

24. 50.6%

Convert each fraction or mixed number to a percent. Round your answer to the nearest percent if rounding is necessary.

25. $\frac{8}{50}$

27. $5\frac{3}{5}$

29. $\frac{5}{12}$

26. $\frac{7}{25}$

28. $10\frac{2}{3}$

30. $\frac{8}{9}$

Convert each percent to a fraction or mixed number. Simplify.

31. 60%

33. 5%

35. 84%

32. 22%

34. 175%

36. 23%

Solve each problem. Simplify all fractions.

37. A survey showed that $\frac{4}{5}$ of moviegoers think tickets are too expensive. What percent of those surveyed think tickets are too expensive?

38. Bob has completed 65% of the levels on a video game. What fraction of the levels has Bob completed?

39. A bank paid 3.4% interest on a savings account. What is 3.4% in decimal form?

40. A restaurant found that 80% of employees liked working on Mondays. What fraction of the employees liked working on Mondays?

41. Doug has finished reading 220 pages of a 500-page book. What percent of the book has Doug read so far?

42. A scientist found that 12 of 18 birds had a red spot on their heads. What fraction of the birds had a red spot on their head?

*43. **Challenge** Order the following sets of numbers from least to greatest.

A. $\frac{1}{4}$, 0.32, 28%

B. 0.05, 0.5%, $\frac{1}{5}$

Similarity and Scale

Similar figures are figures that have the exact same shape but not necessarily the same size.

REMEMBER

Congruent angles are angles having equal measures.

Figures are similar if corresponding angles are congruent and corresponding sides are proportional.

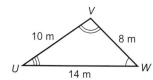

$\triangle UVW$ is similar to $\triangle XYZ$ so

$$\angle U \cong \angle X, \qquad \angle V \cong \angle Y, \qquad \angle W \cong \angle Z$$

TIP

UV means the length of $\overline{UV}$.

$$\frac{UV}{XY} = \frac{VW}{YZ}; \frac{UV}{XY} = \frac{WU}{ZX}; \frac{VW}{YZ} = \frac{WU}{ZX}$$

$$\frac{10}{5} \overset{?}{=} \frac{8}{4} \qquad \frac{10}{5} \overset{?}{=} \frac{14}{7} \qquad \frac{8}{4} \overset{?}{=} \frac{14}{7}$$

$$10 \cdot 4 \overset{?}{=} 5 \cdot 8 \qquad 10 \cdot 7 \overset{?}{=} 5 \cdot 14 \qquad 8 \cdot 7 \overset{?}{=} 4 \cdot 14$$

$$40 = 40 \checkmark \qquad 70 = 70 \checkmark \qquad 56 = 56 \checkmark$$

Cross multiply to see if the fractions are equal.

Determining Whether Two Figures Are Similar

Example 1 Determine whether $ABCD$ and $EFGH$ are similar.

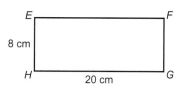

(continued)

Solution

Step 1   Check corresponding angles.

Because both figures are rectangles, all angles measure 90°. So, $\angle A \cong \angle E$; $\angle B \cong \angle F$; $\angle C \cong \angle G$; $\angle D \cong \angle H$.

Therefore, corresponding angles are congruent.

Step 2   Check corresponding sides.

If corresponding sides are proportional, then $\dfrac{AD}{EH} = \dfrac{AB}{EF}$.

$\dfrac{2}{8} \stackrel{?}{=} \dfrac{5}{20}$ Write the measures of the side lengths as a proportion and check to see if the proportion is true.

$2 \cdot 20 \stackrel{?}{=} 8 \cdot 5$ Cross multiply to see if the fractions are equal.

$40 = 40$ ✓

Because corresponding angles are congruent and corresponding sides are proportional, the rectangles are similar. ■

Using Similarity to Find Missing Side Lengths

You can use the properties of similar figures to find a missing side.

Example 2 $\triangle GHI$ and $\triangle JKL$ are similar. What is the length of $\overline{JK}$?

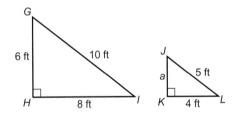

Solution $\overline{GH}$ corresponds to $\overline{JK}$. $\overline{HI}$ corresponds to $\overline{KL}$. Set up the corresponding sides as a proportion. Then solve for a.

$\dfrac{6}{a} = \dfrac{8}{4}$ Write a proportion.

$6 \cdot 4 = 8a$ Cross multiply.

$\dfrac{24}{8} = \dfrac{8a}{8}$ Divide both sides by 8.

$3 = a$ Simplify.

The length of $\overline{JK}$ is 3 ft. ■

> **REMEMBER**
>
> In the proportion $\dfrac{a}{b} = \dfrac{c}{d}$, a and d are the extremes, and b and c are the means. The product of the means equals the product of the extremes.

Determining Scale

Scale factor is a ratio of one measure to another. You can find a scale factor of a figure by using the ratio of corresponding parts.

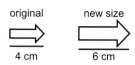

original   new size

4 cm   6 cm

The new size is an enlargement. To find the scale factor, write a ratio comparing corresponding sides.

$$\frac{\text{new size}}{\text{original size}} = \frac{6 \text{ cm}}{4 \text{ cm}} = \frac{3}{2}$$ The scale factor for the arrows is 3 : 2 or 1.5.

Example 3   The regular pentagons shown are similar. What is the scale factor?

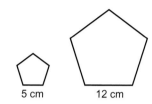

5 cm   12 cm

THINK ABOUT IT

All regular pentagons are similar to each other.

Solution   This is an enlargement so the scale factor is greater than 1. The scale factor is $\frac{12}{5}$. ∎

Using Scale Factor

A scale factor greater than 1 indicates an enlargement. A scale factor less than 1 indicates a reduction. A scale factor equal to 1 means there is no change in size.

Example 4   An equilateral triangle with side length of 8 cm is multiplied by the scale factors below. State whether the new triangle is an enlargement or a reduction. Then find the side length of the new size.

Ⓐ $\frac{3}{4}$

Solution   This is a reduction because the scale factor is less than 1. Multiplying by the scale factor we have $\frac{3}{4} \cdot 8 = 6$. The new side measure is 6 cm. ∎

Ⓑ 8 : 1

Solution   The scale factor is $\frac{8}{1} = 8$. This is an enlargement because 8 is greater than 1. Multiplying by the scale factor we have $8 \cdot 8 = 64$. The new side measure is 64 cm. ∎

Ⓒ 2.2

Solution   This is an enlargement because the scale factor is greater than 1. Multiplying by the scale factor we have $2.2 \cdot 8 = 17.6$. The new side measure is 17.6 cm. ∎

Application: Photography

Example 5   A rectangular picture is 2.5 inches wide and 4 inches long. If the picture is enlarged so that it is 10 inches long, what is the new width?

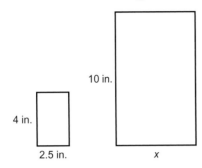

Solution   Because this is an enlargement, the pictures will be similar.

$$\frac{2.5}{x} = \frac{4}{10}$$ Set up a proportion using corresponding sides.

$2.5 \cdot 10 = 4x$ Cross multiply.

$$\frac{25}{4} = \frac{4x}{4}$$ Divide both sides by 4.

$6.25 = x$ Simplify.

The width of the enlarged picture is 6.25 inches. ■

Problem Set

1. Determine whether *GHIJ* and *KLMN* are similar.

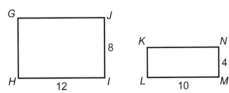

2. The corresponding angles of the triangles are congruent. Determine whether $\triangle ABC$ and $\triangle DEF$ are similar.

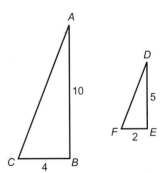

Each pair of figures is similar. Find the value of x.

3.

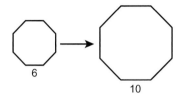

4.

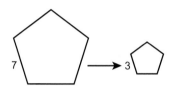

5.

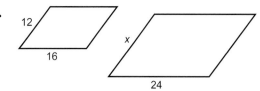

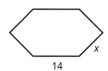

6.

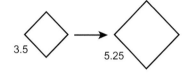

Each set of figures is similar. State the scale factor. Determine whether the scale factor is an enlargement or a reduction.

7.

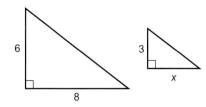

8.

9.

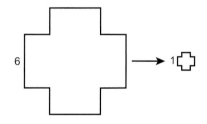

10.

Solve each problem.

11. A regular pentagon has sides measuring 5 centimeters. The pentagon is enlarged using a scale factor of $\frac{3}{2}$. What are the lengths of each side of the enlarged pentagon?

12. A photograph measures 10 inches wide by 18 inches long. If the picture is reduced so that the length is 6 inches, what is the new width?

* **13.** **Challenge** An equilateral triangle has a perimeter of 33 centimeters. If the triangle is enlarged using a scale factor of 4, what is the length of one side of the triangle?

* **14.** **Challenge** A square with side lengths of 12 centimeters is multiplied by a scale factor of $\frac{3}{4}$.

    A. State whether the new square is an enlargement or a reduction.

    B. Find the side lengths of the new square.

    C. How did the perimeter of the square change after the scale factor was applied? Explain.

    D. How did the area of the square change after the scale factor was applied? Explain.

Working with Percent

You can use percent to solve problems that involve parts of whole amounts.

Using the Percent Proportion

You can use the following proportion to solve percent problems.

$$\frac{\text{part}}{\text{whole}} = \frac{\text{percent}}{100}$$

For example,

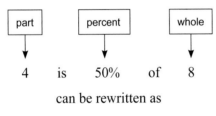

can be rewritten as

$$\frac{4}{8} = \frac{50}{100}.$$

Example 1   What is 20% of 250?

Solution   Write the percent proportion and fill in the known information. Use x for the unknown.

$$\frac{\text{part}}{\text{whole}} = \frac{\text{percent}}{100}$$

$\dfrac{x}{250} = \dfrac{20}{100}$ The part is the unknown.

$100x = 250 \cdot 20$ Cross multiply.

$100x = 5000$ Multiply.

$\dfrac{100x}{100} = \dfrac{5000}{100}$ Divide each side by 100.

$x = 50$ Simplify.

Twenty percent of 250 is 50. ■

> **TIP**
>
> The word "of" means to multiply.
>
> $20\% \text{ of } 250 = 20\% \cdot 250$
>
> $= 0.20 \cdot 250$
>
> $= 50$

Example 2 Eighteen is what percent of 72?

Solution Write and solve a percent proportion.

$$\frac{\text{part}}{\text{whole}} = \frac{\text{percent}}{100}$$

$$\frac{18}{72} = \frac{x}{100} \qquad \text{The percent is the unknown.}$$

$$18 \cdot 100 = 72x \qquad \text{Cross multiply.}$$

$$1800 = 72x \qquad \text{Multiply.}$$

$$\frac{1800}{72} = \frac{72x}{72} \qquad \text{Divide each side by 72.}$$

$$25 = x \qquad \text{Simplify.}$$

Eighteen is 25% of 72. ■

Example 3 One hundred nineteen is 70% of what number?

Solution Write and solve a percent proportion.

$$\frac{\text{part}}{\text{whole}} = \frac{\text{percent}}{100}$$

$$\frac{119}{x} = \frac{70}{100} \qquad \text{The whole is the unknown.}$$

$$119 \cdot 100 = 70x \qquad \text{Cross multiply.}$$

$$11{,}900 = 70x \qquad \text{Multiply.}$$

$$\frac{11{,}900}{70} = \frac{70x}{70} \qquad \text{Divide each side by 70.}$$

$$170 = x \qquad \text{Simplify.}$$

One hundred nineteen is 70% of 170. ■

Application: Biology

Example 4 At birth, an elephant weighs about 2.5% of its adult weight. If an elephant weighs 8000 pounds as an adult, about how many pounds did the elephant weigh at birth?

Solution Write and solve a percent proportion.

$$\frac{\text{part}}{\text{whole}} = \frac{\text{percent}}{100}$$

$$\frac{x}{8000} = \frac{2.5}{100} \qquad \text{The part is unknown.}$$

$$100x = 8000 \cdot 2.5 \qquad \text{Use the means-extremes product property.}$$

$$100x = 20{,}000 \qquad \text{Multiply.}$$

$$\frac{100x}{100} = \frac{20{,}000}{100} \qquad \text{Divide each side by 100.}$$

$$x = 200 \qquad \text{Simplify.}$$

The elephant weighed about 200 pounds at birth. ■

Problem Set

Write a proportion to solve the problem. Then solve the proportion.

1. What is 76% of 30?
2. Seven is 20% of what number?
3. Thirteen is what percent of 15?
4. What is 85% of 81?
5. Twenty is 10% of what number?
6. What is 34% of 57?
7. Seventeen is 20% of what number?
8. What is 72% of 29?
9. Fifteen is what percent of 30?
10. What is 44% of 55?
11. One hundred thirty-three is 35% of what number?
12. What is 105% of 380?
13. Ninety-nine is what percent of 150?
14. What is 15% of 260?
15. Seventeen is what percent of 85?
16. Thirty-five is what percent of 7?
17. What is 34% of 50?
18. Twenty is 150% of what number?
19. Twenty-one is what percent of 28?
20. What is 44% of 325?
21. Seven is 14% of what number?
22. What is 42% of 25?
23. One hundred forty-seven is what percent of 210?
24. Ninety-five is what percent of 57?
25. What is 150% of 65?
26. Fifteen is 108% of what number?
* 27. **Challenge** What is 6% of 3.5?
* 28. **Challenge** Twenty-two and seventy-seven hundredths is 46% of what number?
* 29. **Challenge** Five and seven hundredths is what percent of 65?
* 30. **Challenge** What is 82.5% of 145.8?

Solve each problem.

31. A cell phone costs $170 and has a tax rate of 7%. Write and solve a proportion to find how much tax is paid on the cell phone.

32. Maureen spent $48 on books. That is 70% of her savings. Write and solve a proportion to find the total amount of Maureen's savings.

33. There are 260 students in the 6th grade, which accounts for 40% of the school population. Write and solve a proportion to find the total number of students at the school.

34. A window measures 45 inches long. The wall is 210 inches long. Write and solve a proportion to find the percent of the wall's length that is taken up by the window.

35. A music player has 1230 songs. Three hundred of the songs are hip-hop songs. Write and solve a proportion to find the percent of songs that are hip-hop.

36. The music club spent $400 on snacks for an after concert party. That expenditure was 25% of the total budget. Write and solve a proportion to find the total budget for the music club.

37. Mia received 420 total text messages last month, of which 140 were from Shannon. Write and solve a proportion to find the percent of text messages that were sent by Shannon.

38. A used book store sold 150 fiction books in one week. That number accounted for 75% of all books sold that week. Write and solve a proportion to find the total number of books sold.

Percent of Increase or Decrease

A percent of change shows how much an amount increases or decreases.

AMOUNT AND PERCENT OF CHANGE

amount of change = new amount − original amount

$$\text{percent of change} = \frac{\text{amount of change}}{\text{original amount}} \cdot 100\%$$

Finding Percent Increase and Decrease

Example 1

A Find the percent increase from 10 to 15.

Solution

$$\frac{\text{amount of}}{\text{change}} = \frac{\text{new}}{\text{amount}} - \frac{\text{original}}{\text{amount}}$$

Find the amount of change.

$$= 15 - 10$$

Substitute 15 for new amount and 10 for original amount. Subtract.

$$= 5$$

$$\frac{\text{percent of}}{\text{change}} = \frac{\text{amount of change}}{\text{original amount}} \cdot 100\%$$

$$= \frac{5}{10} \cdot 100\%$$

Substitute 5 for the amount of change. Divide.

$$= 0.5 \cdot 100\%$$

Multiply.

$$= 50\%$$

The percent increase is 50%. ∎

B Find the percent decrease from 15 to 10.

Solution

$$\frac{\text{amount of}}{\text{change}} = \frac{\text{new}}{\text{amount}} - \frac{\text{original}}{\text{amount}}$$

Find the amount of change.

$$= 10 - 15$$

Substitute 10 for new amount and 15 for original amount.

$$= -5$$

Subtract.

(continued)

$$\text{percent of change} = \frac{\text{amount of change}}{\text{original amount}} \cdot 100\%$$

$$= -\frac{5}{15} \cdot 100\%$$ Substitute -5 for the amount of change. Divide.

$$= -0.33\tfrac{1}{3} \cdot 100\%$$ Multiply.

$$= -33\tfrac{1}{3}\%$$

The percent decrease is $33\tfrac{1}{3}\%$. ■

THINK ABOUT IT

A percent increase is not offset by the same percent decrease. For example, if an item that costs $10 is marked up to $15, the percent increase is 50%. If that item that costs $15 is discounted to $10, the percent decrease is $33\tfrac{1}{3}\%$.

Example 2

A The population of Smalltown changed from 125 to 150. What was the percent increase?

Solution

$$\text{percent of change} = \frac{\text{amount of change}}{\text{original amount}} \cdot 100\%$$

$$= \frac{150 - 125}{125} \cdot 100\% = \frac{25}{125} \cdot 100\% = 0.2 \cdot 100\% = 20\%$$

The percent increase was 20%. ■

B Juan bought a new car for $16,000. One year later, its value was $13,600. What was the percent decrease in the value of the car in one year?

Solution

$$\text{percent of change} = \frac{\text{amount of change}}{\text{original amount}} \cdot 100\%$$

$$= \frac{13,600 - 16,000}{16,000} \cdot 100\% = \frac{-2400}{16,000} \cdot 100\% = -0.15 \cdot 100\% = -15\%$$

The percent decrease was 15%. ■

Using Percent Increase and Decrease

You can use a known percent of change to find a new value.

Example 3

A A worker's salary is increased by 5%. If the old salary was $12,000 per year, what is the worker's new salary?

Solution Find the amount of increase, and then add that amount to the original amount.

increase $= 5\%$ of $12,500$ Find the increase.

$$= 0.05 \times 12,500$$

$$= 625$$

original amount $+$ increase $=$ new amount

$12,500 + 625 = 13,125$ Add the increase to the original amount.

The worker's new salary is $13,125. ■

TIP

For problems that involve percent of change, be careful to answer the question. If asked for a new value, do not answer with the amount of change.

B Nathan weighed 180 pounds. He went on a diet and lost 10% of his weight. What was Nathan's new weight?

Solution   Find the amount of decrease, and then subtract this amount from the original amount.

$$\text{decrease} = 10\% \text{ of } 180 \qquad \text{Find the decrease.}$$
$$= 0.10 \times 180$$
$$= 18$$

original amount − decrease = new amount

$$180 - 18 = 162 \qquad \text{Subtract the decrease from the original amount.}$$

Nathan's new weight was 162 pounds. ■

Application: Zoology

Example 4   Camels can go for a week without drinking water. A camel can survive a 40% weight loss due to lack of water. If a camel starts off weighing 1200 pounds, how much will the camel weigh after a 40% weight loss?

Solution

$$\text{decrease} = 40\% \text{ of } 1200 \qquad \text{Find the decrease.}$$
$$= 0.40 \times 1200$$
$$= 480$$

original amount − decrease = new amount

$$1200 - 480 = 720 \qquad \text{Subtract the decrease from the original amount.}$$

After a 40% weight loss, a camel originally weighing 1200 pounds would weigh 720 pounds. ■

Application: Real Estate

Example 5   Mariah's house has appreciated in value over the last three years. It has gone from being worth $125,000 to being worth $175,000. What is the percent increase in the value of Mariah's house?

Solution

$$\text{percent of change} = \frac{\text{amount of change}}{\text{original amount}} \cdot 100\%$$

$$= \frac{175,000 - 125,000}{125,000} \cdot 100\% = \frac{50,000}{125,000} \cdot 100\% = 0.4 \cdot 100\% = 40\%$$

There has been a 40% percent increase in the value of Mariah's house. ■

Application: Sports

Example 6

Ⓐ The chart shows Nathan's bowling scores. What was the percent increase in his score from game 1 to game 2?

Nathan's Bowling Scores	
Game	Score
1	180
2	200
3	180

Solution

$$\text{percent of change} = \frac{\text{amount of change}}{\text{original amount}} \cdot 100\%$$

$$= \frac{200 - 180}{180} \cdot 100\% = \frac{20}{180} \cdot 100\% \approx 0.11 \cdot 100\% = 11\%$$

Nathan's score increased about 11% percent from game 1 to game 2. ■

Ⓑ What was the percent decrease in Nathan's score from game 2 to game 3?

Solution

$$\text{percent of change} = \frac{\text{amount of change}}{\text{original amount}} \cdot 100\%$$

$$= \frac{180 - 200}{200} \cdot 100\% = \frac{-20}{200} \cdot 100\% = -0.1 \cdot 100\% = -10\%$$

Nathan's score decreased 10% percent from game 2 to game 3. ■

Problem Set

Find each percent increase or decrease. Round each percent to the nearest tenth, if necessary.

1. 25 to 15

2. 20 to 45

3. 95 to 60

4. 3 to 40

5. 150 to 230

6. 110 to 40

7. 250 to 100

8. 35 to 90

* 9. Challenge 23.5 to 119

* 10. Challenge 0.05 to 1.5

The chart shows the population each year for a small town. Use the chart to find the percent increase or decrease in population.

11. Year 1 to Year 2

12. Year 2 to Year 3

13. Year 3 to Year 4

14. Year 4 to Year 5

15. Year 1 to Year 5

Year	Population
Year 1	2150
Year 2	2500
Year 3	2240
Year 4	3200
Year 5	3650

The chart below shows the average temperature for each month for a certain city. Use the information to find the percent increase or decrease in temperature.

Month	Jan.	Feb.	Mar.	Apr.	May	June	July	Aug.	Sep.	Oct.	Nov.	Dec.
Temp. °F	24	28	33	40	47	54	56	55	50	42	33	28

16. January to February

17. January to June

18. March to August

19. November to April

20. December to July

21. April to October

*22. **Challenge** Between which two consecutive months is there about a 9% decrease in temperature? Explain.

*23. **Challenge** Between which two consecutive months is there about a 15% decrease in temperature? Explain.

Solve each problem.

24. An e-waste collection drive gathered 3500 pounds of e-waste last year. This year the collection drive gathered 5200 pounds of e-waste. What is the percent of increase?

25. A cell phone plan allowed 500 minutes of calling each month. The new plan will increase the number of minutes by 150%. What is the number of minutes allowed on the new plan?

26. Last year Dale mowed the lawn in 45 minutes. This year, it took Dale 38 minutes to mow the lawn. What is the percent decrease?

27. A movie ticket sold for $6.50 ten years ago. Now a movie ticket costs $9.50. What is the percent increase?

28. An airplane was at an altitude of 33,000 feet. The plane decreased the altitude by 5%. What is the new altitude of the plane?

29. The temperature at one point during the day was 73°F. During the next hour it dropped to 68°F. What was the percent decrease?

30. Patrick reached a score of 1750 on a computer game. The next day he reached a score of 2300. What was the percent increase?

*31. **Challenge** Doug's height was 5 feet. The next year Doug was 5 feet 4 inches tall. What is the percent increase?

Simple Interest

When someone borrows money from a bank to purchase a car or a house, the bank charges **interest.** When a bank regularly adds money to a savings account, the account is collecting **interest.**

Interest is the cost to borrow money. **Principal** is money that earns interest at a given rate over time. The **interest rate** is the percentage of the original amount of money that the interest is based on. **Simple interest** is interest earned at a fixed percent of the initial deposit, or **principal** amount.

SIMPLE INTEREST FORMULA

The interest I paid for principal P with interest rate r and time t is:

$$I = Prt$$

Borrowing Money

Example 1

A Laura borrowed $48,000 at a 6% interest rate for 7 years. What was the total interest?

Solution

$I = Prt$

$\quad = \$48{,}000 \cdot 0.06 \cdot 7 \qquad$ Substitute.

$\quad = \$20{,}160 \qquad\qquad$ Multiply.

The total interest was $20,160. ■

B Bryan borrowed $12,800 at a 4.8% interest rate for 6 years. What was the total interest?

Solution

$I = Prt$

$\quad = \$12{,}800 \cdot 0.048 \cdot 6 \qquad$ Substitute.

$\quad = \$3686.40 \qquad\qquad$ Multiply.

The total interest was $3686.40. ■

> **REMEMBER**
>
> To write a percent as a decimal, move the decimal point two places to the left.

Saving Money

Example 2   Cecil deposited $5600 in a savings account earning 2.5% interest over 8 years. What was the total interest earned after 8 years?

Solution

$I = Prt$

$\quad = \$5600 \cdot 0.025 \cdot 8$ Substitute.

$\quad = \$1120$ Multiply.

The account earned $1120 in interest. ■

Using the Simple Interest Formula to Calculate Other Values

Example 3

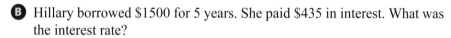 Fritz borrowed $8000 at an interest rate of 6%. He paid $1440 interest. Fritz borrowed the money for how much time?

Solution

$\qquad I = Prt$

$\$1400 = \$8000 \cdot 0.06 \cdot t$ Substitute and solve for t.

$\$1440 = \$480t$ Multiply.

$\dfrac{\$1440}{\$480} = \dfrac{\$480t}{\$480}$ Divide each side by $480.

$\qquad 3 = t$

Fritz borrowed the money for 3 years. ■

B Hillary borrowed $1500 for 5 years. She paid $435 in interest. What was the interest rate?

Solution

$\qquad I = Prt$

$\$435 = \$1500 \cdot r \cdot 5$ Substitute and solve for r.

$\$435 = \$7500r$ Multiply.

$\dfrac{\$435}{\$7500} = \dfrac{\$7500r}{\$7500}$ Divide each side by $7500.

$0.058 = r$

$5.8\% = r$

The interest rate was 5.8%. ■

(continued)

C Sue earned $99.75 in interest from her savings account. If the interest rate is 2.5% over 7 years, what amount did Sue deposit?

Solution

$$I = Prt$$

$$\$99.75 = P \cdot 0.025 \cdot 7 \qquad \text{Substitute and solve for } P.$$

$$\$99.75 = 0.175P \qquad \text{Multiply.}$$

$$\frac{\$99.75}{0.175} = \frac{0.175P}{0.175} \qquad \text{Divide each side by 0.175.}$$

$$\$570 = P$$

Sue deposited $570. ∎

Problem Set

Use the simple interest formula $I = Prt$ to solve.

1. Find the interest if the principal is $500, the interest rate is 3%, and the time is 5 years.

2. Find the interest if the principal is $2300, the interest rate is 4%, and the time is 3 years.

3. Find the interest if the principal is $10,000, the interest rate is 2%, and the time is 8 years.

4. Find the principal if the interest is $264, the interest rate is 5.5%, and the time is 6 years.

5. Find the principal if the interest is $857.50, the interest rate is 3.5%, and the time is 7 years.

6. Find the interest rate if the principal is $8900, the interest is $4272, and the time is 10 years.

7. Find the interest rate if the principal is $25,000, the interest is $10,875, and the time is 15 years.

8. Find the time if the principal is $32,500, the interest is $12,870, and the interest rate is 3.3%.

9. Find the time if the principal is $5300, the interest is $1335.60, and the interest rate is 7.2%.

10. Find the interest if the principal is $8400, the interest rate is 6.3%, and the time is $6\frac{3}{4}$ years.

Solve each problem.

11. Mark deposited $750 in a savings account earning 3% interest over 9 years. What was the total interest earned after 9 years?

12. Taylor borrowed $14,000 at a 6% interest rate for 5 years. What was the total interest?

13. You borrow $5000 at an interest rate of 4%. The interest paid is $1800. For how long did you borrow the money?

14. Jerry borrows $6200 for 8 years. The interest paid is $2579.20. What was the interest rate?

15. Ryan earned $212 in interest from his savings account. If the interest rate is 3% over 8 years, what amount did Ryan deposit?

16. Morgan borrowed $28,000 at an 8% interest rate for 10 years. What was the total interest?

17. Milo borrows $15,000 for 12 years. The interest paid is $7200. What was the interest rate?

18. Casey borrowed $10,000 at a 5.5% interest rate for 7 years. What was the total interest?

19. Bella earned $85.60 in interest from her savings account. If the interest rate is 2% over 6 years, what amount did Bella deposit?

20. Alfredo deposited $3500 in a savings account earning 5% interest over 7 years. What was the total interest earned after 7 years?

21. Rita borrowed $7500 at an interest rate of 3%. The interest paid is $1462.50. For how long did she borrow the money?

22. Corinne deposited $15,000 in a savings account earning 3.5% interest over 6 years. What was the total interest earned after 6 years?

23. Christa earned $1400 in interest from her savings account. If the interest rate is 3.5% over 10 years, what amount did Christa deposit?

24. You borrow $11,000 for 6 years. The interest paid is $1800. What is the interest rate?

25. Francesca deposited $920 in a savings account earning 2% interest over 12 years. What was the total interest earned after 12 years?

26. Carrie borrows $2600 at an interest rate of 2.5%. The interest paid is $536.25. For how long did she borrow money?

27. Sam borrowed $7000 at a 5% interest rate for 12 years. What is the total amount Sam must pay?

28. Carson deposited $2350 in a savings account at a 4.5% interest rate for 15 years. What is the total amount Carson will have in the savings account at the end of 15 years?

*29. **Challenge** Allison deposited $5000 in a savings account that pays 3% interest.

   A. What is the total amount Allison will have after 1 year? 2 years? 3 years?

   B. Allison's savings will double after how many years?

Compound Interest

Compound interest is interest earned on both the principal and on any interest that has already been earned.

Using the Distributive Property to Find Compound Interest

You can use the distributive property to help with calculations. Let P_0 represent the original principal, and let P_1 and P_2 represent the principal after compounding the interest over the first and second time periods, respectively.

$P_1 = P_0 + P_0 I$ After compounding interest over one time period, the new principal is the sum of the original principal and the interest earned on the original principal.

$P_1 = P_0(1 + I)$ Apply the distributive property.

You can find P_2, the principal at the end of the second time period, in a similar manner, except now P_1 replaces P_0 and P_2 replaces P_1 in the previous equations.

$P_2 = P_1 + P_1 I$

$P_2 = P_1(1 + I)$ Apply the distributive property.

This pattern continues for any number of time periods.

$P_1 = P_0 + P_0 I = P_0(1 + I)$

$P_2 = P_1 + P_1 I = P_1(1 + I)$

$P_3 = P_2 + P_2 I = P_2(1 + I)$

$$\vdots$$

For example, suppose you invested \$2000 at 3% interest compounded annually. Find the amount of money you have after one year.

$2000 + 2000 \cdot 0.03 = 2000(1 + 0.03)$ $P_0 + P_0 I = P_0(1 + I)$

$= 2000 \cdot 1.03$

Interest Compounded Annually

Interest may be compounded yearly, half-yearly, quarterly, monthly, daily, or some other time period. Interest compounded annually means the interest is calculated once each year.

Example 1 If $1500 is deposited in an account that pays 4% interest compounded annually, how much is in the account after 3 years?

Solution

Year	Principal	Principal + Compound Interest
1	$1500.00	$1500.00 · 1.04 = $1560.00
2	$1560.00	$1560.00 · 1.04 = $1622.40
3	$1622.40	$1622.40 · 1.04 = $1687.30

The account will have $1687.30 at the end of three years. ■

> **THINK ABOUT IT**
>
> Using simple interest, the interest earned for Example 2 would be
>
> $$I = Prt$$
> $$= \$1500 \cdot 0.04 \cdot 3$$
> $$= \$180$$
>
> So the total amount in the account would be
>
> $$\$1500 + \$180 = \$1680$$

Interest Compounded Quarterly

Interest compounded quarterly means the interest is calculated four times each year. Divide the yearly interest rate by 4 to find the interest rate for each quarter.

Example 2 If $500 is deposited in an account that pays 8% interest compounded quarterly, how much is in the account after 1 year?

Solution Divide the interest by 4 to find the interest earned each quarter. So $\frac{8}{4} = 2$ means you will calculate 2% interest each quarter. There are 4 quarters in each year so you must calculate the interest 4 times.

Quarter	Principal	Principal + Compound Interest
1	$500.00	$500.00 · 1.02 = $510.00
2	$510.00	$510.00 · 1.02 = $520.20
3	$520.20	$520.20 · 1.02 = $530.60
4	$530.60	$530.60 · 1.02 = $541.21

The account will have $541.21 at the end of one year. ■

Interest Compounded Monthly

Interest compounded monthly means the interest is calculated 12 times each year. Divide the interest by 12 to find the interest rate for each month.

Example 3 If $2000 is deposited in an account that pays 6% interest compounded monthly, how much is in the account after 2 months?

Solution Divide the interest by 12 to find the percent earned each month. So $\frac{6}{12} = 0.5$ means you will calculate with 0.5% interest each month.

Month	Principal	Principal + Compound Interest
1	$2000.00	$2000.00 · 1.005 = $2010.00
2	$2010.00	$2010.00 · 1.005 = $2020.05

The account will have $2020.05 at the end of two months. ■

> **REMEMBER**
>
> Move the decimal two places to the left to change a percent to a decimal. So 0.5% = 0.005.

Application: Consumer Finance

Example 4 Nigel has $3500 to deposit in a savings account. Bank A offers an account with a simple interest rate of 3.5%. Bank B offers an interest rate of 3.4% compounded annually. After 3 years, in which bank will Nigel have the greatest total? Show your work.

Solution

Step 1 Find the interest earned for Bank A.

$I = Prt$

$= \$3500 \cdot 0.035 \cdot 3$

$= \$367.50$

The total amount in the account is $3500 + $367.50 = $3867.50.

Step 2 Find the total amount for Bank B.

Year	Principal	Principal + Compound Interest
1	$3500.00	$3500 · 1.034 = $3619.00
2	$3619.00	$3619 · 1.034 = $3742.05
3	$3742.05	$3742.05 · 1.034 = $3869.28

Bank A will have a total of $3867.50. Bank B will have a total of $3869.28. Nigel should choose Bank B because compounded interest increases the amount of interest earned. ■

Problem Set

1. Three thousand dollars is deposited in an account that pays 5% interest compounded annually. Complete the table below, filling in the blanks to find how much is in the account after 4 years.

Year	Principal	Principal + Compound Interest
1	$3000.00	$3000.00 · 1.05 = $3150.00
2	$_____	$_____ · 1.05 = $3307.50
3	$_____	$_____ · 1.05 = $_____
4	$_____	$_____ · 1.05 = $_____

Find the total amount in each account if interest is compounded annually.

2. Principal: $800; Interest rate: 5%; Time: 2 years

3. Principal: $3000; Interest rate: 2%; Time: 3 years

4. Principal: $450; Interest rate: 4%; Time: 2 years

5. Principal: $1200; Interest rate: 6.5%; Time: 4 years

6. Principal: $2000; Interest rate: 2.75%; Time: 3 years

7. Principal: $400; Interest rate: 4.25%; Time: 2 years

Find the total amount in each account if the interest is compounded quarterly.

8. Principal: $1000; Interest rate: 8%; Time: 1 year

9. Principal: $400; Interest rate: 4%; Time: 1 year

*10. **Challenge** Principal: $5000; Interest rate: 2%; Time: 0.25 years

*11. **Challenge** Principal: $1200; Interest rate: 1%; Time: 0.5 years

Find the total amount in each account if the interest is compounded monthly.

12. Principal: $7000; Interest rate: 6%; Time: 1 month

13. Principal: $8500; Interest rate: 3%; Time: 3 months

14. Principal: $500; Interest rate: 12%; Time: 4 months

*15. **Challenge** Principal: $28,000; Interest rate: 3%; Time: 3 months

Solve each problem.

16. Manuel has $10,000 to deposit for 1 year. The bank offers a 6% interest rate. Fill in the chart to find the difference in interest when the interest is compounded annually and quarterly.

Annually	Quarterly
10,000 · 1.06 = _____	10,000 · 1.015 = _____
	_____ · 1.015 = _____
	_____ · 1.015 ≈ _____
	_____ · 1.015 ≈ _____

17. If $2300 is deposited in an account that pays 5% interest compounded annually, how much is in the account after 4 years?

18. If $600 is deposited in an account that pays 12% interest compounded quarterly, how much is in the account after 1 year?

19. If $3000 is deposited in an account that pays 6% interest compounded monthly, how much is in the account after 3 months?

UNIT 9   Analytic Geometry

An air traffic controller uses algebra and geometry to help airplanes get from one point to another.

A pilot uses numbers to locate the airport she is flying to. An air traffic controller uses numbers on a radar screen to locate each airplane approaching the airport. Without a system of locating points, airplanes would have a hard time getting anywhere safely.

Big Idea

▶ Analytic geometry combines the tools of algebra with geometry to solve many real-world problems.

Unit Topics

▶ Points on the Plane

▶ Two-Variable Equations

▶ Linear Equations and Intercepts

▶ Slope

▶ Applications: Linear Graphs

▶ Relations and Functions

▶ Systems of Linear Equations

Points on the Plane

You can use a single number to describe the location of a point on a line, but on a coordinate plane it takes two numbers to describe the location of any point.

Identifying Axes and Quadrants

A **coordinate plane** is formed by two perpendicular number lines called **axes**. The *x*-axis is a horizontal line. The *y*-axis is a vertical line. The axes intersect at the point at which they both have coordinate zero. This point is called the **origin**. The axes separate the plane into four **quadrants**. On the axes, positive *x* goes right and positive *y* goes up. Negative *x* goes left and negative *y* goes down.

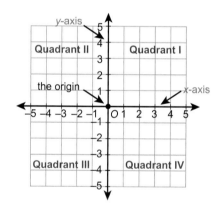

> **TIP**
>
> The quadrants are numbered counterclockwise. To identify Quadrant I, think of where the numeral "1" is on a clock.

Example 1   For each point, name the axis it is on or the quadrant it lies in.

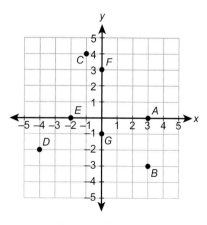

Solution

Points *A* and *E* lie on the *x*-axis.

Points *F* and *G* lie on the *y*-axis.

Point *C* lies in Quadrant II.

Point *D* lies in Quadrant III.

Point *B* lies in Quadrant IV. ■

> **TIP**
>
> Every point in a coordinate plane lies either on an axis or in a quadrant, but not both.

Using an Ordered Pair to Describe a Location

To describe the location of a point, use an **ordered pair**. An ordered pair has the form (x, y). The number x (the **x-coordinate**) describes the point's horizontal (left-right) distance from the origin. The number y (the **y-coordinate**) describes the point's vertical (up-down) distance from the origin. The numbers in an ordered pair are called **coordinates**.

To name the coordinates of a point, determine how you can get to the point from the origin by first counting right or left and then counting up or down.

Example 2   Name the ordered pair for each point.

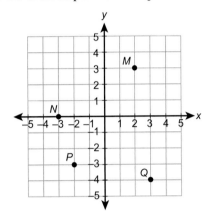

Solution

Ⓐ Point M

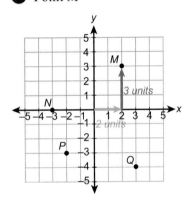

Start at the origin.

Go 2 units to the right.

Go 3 units up.

THINK ABOUT IT

Point *M* is directly above 2 on the x-axis and directly to the right of 3 on the y-axis. Therefore, its coordinates are (2, 3).

The ordered pair for point M is $(2, 3)$. ■

Ⓑ Point N

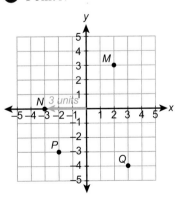

Start at the origin.

Go 3 units to the left.

Go 0 units vertically (up or down).

The ordered pair for point N is $(-3, 0)$. ■

C Point *P*

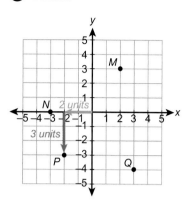

Start at the origin.

Go 2 units to the left.

Go 3 units down.

The ordered pair for point *P* is (−2, −3). ∎

D Point *Q*

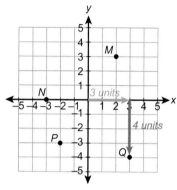

Start at the origin.

Go 3 units to the right.

Go 4 units down.

The ordered pair for point *Q* is (3, −4). ∎

Graphing an Ordered Pair

Example 3   Graph each ordered pair on the coordinate plane. Name the quadrant in which the point lies or the axis on which the point lies.

A (−1, 4)

Solution

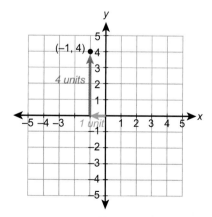

Start at the origin.

The *x*-coordinate is −1. Go 1 unit left.

The *y*-coordinate is 4. Go 4 units up.

Draw and label a dot.

The point (−1, 4) lies in Quadrant II. ∎

(continued)

B $(0, -3)$

Solution

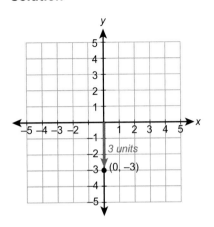

Start at the origin.

The x-coordinate is 0, so do not move left or right.

The y-coordinate is -3. Go 3 units down.

Draw and label a dot.

The point $(0, -3)$ lies on the y-axis. ■

C $(4, -4)$

Solution

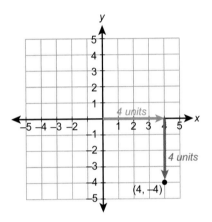

Start at the origin.

The x-coordinate is 4. Go 4 units right.

The y-coordinate is -4. Go 4 units down.

Draw and label a dot.

The point $(4, -4)$ lies in Quadrant IV. ■

THINK ABOUT IT

Every point on the x-axis has y-coordinate 0. Every point on the y-axis has x-coordinate 0.

Problem Set

Use the coordinate plane below for problems 1–10.

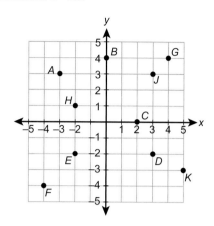

For each point,

A. Name the axis it is on or the quadrant it lies in.
B. Name the ordered pair.

1. A

2. B

3. C

4. D

5. E

6. F

7. G

8. H

9. J

10. K

Graph each ordered pair on a coordinate plane.

11. $(1, -4)$

12. $(-3, -1)$

13. $(0, 4)$

14. $(5, 0)$

15. $(2, -2)$

16. $(3, 5)$

17. $(-4, 2)$

18. $(2, -3)$

19. $(4, -5)$

20. $(-3, 4)$

Solve.

*21. **Challenge** Start at the origin. Go 3 units right, 4 units down, 6 units left, 8 units right, and 5 units up. Which quadrant are you in?

Two-Variable Equations

A solution of a one-variable equation is a single number. For example, the solution of $3x = 12$ is 4. But a solution of a two-variable equation is an ordered pair of numbers.

Determining Whether an Ordered Pair Is a Solution

An ordered pair is a **solution to a two-variable equation** in x and y if substituting the first coordinate for x and the second coordinate for y results in a true equation.

Example 1   Determine if the ordered pair is a solution of the equation.

Ⓐ Is $(2, 4)$ a solution of $3x + 8y = 38$?

Solution

$$3x + 8y = 38 \qquad \text{Write the two-variable equation.}$$

$$3 \cdot 2 + 8 \cdot 4 \stackrel{?}{=} 38 \qquad \text{Substitute 2 for } x \text{ and 4 for } y.$$

$$6 + 32 \stackrel{?}{=} 38 \qquad \text{Multiply.}$$

$$38 = 38 \ \checkmark \quad \text{Add.}$$

Yes, $(2, 4)$ is a solution of $3x + 8y = 38$. ∎

Ⓑ Is $(8, -13)$ a solution of $s = -3r - 2$?

Solution

$$s = -3r - 2 \qquad \text{Write the two-variable equation.}$$

$$-13 \stackrel{?}{=} -3 \cdot 8 - 2 \qquad \text{Substitute 8 for } r \text{ and } -13 \text{ for } s.$$

$$-13 \stackrel{?}{=} -24 - 2 \qquad \text{Multiply.}$$

$$-13 \neq -26 \qquad \text{Subtract.}$$

No, $(8, -13)$ is not a solution of $s = -3r - 2$. ∎

Ⓒ Is $(0.5, -3)$ a solution of $-2x - 4y = 11$?

Solution

$$-2x - 4y = 11 \qquad \text{Write the two-variable equation.}$$

$$-2 \cdot 0.5 - 4 \cdot (-3) \stackrel{?}{=} 11 \qquad \text{Substitute 0.5 for } x \text{ and } -3 \text{ for } y.$$

$$-1 + 12 \stackrel{?}{=} 11 \qquad \text{Simplify.}$$

$$11 = 11 \ \checkmark \quad \text{Add.}$$

Yes, $(0.5, -3)$ is a solution of $-2x - 4y = 11$. ∎

> **TIP**
>
> Most equations with two variables have countless ordered-pair solutions.

> **TIP**
>
> In the equation $s = -3r - 2$, the ordered pairs are traditionally written in the form (r, s) because r comes before s in the alphabet.

Finding Solutions of an Equation

In the equation $y = x + 3$, you can choose any value for the variable x. Once you substitute a value for x, you can solve to find the corresponding value of y. You could also start with a value of y.

Example 2   Find three solutions of each equation.

Ⓐ $y = 2x - 4$

Solution   Choose any values for x. Find the corresponding values of y.

Let $x = -1$.	Let $x = 0$.	Let $x = 1$.
$y = 2x - 4$	$y = 2x - 4$	$y = 2x - 4$
$y = 2 \cdot (-1) - 4$	$y = 2 \cdot 0 - 4$	$y = 2 \cdot 1 - 4$
$y = -2 - 4$	$y = 0 - 4$	$y = 2 - 4$
$y = -6$	$y = -4$	$y = -2$
$(-1, -6)$ is a solution.	$(0, -4)$ is a solution.	$(1, -2)$ is a solution.

Three solutions of $y = 2x - 4$ are $(-1, -6)$, $(0, -4)$, and $(1, -2)$. ∎

> **THINK ABOUT IT**
>
> The number of possible choices for x is unlimited, so the number of ordered-pair solutions is unlimited.

Ⓑ $9 - 6x = 3y$

Solution

Step 1   Solve for y.

$9 - 6x = 3y$ Write the equation.

$\dfrac{9}{3} - \dfrac{6x}{3} = \dfrac{3y}{3}$ Divide both sides by 3.

$3 - 2x = y$ Simplify.

Step 2   Choose values for x and find the corresponding values for y.

Let $x = -2$.	Let $x = 3$.	Let $x = 5$.
$3 - 2x = y$	$3 - 2x = y$	$3 - 2x = y$
$3 - 2 \cdot (-2) = y$	$3 - 2 \cdot 3 = y$	$3 - 2 \cdot 5 = y$
$3 + 4 = y$	$3 - 6 = y$	$3 - 10 = y$
$7 = y$	$-3 = y$	$-7 = y$
$(-2, 7)$ is a solution.	$(3, -3)$ is a solution.	$(5, -7)$ is a solution.

Three solutions of $9 - 6x = 3y$ are $(-2, 7)$, $(3, -3)$, and $(5, -7)$. ∎

Graphing an Equation

The graphs of all the ordered-pair solutions of an equation form the **graph of the equation**. You can record several solutions in a table of values and then graph those ordered pairs. After graphing several ordered pairs, you can use the pattern you have formed to draw the graph of the equation.

Example 3   Graph $y - 4 = -2x$.

Solution   First, solve the equation for y.

$y - 4 = -2x$ Write the equation.

$y - 4 + 4 = -2x + 4$ Add 4 to both sides.

$y = -2x + 4$ Simplify.

(continued)

Next, record several ordered pair solutions in a table of values.

x	$-2x + 4$	y	(x, y)
-3	$-2 \cdot (-3) + 4 = 6 + 4 = 10$	10	$(-3, 10)$
-1	$-2 \cdot (-1) + 4 = 2 + 4 = 6$	6	$(-1, 6)$
0	$-2 \cdot 0 + 4 = 0 + 4 = 4$	4	$(0, 4)$
2	$-2 \cdot 2 + 4 = -4 + 4 = 0$	0	$(2, 0)$
4	$-2 \cdot 4 + 4 = -8 + 4 = -4$	-4	$(4, -4)$

TIP

Choose values for x that are easy to work with. Zero is usually an easy value to work with.

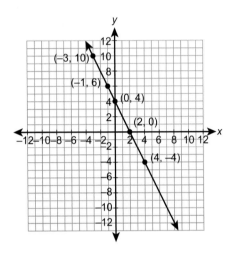

Graph the ordered pairs.

The points lie in a line. Draw a line through the points. The line is the graph of $y - 4 = -2x$. ∎

THINK ABOUT IT

Any linear equation has an infinite number of solutions. Their corresponding points form a line, which has infinitely many points.

Determining Dependent Variables and Independent Variables

In a two-variable equation, the **independent variable** is the input variable and the **dependent variable** is the output variable.

Sometimes you need to determine which variable is dependent and which variable is independent. Consider these two variables: price p and sales tax t. It is not reasonable to say that the price of an item depends on the amount of sales tax charged on that item. Instead, it is reasonable to say that the amount of sales tax t depends on the price p. So in this case, the dependent variable is t and the independent variable is p.

Example 4 Identify the dependent variable and the independent variable in each situation. Explain your answer.

Ⓐ Mai is a sales associate. She earns a salary of \$650 per week and a 5% commission on sales. If s is the amount of Mai's sales in dollars and p is Mai's total pay, then the variables s and p are related by the equation $-0.05s + p = 650$.

Solution Because Mai's total pay p depends on the amount of her sales s, the dependent variable is p and the independent variable is s. ∎

TIP

In an ordered pair, the independent variable is first and the dependent variable is second.

B Rico has 12 gallons of gasoline in his car's tank when he begins a road trip. During the trip, g is the number of gallons remaining in the tank and m is the number of miles he has driven. The variables are related by the equation $0.04m + g = 12$.

Solution Because the number of remaining gallons g depends on the number of miles driven m, the dependent variable is g and the independent variable is m. ■

C Tickets to a school play cost \$5.50 for adults and \$3 for students. On opening night, \$960 is collected in ticket sales. If a is the number of adult tickets sold and s is the number of student tickets sold, then the variables are related by the equation $5.50a + 3s = 960$.

Solution There is no way to determine whether sales of one type of ticket affect sales of the other type of ticket. So in this case, it is not reasonable to say that either variable depends on the other. If you need to decide that one variable is dependent and the other is independent, then you can decide either way. ■

Problem Set

Determine if the ordered pair is a solution of the equation.

1. Is $(0, 0)$ a solution of $y = x$?

2. Is $(1, 3)$ a solution of $y = 3x$?

3. Is $(4, 2)$ a solution of $y = 3x - 4$?

4. Is $(3, -1)$ a solution of $y + 3x = 4$?

5. Is $(5, 3)$ a solution of $2x + 3y = 19$?

6. Is $(8, -2)$ a solution of $12x + 2y = 92$?

7. Is $(6, -3)$ a solution of $4x - 2y = 30$?

8. Is $(0, -7)$ a solution of $9x + 2y = 14$?

9. Is $(2, 7)$ a solution of $2y = 3x + 8$?

10. Is $\left(-5, \frac{1}{2}\right)$ a solution of $8y = 2x + 14$?

11. Is $(3, -1)$ a solution of $-2x - 5y = -1$?

12. Is $(1.5, 2.5)$ a solution of $8x + 4y = 20$?

Find three solutions of each equation.

13. $y = 4x$

14. $q = 2p + 6$

15. $f = \frac{1}{2}e - 5$

16. $2h = 8g - 12$

17. $20 - 4x = 4y$

18. $y - 4x = 9$

*19. **Challenge** $3y - 9x = 12$

*20. **Challenge** $8y - 10 = 3y + 15x$

Make a table of values, and then graph each equation.

21. $y = 2x$

22. $y = \frac{1}{3}x$

23. $y = x - 4$

24. $y + 4x = 8$

25. $4x - 2y = 12$

*26. **Challenge** $5y - 2y = 3x + 6y$

*27. **Challenge** $-2x - 4y = 6x + 12$

Identify the dependent variable and the independent variable in each situation. Explain your answer.

28. Marty borrowed money from his mother to buy a new car. He makes a payment of $250 to her each month. The total amount a that Marty still owes his mother is given by the equation $a = 5000 - 250m$ where m is the number of monthly payments Marty has already made.

29. An adventure fitness club charges a $25 membership fee. A one-hour session of rock-wall climbing costs $4. If n is the number of climbing sessions and t is the total amount spent in fees and climbing sessions combined, then the variables n and t are related by the equation $t - 4n = 25$.

30. Caroline has n nickels and d dimes in her pocket. The total value of the coins is $4.25. The variables are related by the equation $0.05n + 0.10d = 4.25$.

31. A prepaid cellular phone is loaded with a $100 card. Each minute of talk costs $0.25. If r is the remaining balance on the card and t is the number of minutes talked, then the variables are related by the equation $4r + t = 400$.

Linear Equations and Intercepts

A **line** is made up of an infinite number of points and extends without end in two opposite directions.

Identifying the Intercepts of a Line

When you graph a line on a coordinate plane, it crosses at least one axis.

> **DEFINITIONS**
>
> The **x-intercept** of a line is the x-coordinate of the point where the line intersects the x-axis. The **y-intercept** of a line is the y-coordinate of the point where the line intersects the y-axis.

Example 1 Name the intercepts of each line.

 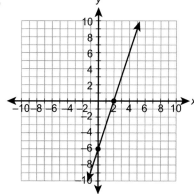

Solution The line intersects the x-axis at (2, 0). The x-intercept is 2. The line intersects the y-axis at (0, −6). The y-intercept is −6. ∎

 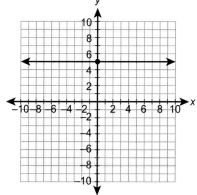

Solution The line is horizontal. It does not intersect the x-axis, so it has no x-intercept. The line intersects the y-axis at (0, 5). The y-intercept is 5. ∎

Using Intercepts to Graph $Ax + By = C$

If the graph of an equation is a line, the equation is a **linear equation**. The graph of an equation in the form $Ax + By = C$ (where A, B, and C are integers and A and B are not both zero) is a line. An equation in this form is called the **standard form of a linear equation**. If A and B are both nonzero, the line is neither horizontal nor vertical, and it will intersect both axes.

GRAPHING A LINEAR EQUATION BY FINDING ITS INTERCEPTS

Step 1 Find the x-intercept by letting $y = 0$ and solving for x.
Step 2 Find the y-intercept by letting $x = 0$ and solving for y.
Step 3 Graph the intercepts. Draw the line through both points.

Example 2 Graph each equation.

A $4x + 3y = 12$

Solution First, find the intercepts.

$$4x + 3y = 12 \qquad \text{Write the equation.}$$
$$4x + 3 \cdot 0 = 12 \qquad \text{To find the } x\text{-intercept, let } y = 0.$$
$$4x = 12 \qquad \text{Simplify.}$$
$$x = 3 \qquad \text{Solve for } x.$$

The x-intercept is 3. The line intersects the x-axis at $(3, 0)$.

Next, find the y-intercept.

$$4x + 3y = 12 \qquad \text{Write the equation.}$$
$$4 \cdot 0 + 3y = 12 \qquad \text{To find the } y\text{-intercept, let } x = 0.$$
$$3y = 12 \qquad \text{Simplify.}$$
$$y = 4 \qquad \text{Solve for } y.$$

The y-intercept is 4. The line intersects the y-axis at $(0, 4)$.

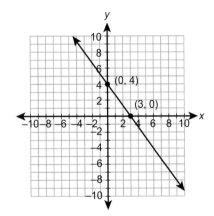

Graph the intercepts.

Draw the line that contains both points.

The line is the graph of $4x + 3y = 12$. ∎

B $-2x - 6 = 3y$

Solution First, write the equation in standard form.

$$-2x - 6 = 3y \qquad \text{Write the equation.}$$
$$-2x - 6 + 6 = 3y + 6 \qquad \text{Add 6 to both sides.}$$
$$-2x = 3y + 6 \qquad \text{Simplify.}$$
$$-2x - 3y = 3y + 6 - 3y \qquad \text{Subtract } 3y \text{ from both sides.}$$
$$-2x - 3y = 6 \qquad \text{The equation is in standard form.}$$

Next, find the intercepts.

$$-2x - 3y = 6 \qquad\qquad -2x - 3y = 6$$
$$-2x - 3 \cdot 0 = 6 \qquad\qquad -2 \cdot 0 - 3y = 6$$
$$-2x = 6 \qquad\qquad\qquad -3y = 6$$
$$x = -3 \qquad\qquad\qquad y = -2$$

The x-intercept is -3.   The y-intercept is -2.

REMEMBER

Equations that have all the same solutions are equivalent. In Example 2B, the equations $-2x - 6 = 3y$ and $-2x - 3y = 6$ are equivalent.

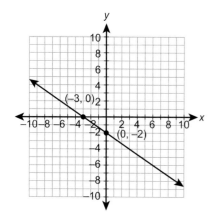

Graph the intercepts.

Draw the line through both points.

The line is the graph of $-2x - 6 = 3y$. ∎

Graphing $y = b$

The graph of an equation in the form $y = b$, where b is a constant, is a horizontal line with y-intercept b.

Example 3 Graph $y = -5$.

Solution The graph is the horizontal line with y-intercept -5.

THINK ABOUT IT

Some solutions to the equation $y = -5$ are $(0, -5)$, $(2, -5)$, and $(-23, -5)$. The y-coordinate of every point on the line is -5.

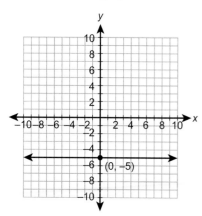

Graph the y-intercept.

Draw a horizontal line through the point.

The line is the graph of $y = -5$. ∎

Graphing $x = a$

The graph of an equation in the form $x = a$, where a is a constant, is a vertical line with x-intercept a.

Example 4 Graph $x = 3$.

Solution The graph is the vertical line with x-intercept 3.

REMEMBER

The graph of $x = a$ is a vertical line.

The graph of $y = b$ is a horizontal line.

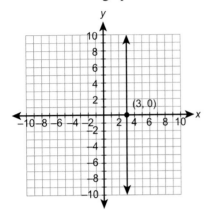

Graph the x-intercept.

Draw a vertical line through the point.

The line is the graph of $x = 3$. ∎

Using Intercepts to Write an Equation of a Line

USING INTERCEPTS TO WRITE AN EQUATION OF A LINE

Step 1 Let C equal the product of the intercepts.

Step 2 Substitute the ordered pairs that contain the intercepts into $Ax + By = C$ to find the values of A and B.

Step 3 Substitute the values of A, B, and C into $Ax + By = C$.

Example 5 Write a linear equation for the graph that is shown.

THINK ABOUT IT

You could use any nonzero value for C, but using the product of the intercepts makes for neater numbers.

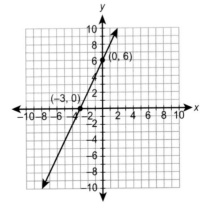

Solution The intercepts are -3 and 6. The product is $-3 \cdot 6 = -18$. Use $(0, 6)$ and $(-3, 0)$ to find the values of A and B.

Substitute $(0, 6)$

$$Ax + By = -18$$
$$A \cdot 0 + B \cdot 6 = -18$$
$$B \cdot 6 = -18$$
$$B = -3$$

Substitute $(-3, 0)$

$$Ax + By = -18$$
$$A \cdot (-3) + B \cdot 0 = -18$$
$$-3A = -18$$
$$A = 6$$

TIP

Check your equation by finding the intercepts.

Since $A = 6$, $B = -3$, and $C = -18$, the equation is $6x - 3y = -18$. ∎

Problem Set

Name the intercepts of each line.

1.

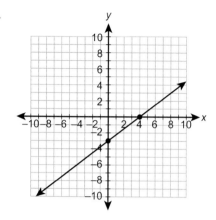

2.

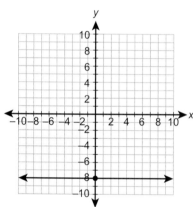

3.

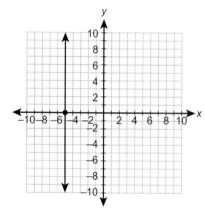

4.

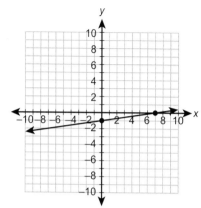

5.

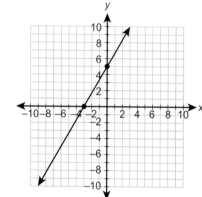

6.

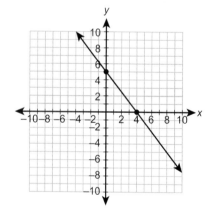

Find the intercepts of the graph of the line.

7. $2x + 4y = 8$

8. $x - y = 5$

9. $x + 3y = 9$

10. $5x - y = 10$

11. $9x + 4y = 18$

12. $-4x - 2y = 16$

Graph each equation.

13. $x - y = 4$

14. $x + 2y = 8$

15. $y = -7$

16. $x = 2$

17. $4x - 2y = 12$

18. $x = 5$

19. $x = -4$

20. $y = 1$

21. $-x + 4 = 2y$

22. $y = -2$

23. $-5x = 2y - 10$

24. $x + 3y = 9$

*25. **Challenge** $4x + 2y = 12 + x$

*26. **Challenge** $\frac{1}{2}x + \frac{2}{3}y = 4$

Write a linear equation for the graph that is shown.

27.
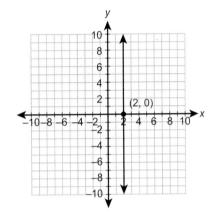

30.
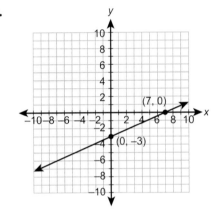

28.
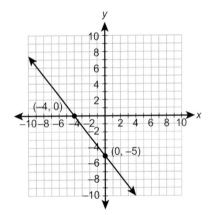

31.
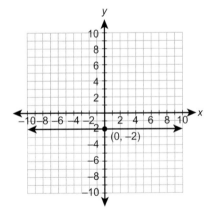

29.
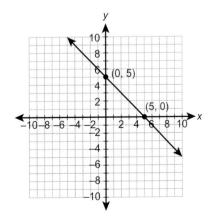

32.
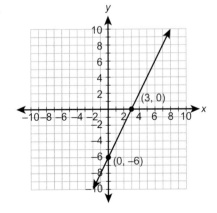

Slope

Lines can vary in steepness. They can also vary in whether they slant up to the left, up to the right, or not at all. *Slope* describes all those variations.

Calculating Slope

Let (x_1, y_1) and (x_2, y_2) be two points on a line. When moving from (x_1, y_1) to (x_2, y_2) on the line, the vertical change, or **rise**, equals $y_2 - y_1$ and the horizontal change, or **run**, equals $x_2 - x_1$.

TIP

x_1 is read "x sub 1," and means "the x-coordinate of the first point."

SLOPE

The **slope** of a line is the ratio of the rise to the run.

$$\text{slope} = \frac{\text{rise}}{\text{run}} = \frac{\text{vertical change}}{\text{horizontal change}} = \frac{y_2 - y_1}{x_2 - x_1}$$

Example 1   Find the slope of the line.

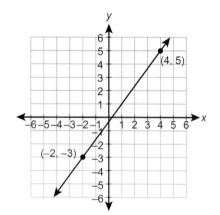

Solution   You can count the rise and the run from one point to another. Or, you can use the slope formula. Let $(-2, -3)$ be (x_1, y_1) and let $(4, 5)$ be (x_2, y_2). Substitute the values of x_1, y_1, x_2, and y_2 into the formula.

(continued)

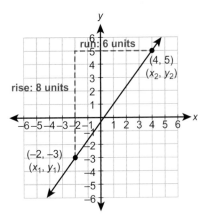

$$\text{slope} = \frac{\text{rise}}{\text{run}} = \frac{y_2 - y_1}{x_2 - x_1}$$

$$= \frac{5 - (-3)}{4 - (-2)}$$

$$= \frac{5 + 3}{4 + 2}$$

$$= \frac{8}{6}$$

$$= \frac{4}{3}$$

The slope is $\frac{4}{3}$. ■

Calculating Slope More Than One Way

To find the slope of a line, use any pair of points on the line. And for any pair of points, you can use either order.

Example 2 Find the slope of the line. Use two different pairs of points and change the order for one pair of points.

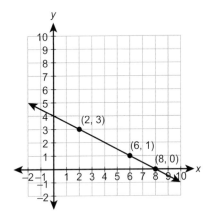

Solution

(x_1, y_1)	(x_2, y_2)	slope $= \frac{y_2 - y_1}{x_2 - x_1}$
$(2, 3)$	$(6, 1)$	slope $= \frac{1 - 3}{6 - 2} = \frac{-2}{4} = -\frac{1}{2}$
$(8, 0)$	$(6, 1)$	slope $= \frac{1 - 0}{6 - 8} = \frac{1}{-2} = -\frac{1}{2}$
$(6, 1)$	$(8, 0)$	slope $= \frac{0 - 1}{8 - 6} = \frac{-1}{2} = -\frac{1}{2}$

This is the same pair of points in a different order.

The slope is $-\frac{1}{2}$. ■

Calculating the Slope of a Horizontal Line

Example 3   Find the slope of the horizontal line.

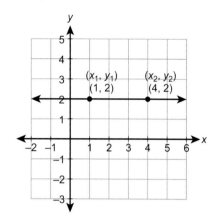

Solution   slope $= \dfrac{y_2 - y_1}{x_2 - x_1} = \dfrac{2-2}{4-1} = \dfrac{0}{3} = 0$ The slope is 0. ■

> **REMEMBER**
>
> Any fraction with a numerator of zero and a nonzero denominator equals zero.
>
> $\dfrac{0}{a} = 0$ if $a \neq 0$

Describing the Slope of a Vertical Line

Example 4   Find the slope of the vertical line.

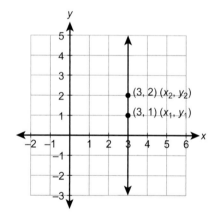

Solution   slope $= \dfrac{y_2 - y_1}{x_2 - x_1} = \dfrac{2-1}{3-3} = \dfrac{1}{0}$ The slope is undefined. ■

> **REMEMBER**
>
> Any fraction with denominator zero is undefined.
>
> $\dfrac{a}{0}$ is undefined for all values of a.

Using Slope to Classify and Describe Lines

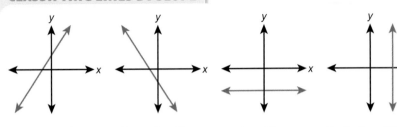

Positive Slope
The line rises
left to right.

Negative Slope
The line falls
left to right.

Zero Slope
The line is
horizontal.

Undefined Slope
The line is
vertical.

Example 5   Find the slope of the line that passes through the points $(2, 0)$ and $(-1, 3)$. Describe the line.

Solution   Let $(2, 0)$ be (x_1, y_1) and let $(-1, 3)$ be (x_2, y_2).

$$\text{slope} = \frac{y_2 - y_1}{x_2 - x_1} = \frac{3 - 0}{-1 - 2} = \frac{3}{-3} = -1$$

The line falls from left to right because it has a negative slope. ■

> **TIP**
>
> You can let either point be (x_1, y_1). Then let the other point be (x_2, y_2).

Using Slope to Compare the Steepness of Lines

The slope is a measure of the steepness of a line, that is, the angle the line makes with the horizontal. The steeper of two lines has the greater absolute value of slope.

Example 6   Which is the slope of the steeper line, $-\frac{10}{3}$ or 2?

Solution   Compare the absolute values of the slopes.

$$\left| -\frac{10}{3} \right| = \frac{10}{3} = 3\frac{1}{3} \text{ and } |2| = 2.$$

Since $3\frac{1}{3} > 2$, $-\frac{10}{3}$ is the slope of the steeper line. ■

> **THINK ABOUT IT**
>
> When you think about the steepness of a line, think about riding a bike or skateboard downhill on a street with that slope. The steeper the slope (greater absolute value), the faster you will go.

Finding the Slope of a Line, Given the Equation in Standard Form

You can use the intercepts as two points to find the slope of a line.

Example 7   Find the slope of the graph of $2x - 4y = 12$.

Solution

Find the x-intercept.	Find the y-intercept.
$2x - 4y = 12$	$2x - 4y = 12$
$2x - 4 \cdot 0 = 12$	$2 \cdot 0 - 4y = 12$
$2x = 12$	$-4y = 12$
$x = 6$	$y = -3$
x-intercept: $(6, 0)$	y-intercept: $(0, -3)$

Graph the line. Find the rise and run.

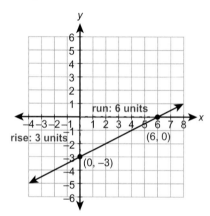

Finally, calculate the slope.

$$\text{slope} = \frac{\text{rise}}{\text{run}} = \frac{3}{6} = \frac{1}{2} \quad \blacksquare$$

SLOPE OF THE GRAPH OF $Ax + By = C$

The slope of the graph of a linear equation in standard form

$Ax + By = C$ is $-\dfrac{A}{B}$.

Example 8   Find the slope of the graph of $2x - 4y = 12$.

Solution   Identify the values of A and B, and then find the slope.

$$Ax + By = C$$
$$\downarrow \quad \downarrow \qquad A = 2 \text{ and } B = -4.$$
$$2x - 4y = 12$$

$$\text{slope} = -\frac{A}{B} = -\frac{2}{-4} = \frac{1}{2} \quad \blacksquare$$

THINK ABOUT IT

Examples 7 and 8 have the same answer because they have the same equation.

Example 8 illustrates the slope property for a linear equation in standard form.

Problem Set

Use the graph to find the slope of each line.

1.

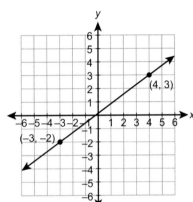

4.

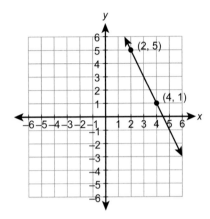

2.

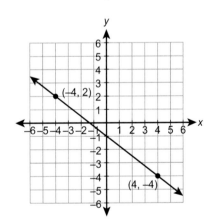

5.

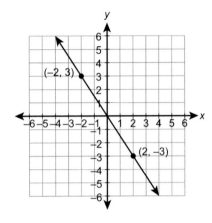

3.

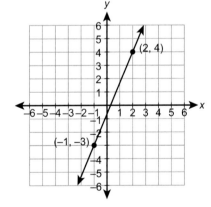

6.

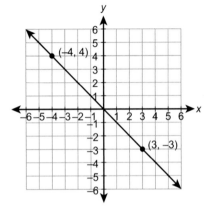

Find the slope of the line that passes through the points.

7. $(2, 3)$ and $(4, 5)$

8. $(0, 2)$ and $(6, 7)$

9. $(0, 0)$ and $(-5, 2)$

10. $(3, 2)$ and $(-7, 2)$

11. $(2, -9)$ and $(3, -1)$

12. $(-4, 8)$ and $(-4, 5)$

13. $(6, 10)$ and $(3, -7)$

***14.** **Challenge** $\left(\frac{2}{3}, \frac{1}{2}\right)$ and $\left(\frac{1}{3}, \frac{1}{4}\right)$

Find the slope of the line with the given equation.

15. $2x + 4y = 12$

16. $3x + 2y = 6$

17. $y = 3$

18. $9x - y = 18$

19. $x = -5$

20. $6x - 2y = 18$

*21. **Challenge** $y = 4x - 7$

*22. **Challenge** $\frac{1}{2}x + 4y = 3y - 7$

State whether the slope of the line is positive, negative, zero, or undefined.

23.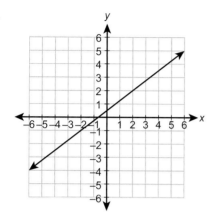

26.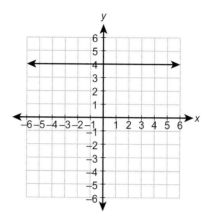

24.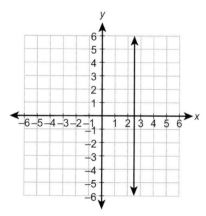

27.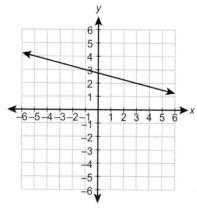

25.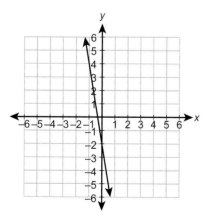

28.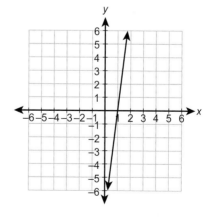

Which is the slope of the steepest line?

29. 8 or −2

30. $\frac{5}{2}$, $-\frac{3}{2}$, or 3

31. $-\frac{2}{3}$ or $\frac{1}{2}$

Applications: Linear Graphs

Many applications can be modeled with linear equations.

TIP

When you infer, you make an educated guess.

When data form a linear pattern, you can use a linear graph to make inferences and predictions.

Application: Health

DEFINITION

Interpolation is a process of inferring, or estimating, an unknown value that is between known values.

THINK ABOUT IT

Interpolate comes from the Latin *inter* meaning "between" and *polus* meaning "point."

Example 1   Mr. Nelson has been losing weight steadily for 10 months. The graph shows data about his weight over time. What is a reasonable guess for Mr. Nelson's weight in month 7?

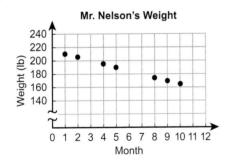

Solution   The data points form a linear pattern. Draw the line through the points. Then interpolate to infer the weight for month 7.

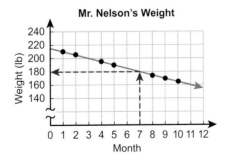

It is reasonable to infer that Mr. Nelson's weight in month 7 was 180 pounds. ∎

Application: Personal Finance

DEFINITION

Extrapolation is a process of inferring, estimating, or predicting a value that is outside of known values.

THINK ABOUT IT

Extrapolate comes from the Latin *extra* meaning "outside" and *polus* meaning "point."

When you extrapolate, you make an inference about values that are outside the known points.

Example 2   Sheila has been saving money at a steady rate. She is saving for a new television that costs $2400. A graph of her savings is shown below. What is a reasonable prediction of when Sheila will have enough money saved to buy the television set?

Month	Total Saved ($)
1	300
2	600
3	900
4	1200
5	1500

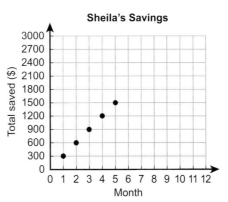

Solution   The data points form a linear pattern. Draw the line through the points. Then extrapolate to predict the first month in which Sheila's total savings will be at least $2400.

Month	Total Saved ($)
1	300
2	600
3	900
4	1200
5	1500

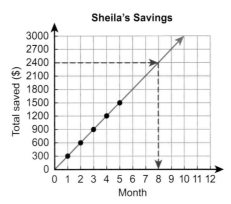

Sheila should reach her savings goal in Month 8. The prediction is reasonable because Sheila is saving $300 per month. If she continues saving at the same rate, she will have $2400 saved in month 8. ∎

Application: Sports

In some cases, using extrapolation will not yield a reasonable prediction.

Example 3   The number of runs scored by a baseball team in each of its first four games of a season are shown in the graph below. Use extrapolation to predict the number of runs the team will score in the 20th game of the season. Is the prediction reasonable? Explain.

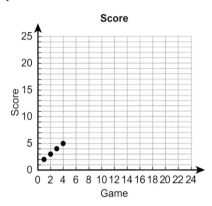

Game	Score
1	2
2	3
3	4
4	5

Solution   The data points form a linear pattern. Draw the line through the points. Then extrapolate to predict the number of runs the team will score in the 20th game.

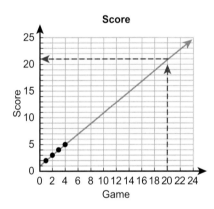

Game	Score
1	2
2	3
3	4
4	5

If the pattern continues, the team will score 21 runs in the 20th game. This prediction is not reasonable because it is not reasonable to expect the pattern to continue. A constant increase of one run per game is not likely over more than a few games. ■

Problem Set

Solve. For each set of problems use the given graph and information.

Use the following information to solve problems 1−5. Because of a drought, the water level in a lake has been decreasing steadily for the past 8 months. The graph shows data about the water level over time.

Use the following information to solve problems 6−10. Washington Elementary School has experienced an increase in enrollment each year since it opened. The graph shows data about the student population over time.

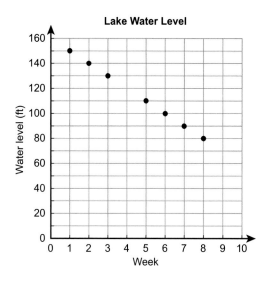

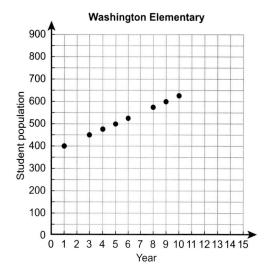

1. What is a reasonable inference for the water level in Week 4?

2. What is a reasonable prediction for the water level in Week 9?

3. What is a reasonable prediction for the water level in Week 10?

4. A state of emergency will be declared when the water level in the lake reaches 40 feet. Use extrapolation to predict when a state of emergency will be declared.

5. Is the prediction you made in problem 4 reasonable? Explain.

6. What is a reasonable inference for the student population in Year 2?

7. What is a reasonable inference for the student population in Year 7?

8. What is a reasonable prediction for the student population in Year 11?

9. School administrators plan to build a new elementary school when the student population at Washington Elementary reaches 700. Use extrapolation to predict the year in which that might happen.

10. Is the prediction you made in problem 9 reasonable? Explain.

Use the following information for problems 11–15.
A new car loses value as it ages. The value of a certain car during its first five years is shown in the graph.

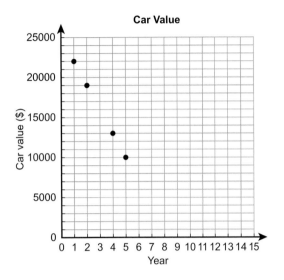

Car Value

Use the following information for problems 16–20.
Marvin is lifting weights to build muscle. During his first four weeks of weight training, he tracks the greatest weight he can bench press each week in a graph.

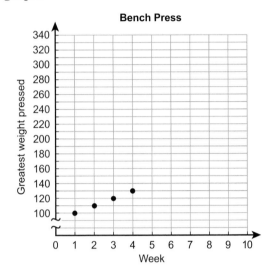

Bench Press

11. What is a reasonable inference for the value of the car in Year 3?

12. What is a reasonable prediction for the value of the car in Year 6?

13. If you extrapolate from the data in the graph, what will be the value of the car in Year 9?

14. Use extrapolation to predict the year in which the car will be worth nothing.

15. Is the prediction you made in problem 14 reasonable? Explain.

16. During the first four weeks, how much does Marvin's heaviest press increase each week?

17. What is a reasonable prediction for Marvin's heaviest press in Week 5?

18. What is a reasonable prediction for Marvin's heaviest press in Week 6?

19. Use extrapolation to predict Marvin's heaviest press in Week 20.

20. Is the prediction you made in problem 19 reasonable? Explain.

Relations and Functions

A relation describes how two sets are related to each other.

Identifying Domain and Range

Example 1   Identify the domain and range.

A $\{(-3, 4), (-2, 1), (-1, 0), (1, 7), (3, 7)\}$

Solution   Identify the first elements. Identify the second elements.

Domain: $\{-3, -2, -1, 1, 3\}$ Range: $\{4, 1, 0, 7\}$ ■

B

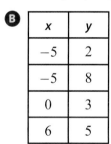

x	y
−5	2
−5	8
0	3
6	5

Solution   The domain is the set of *x*-values. The range is the set of *y*-values.

Domain: $\{-5, 0, 6\}$ Range: $\{2, 8, 3, 5\}$ ■

Determining Whether a Relation Is a Function

(continued)

Example 2 Determine whether each relation is a function.

Ⓐ {(−3, 4), (−2, 0), (−2, 1), (1, 3), (3, 7)}

Solution Look at the ordered pairs (−2, 0) and (−2, 1). The input −2 is assigned two different outputs: 0 and 1. This relation *is not* a function. ∎

Ⓑ

x	y
−6	3
−4	−4
1	0
1	3
2	8

Ⓒ

x	y
1	2
0	4
−1	6
−2	8

TIP

If an *x*-value is repeated, appearing in different ordered pairs, then the relation is not a function.

Solution The input 1 is assigned two different outputs: 0 and 3. This relation *is not* a function. ∎

Solution Each input is assigned exactly one output. This relation *is* a function. ∎

Applying the Vertical Line Test

All relations can be graphed. When a relation is graphed, use the vertical line test to determine whether it is a function.

VERTICAL LINE TEST

If any vertical line can be drawn to intersect the graph of a relation in more than one point, the relation *is not* a function. If no vertical line exists that intersects the graph in more than one point, the relation *is* a function.

THINK ABOUT IT

If a vertical line hits more than one location on a graph, it means there are two points with the same *x*-coordinate.

Example 3 Apply the vertical line test to determine whether each graph represents a function.

Ⓐ

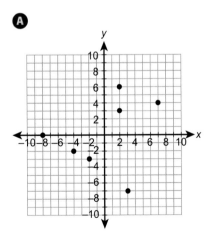

Solution

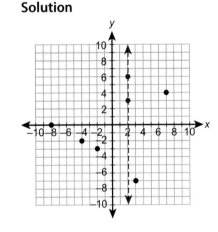

A vertical line intersects the graph in more than one point. The graph fails the vertical line test. The graph *does not* represent a function. ∎

B

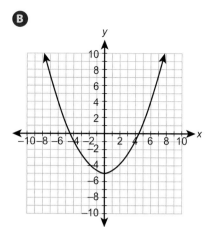

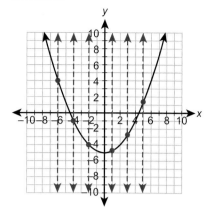

There is no vertical line that intersects the graph in more than one point. The graph passes the vertical line test. The graph *does* represent a function. ∎

C

Solution

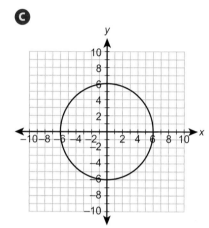

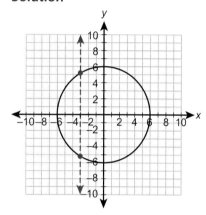

A vertical line intersects the graph in more than one point. The graph fails the vertical line test. The graph *does not* represent a function. ∎

The vertical line test is really just a way of applying the definition of a function. Note that in the preceding Example 3A, the points on the vertical line are (2, 3) and (2, 6). Therefore, the input 2 is assigned two different outputs: 3 and 6. By definition, the relation is not a function.

> **TIP**
>
> The arrowheads on the graph in Example 3B indicate that the graph continues without end.

Evaluating Functions

Many functions can be represented by equations. For instance, the equation $y = x + 3$ represents a function. Two solutions of the equation are (1, 4) and (2, 5). All the solutions of the equation form the set of ordered pairs that make up the function.

    If a function equation has variables x and y, then x is the input (independent) variable, and y is the output (dependent) variable. We sometimes use the notation $f(x)$ in place of the variable y. In **function notation**, x is the input variable. Using function notation, the equation $y = x + 3$ can be written $f(x) = x + 3$. If $x = 1$, then $y = f(x) = f(1) = 1 + 3 = 4$. This is called evaluating the function f for the input $x = 1$. Note that the values $x = 1$ and $y = 4$ are in the ordered pair (1, 4).

> **THINK ABOUT IT**
>
> Read $f(x)$ as "f of x".

> **TIP**
>
> Variables other than x, y, and f can be used for functions. For example, the function $d = 50t$ gives distance d as a function of time t. It can be written $d(t) = 50t$.

(continued)

Example 4 Evaluate the function for the given input.

A Find $f(7)$.

x	$f(x)$
3	-4
0	2
2	3
4	7
7	11
10	15

Solution

x	$f(x)$
3	-4
0	2
2	3
4	7
7	11
10	15

Find the input 7 in the table. The output is 11. $f(7) = 11$ ■

B Find $f(-5)$.

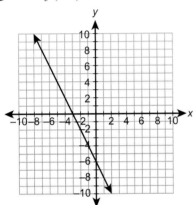

Solution

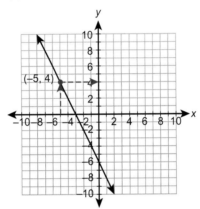

Find the y-coordinate when the x-coordinate is -5. $f(-5) = 4$ ■

C For $f(x) = 8x - 10$, find $f(2)$.

Solution

$f(x) = 8x - 10$	Write the function equation.
$f(2) = 8 \cdot 2 - 10$	Substitute 2 for x.
$= 16 - 10$	Multiply.
$= 6$	Subtract.

$f(2) = 6$ ■

Problem Set

Identify the domain and range.

1. $\{(3, 0), (-3, 1), (2, 0), (0, 4), (3, 2)\}$

2. $\{(-4, 5), (7, -6), (4, 2), (4, 1), (4, -5)\}$

3. $\{(1, 4), (1, -2), (1, 5), (1, -3), (1, -5)\}$

4.

x	y
−2	4
−1	2
0	3
1	2

5.

x	y
−1	1
3	−2
3	5
5	6

6.

x	y
0	0
0	−3
1	1
2	0

Determine whether each relation is a function.

7. $\{(2, 0), (2, 7), (3, −1), (4, 2), (9, 3)\}$

8. $\{(0, 2), (4, 2), (3, 2), (5, 1), (6, 2)\}$

9. $\{(1, 2), (2, 4), (3, 6), (4, 8), (5, 10)\}$

10.

x	y
1	3
1	2
2	2
3	−2

11.

x	y
−2	3
1	2
2	1
4	2

12.

x	y
0	0
2	3
5	0
6	1

Apply the vertical line test to determine whether each graph represents a function.

13.

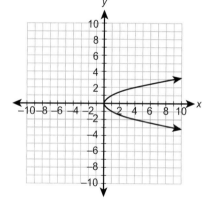

15.

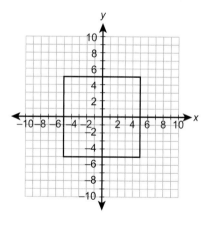

14.

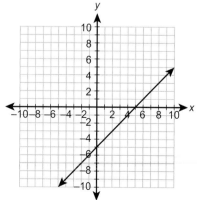

16.

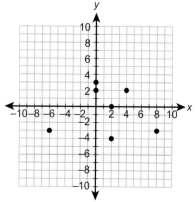

Evaluate the function for the given input.

17. $f(3)$

x	f(x)
0	4
1	5
2	6
3	7
4	8
5	9

18. $g(9)$

x	g(x)
−2	3
2	6
4	8
9	−2
−5	6
0	1

19. $h(-3)$

x	h(x)
2	3
1	2
3	2
−1	−2
−3	6
−8	2

20. $f(-2)$

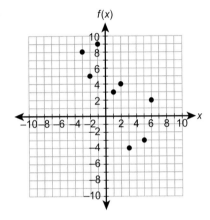

22. $s(3)$

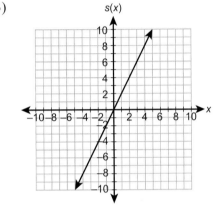

21. $f(5)$

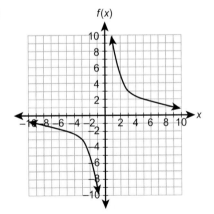

23. $g(9)$

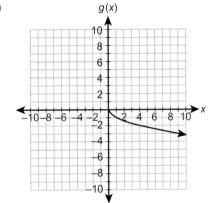

24. $f(x) = 3x$
Find $f(4)$.

25. $g(x) = 2x - 3$
Find $g(-2)$.

26. $f(x) = x^2 + 3x$
Find $f(4)$.

27. $h(x) = \sqrt{2x + 25}$
Find $h(0)$.

Systems of Linear Equations

A **system of linear equations** is made up of two or more linear equations.

A **solution of a system of linear equations** in two variables is an ordered pair that is a solution of each equation in the system.

Solving a System of Linear Equations by Graphing

Example 1   Solve the system by graphing. $y = 3x - 2$
$$y = -x + 6$$

Solution   Graph each equation. The ordered-pair coordinates of the point of intersection is the solution.

x	$y = 3x - 2$
-2	-8
0	-2
3	7

x	$y = -x + 6$
-3	9
0	6
6	0

Make a table of values for each equation.

TIP

Find at least 3 ordered pairs for each line. Choose *x*-values that are spaced apart. This helps ensure that you draw an accurate line.

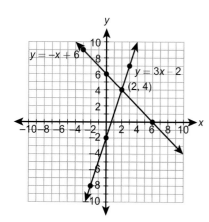

Graph each equation.

Identify the point of intersection.

THINK ABOUT IT

Each equation in the system has an infinite number of ordered-pair solutions, corresponding to the infinite number of points on each line.

But only the point (2, 4) is on both lines. So, (2, 4) is the only solution of the system.

The point of intersection appears to be at (2, 4).

(continued)

Check Substitute (2, 4) into each equation. The solution is correct if each equation is true.

$y = 3x - 2$ $y = -x + 6$

$4 \overset{?}{=} 3 \cdot 2 - 2$ $4 \overset{?}{=} -2 + 6$

$4 \overset{?}{=} 6 - 2$ $4 = 4 \; \checkmark$

$4 = 4 \; \checkmark$

Both equations are true for (2, 4).

The solution of the system is (2, 4). ∎

Determining the Number of Solutions of a System of Linear Equations

A system of linear equations in two variables can have exactly one solution, no solutions, or an infinite number of solutions.

Example 2 Use the graph to determine the number of solutions of the system of equations.

Ⓐ $y = x + 3$

     $y + 5 = x$

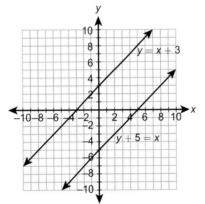

Solution The lines are parallel. There is no point of intersection. The system has no solution. ∎

B $2y = 3x - 6$

   $y = 1.5x - 3$

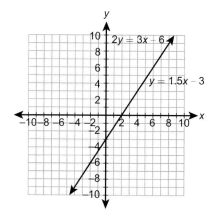

Solution   The two equations in the system describe the same line. Every point on the line is a solution to each equation. The system has an infinite number of solutions. ■

C $x = -6$

   $3x + 2y = -4$

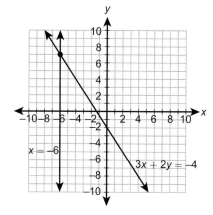

THINK ABOUT IT

The lines in the graph of a linear system can be slanted, vertical, or horizontal.

Solution   The lines intersect in one point. There is exactly one ordered pair that is a solution of both equations in the system. The system has exactly one solution. ■

Solving a System of Linear Equations by Substitution

You can solve a system of linear equations by algebraic methods. One algebraic method is substitution.

SOLVING A SYSTEM OF LINEAR EQUATIONS BY SUBSTITUTION

Step 1   Solve one of the equations for one of the variables.

Step 2   Substitute the expression from Step 1 into the other equation and solve for the other variable.

Step 3   Substitute the value you found in Step 2 into either equation and solve for the remaining variable.

(continued)

Example 3

A Solve the system by substitution.

$5x + y = 20$

$y = x + 2$

Solution

Step 1 The equation $y = x + 2$ is already solved for y.

Step 2 Substitute $x + 2$ for y into the other equation and solve for x.

$5x + y = 20$	Write the first equation.
$5x + x + 2 = 20$	Substitute $x + 2$ for y.
$6x + 2 = 20$	Simplify the left side of the equation.
$6x = 18$	Subtract 2 from both sides.
$x = 3$	Divide both sides by 6.

Step 3 Substitute 3 for x into either equation.

$y = x + 2$	Write the second equation.
$y = 3 + 2$	Substitute 3 for x.
$y = 5$	Simplify to solve the equation.

The result in Step 2 is $x = 3$. The result in Step 3 is $y = 5$. The solution of the system is $(3, 5)$. ■

THINK ABOUT IT

For Step 1, you could solve $5x + y = 20$ for y. Then for Step 2, you would substitute that expression into $y = x + 2$.

TIP

Check the solution by substituting $(3, 5)$ into *both* equations in the system.

B Solve the system by substitution.

$x + 2y = 9$

$x + 3y = 13$

Solution

Step 1 Solve the first equation for x.

$x + 2y = 9$

$x = 9 - 2y$

Step 2 Substitute $9 - 2y$ for x into the second equation and solve for y.

$x + 3y = 13$	Write the second equation.
$9 - 2y + 3y = 13$	Substitute $9 - 2y$ for x.
$9 + y = 13$	Simplify the left side of the equation.
$y = 4$	Subtract 9 from both sides.

Step 3 Substitute 4 for y into either equation.

$x + 2y = 9$	Write the first equation.
$x + 2 \cdot 4 = 9$	Substitute 4 for y.
$x + 8 = 9$	Simplify the left side of the equation.
$x = 1$	Subtract 8 from both sides.

The solution of the system is $(1, 4)$. ■

Application: Ticket Sales

Example 4 Tickets to a school play cost $3 for adults and $2 for students. On opening night, 140 tickets were sold and $370 were collected in ticket sales. How many of each type of ticket were sold?

Solution Let a be the number of adult tickets sold and s be the number of student tickets sold. Write and solve a system of equations.

$a + s = 140$ A total of 140 tickets were sold.

$3a + 2s = 370$ $3a + 2s$ dollars were collected from ticket sales.

Solve the first equation for s.

$s = 140 - a$ Subtract a from both sides.

Substitute this expression for s in the second equation and solve for a.

$3a + 2 \cdot (140 - a) = 370$	Substitute $140 - a$ for s into the second equation.
$3a + 280 - 2a = 370$	Distribute.
$a + 280 = 370$	Simplify the left side of the equation.
$a = 90$	Subtract 280 from both sides.
$s = 140 - a = 140 - 90 = 50$	Substitute 90 for a to find the value of s.

$a = 90$ and $s = 50$.

There were 90 adult tickets and 50 student tickets sold. ∎

THINK ABOUT IT

Example 4 is a case in which it is not reasonable to say that either variable depends on the other. You can choose either variable to be the independent variable. If you choose a to be the independent variable, then ordered pairs are in the form (a, s), and the solution of the system is (90, 50).

Problem Set

Use the graph to determine the number of solutions of the system of equations.

1.

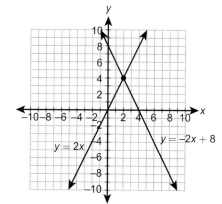

2.

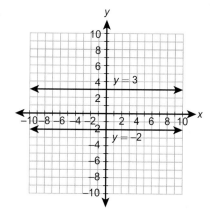

3.

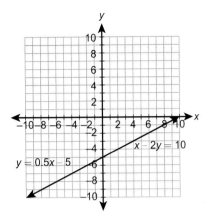

5.

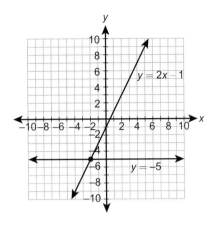

4.

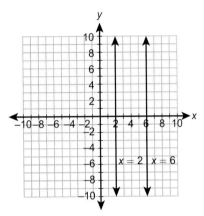

6.

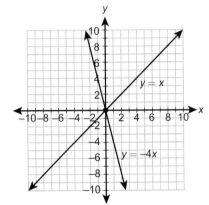

Solve each system by graphing.

7. $x = 2$
   $y = 5$

8. $x = 3$
   $y = x$

9. $y = 2x$
   $y = x - 1$

10. $y = x - 2$
   $y = 2x - 5$

11. $y = 2x - 2$
   $y = 3x - 2$

12. $x + y = 4$
   $y = x - 2$

13. $x + y = 3$
   $2x + y = 8$

14. $3x + y = 9$
   $x - 2y = 10$

Solve each system by substitution.

15. $y = x + 1$
    $x + y = 5$

16. $y = -1$
    $x - y = 5$

17. $x = 2$
    $x = y + 6$

18. $x - y = -2$
    $x + y = 4$

19. $y = 2x$
    $x = y - 2$

20. $x - 2y = 4$
    $x + y = 4$

21. $2x + 3y = 3$
    $x + 2y = 1$

22. $4x + y = -6$
    $3x - y = -1$

23. $y = -6$
    $6x + 2y = -12$

24. $3x - y = -4$
    $x + 3y = 22$

*25. **Challenge** $3x + 4y = -19$
    $2x = 4y - 6$

*26. **Challenge** $4x + 2y = 30$
    $-2x - 5y = -51$

Write and solve a system of equations to answer each question.

27. Mrs. Young teaches flute and piano lessons. She has 9 flute students. The total number of students is 21. How many piano students does Mrs. Young have?

28. The sum of two numbers is 31. The difference of the numbers is 7. What are the two numbers?

29. By weight, a trail mix contains 3 times as much raisins as peanuts. The total weight of the peanuts and raisins in the mixture is 24 ounces. How many ounces of peanuts are in the mixture? How many ounces of raisins?

*30. **Challenge** Charlie bought 2 large pizzas and 4 drinks and paid $38. At the same restaurant, Allen bought 4 large pizzas and 6 drinks and paid $73. What is the cost of a large pizza? What is the cost of a drink?

UNIT 10   Perimeter and Area

An artist uses perimeter and area to determine the amount of materials it takes to produce a piece such as this.

You can find geometric shapes in art. Whether determining the amount of leading or the amount of glass for a piece of stained-glass art, stained-glass artists need to understand perimeter and area to solve many practical problems.

Big Ideas

▶ Several useful aspects of every geometric figure that can be measured, calculated, or approximated. A segment has a finite length that can be measured. Area is a measure of how much material is needed to cover a plane figure.

▶ Many problems can be solved by using the properties of angles, triangles, and circles.

Unit Topics

▶ Types of Polygons

▶ Perimeter

▶ Areas of Rectangles and Triangles

▶ Special Quadrilaterals

▶ Areas of Special Quadrilaterals

▶ Circumference

▶ Areas of Circles

Types of Polygons

Some geometric shapes are polygons.

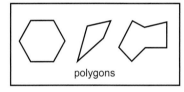

polygons   not polygons

Naming Polygons

A polygon is named by its number of sides. An *n*-sided polygon is called an *n*-gon. Therefore, a polygon with 16 sides is a 16-gon. For fewer numbers of sides, the following terms are commonly used.

3 sides: triangle

4 sides: quadrilateral

5 sides: pentagon

6 sides: hexagon

7 sides: heptagon

8 sides: octagon

9 sides: nonagon

10 sides: decagon

Example 1   Name each polygon.

A

Solution   pentagon ■

B

Solution   quadrilateral ■

C

Solution   octagon ■

D
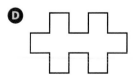

Solution   20-gon ■

Describing Polygons

Tick marks indicate congruent sides and arcs indicate congruent angles.

If a polygon is **equiangular,** all of its angles are congruent.

If a polygon is **equilateral,** all of its sides are congruent.

If a polygon is **regular,** it is both equiangular and equilateral.

Example 2 Determine whether each polygon is equiangular, equilateral, regular, or none of these.

A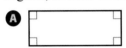

Solution equiangular ■

B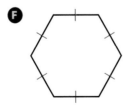

Solution equilateral ■

C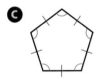

Solution regular ■

D

Solution none of these ■

E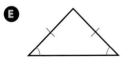

Solution none of these ■

F

Solution equilateral ■

Example 3   The vertices of a polygon are given. Plot and connect the points in the order given. Determine if the polygon appears to be equiangular, equilateral, regular, or none of these.

A (1, 1), (1, 3), (3, 3), (3, 1).

Solution

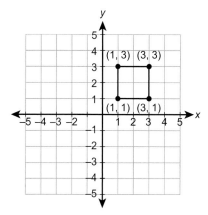

Plot and connect the points.

All 4 sides are congruent.

All the angles are right angles.

The quadrilateral is regular. ■

B (−3, −2), (−3, 1), (3, 1), (3, −2).

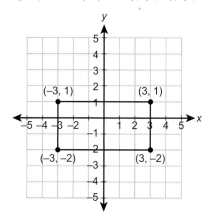

Plot and connect the points.

Both pairs of opposite sides are congruent.

All the angles are right angles.

The quadrilateral is equiangular. ■

Application: Sports

Example 4   The infield of a baseball diamond is bounded by the shape of a regular quadrilateral. At each vertex is a base. The total distance around the infield boundary is 360 feet. What is the distance between each base?

Solution   A figure that is regular is equilateral, so all the sides of the quadrilateral have the same length. Divide the total distance by the number of sides.

$360 \div 4 = 90$

The distance between each pair of consecutive bases is 90 feet. ■

THINK ABOUT IT

A regular quadrilateral is also called a *square*.

Problem Set

Name each polygon.

1.

2.

3.

4.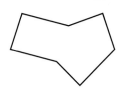

5.

6.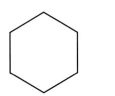

7.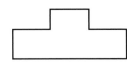

8.

Determine whether each polygon is equiangular, equilateral, regular, or none of these.

9.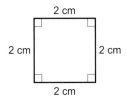

    2 cm

    2 cm   2 cm

    2 cm

10. 2 cm   2 cm

    2 cm   2 cm

11.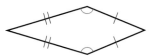

12.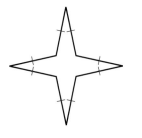

13.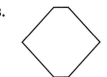

14.

15.

16.

    120° 120°

    120°   120°

    120° 120°

The vertices of a polygon are given. Plot and connect the points in the order given. Determine if the polygon appears to be equiangular, equilateral, regular, or none of these.

17. $(1, 2), (4, 2), (4, 5), (1, 5)$

18. $(1, -2), (-2, -1), (-5, -2), (-2, -3)$

19. $(6, -1), (4, -3), (6, -6)$

20. $(-7, 6), (-5, 6), (-2, 3), (-7, 3)$

Write answers in complete sentences.

21. Why is a circle not a polygon?

22. Which polygon best represents a yield sign?

23. If a polygon has n sides, how many vertices does it have?

24. What is the measure of each angle of a regular octagon if the sum of the measures of all the angles is $1080°$?

25. The sum of the measures of the angles of a regular polygon is $3240°$. One of the angles measures $162°$. Name the polygon.

26. What is the distance around a regular heptagon if each side is 112 inches long?

27. A clock is shaped like a regular 12-gon. The sum of all the angle measures is $1800°$. What is the measure of each angle?

*28. Challenge The sum of the measures of the angles of a quadrilateral is $360°$. Two of the angles are right angles. One of the remaining two angles is twice the measure of the other. What is the measure of the smallest angle in the quadrilateral? What is the measure of the largest angle?

*29. Challenge Connecting one vertex to the other vertices in a polygon forms triangles. The example below shows how to form 3 nonoverlapping triangles inside a pentagon.

How many nonoverlapping triangles are formed by connecting one vertex to the other nonadjacent vertices of a regular hexagon? a regular octagon? a regular n-gon?

Perimeter

The sides of a polygon form the boundary of the figure.

DEFINITION

Perimeter is the distance around a figure.

The perimeter P of a polygon is the sum of the lengths of all its sides. When all sides of a polygon are congruent, as with a regular polygon, you can multiply the length of one side by the number of sides to find the polygon's perimeter.

Finding the Perimeter of a Regular n-gon

A regular polygon has sides that are the same length, so you can use multiplication to find its perimeter.

PERIMETER OF A REGULAR n-GON

The perimeter of a regular polygon with n sides each with length s is

$$P = ns.$$

Example 1

A Each side of a regular hexagon is 12 cm long. Find the perimeter of the hexagon.

Solution A hexagon has 6 sides.

$P = ns$ Write the formula.

$\ = 6 \cdot 12$ Substitute 6 for n and 12 for s.

$\ = 72$ Multiply.

The perimeter is 72 cm. ∎

B Find the perimeter of an equilateral triangle if a side length is 3.5 feet.

Solution A triangle has 3 sides.

$P = ns$ Write the formula.

$\quad = 3 \cdot 3.5$ Substitute 3 for n and 3.5 for s.

$\quad = 10.5$ Multiply.

The perimeter is 10.5 feet. ∎

Finding the Perimeter of a Rectangle

The opposite sides of a rectangle are congruent.

PERIMETER OF A RECTANGLE

The perimeter of a rectangle with width w and length l is

$$P = 2l + 2w.$$

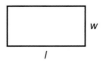

Example 2 Find the perimeter of the rectangle.

6 mm

14 mm

Solution Use the formula.

$P = 2l + 2w$ Write the formula.

$\quad = 2 \cdot 14 + 2 \cdot 6$ Substitute 14 for l and 6 for w.

$\quad = 28 + 12$ Multiply.

$\quad = 40$ Add.

The perimeter is 40 millimeters. ∎

Finding Missing Lengths

You can use perimeter to find a missing side length.

Example 3

A The perimeter of the rectangle is 68 km. The length of the rectangle is 23 km. What is the width of the rectangle?

23 km

(continued)

Solution Substitute the known information into $P = 2l + 2w$. Then solve for w.

$P = 2l + 2w$ Write the formula.

$68 = 2 \cdot 23 + 2w$ Substitute 68 for P and 23 for l.

$68 = 46 + 2w$ Multiply.

$22 = 2w$ Subtract 46 from both sides.

$11 = w$ Divide both sides by 2.

The width is 11 kilometers.

Check $P = 2l + 2w = 2 \cdot 23 + 2 \cdot 11 = 46 + 22 = 68.$ ∎

B The perimeter of a square is 36 meters. What is the length of each side of the square?

Solution A square is a regular quadrilateral. It has 4 congruent sides. Substitute the known information into $P = 4s$ and solve for s.

$P = 4s$ Write the formula.

$36 = 4s$ Substitute 36 for P.

$9 = s$ Divide both sides by 4.

Each side has a length of 9 meters. ∎

Finding Perimeters of Combination Figures

When you are finding the perimeter of a combination figure, the perimeter is the distance around the outside of the figure and does not include any interior segments.

Example 4 Find the perimeter of each figure.

 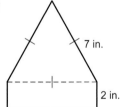

7 in.

2 in.

Solution The tick marks indicate that the length of the rectangle is equal to the side length of the triangle.

Find the sum of the 5 sides around the figure.

$P = 7 + 7 + 2 + 7 + 2$

   $= 25$

The perimeter is 25 inches. ∎

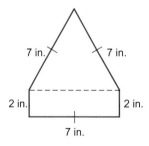

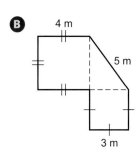

B

4 m

5 m

3 m

Solution Three sides of each square and one side of the triangle form the perimeter.

$P = 3 \cdot 3 + 3 \cdot 4 + 5$

$\quad = 9 + 12 + 5$

$\quad = 26$

The perimeter is 26 meters. ∎

Application: Land Usage

Example 5 Isaac is looking at a map that shows the boundaries of a city park in the shape of a quadrilateral. The lengths of three of the sides are 86 meters, 113 meters, and 94 meters. The length of the remaining side is smudged. Isaac calls the park's office and learns that the entire boundary of the park is 515 meters long. Find the length of the fourth side.

Solution Write and solve an equation.

$86 + 113 + 94 + s = 515$	The sum of the four side lengths equals the perimeter.
$293 + s = 515$	Simplify on the left.
$s = 222$	Subtract 293 from both sides.

The fourth side has a length of 222 meters. ∎

Problem Set

1. Each side of a regular decagon is 15 centimeters long. Find the perimeter of the decagon.

2. Each side of a regular pentagon is 24 inches long. Find the perimeter of the pentagon.

3. Find the perimeter of a square if a side length is 7 meters.

4. Find the perimeter of regular heptagon if a side length is $2\frac{1}{2}$ millimeters.

Find the perimeter of each figure.

5.
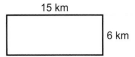
15 km
6 km

6.

1.6 mm

7.

17 cm

8.
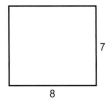
43 in.

9.

7
8

10.
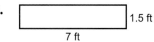
1.5 ft
7 ft

11.
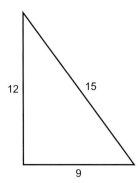
12   15
9

12.
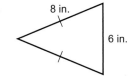
$\frac{1}{2}$ m
$3\frac{1}{2}$ m

13.

1 ft
1 ft

14.
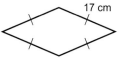
8 in.
6 in.

For problems 15–20, answer each question.

15. The perimeter of the rectangle is 42 units. What is the width of the rectangle?

16

16. The perimeter of the figure is 19.2 meters. What is the length of each side of the figure?

17. The perimeter of the triangle is 51 centimeters. What is the value of x?

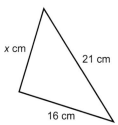
x cm
21 cm
16 cm

18. The perimeter of a square is 48 yards. What is the length of each side of the square?

19. Find the length of a rectangle if its perimeter is 20 units and its width is 3 units.

20. The perimeter of a regular decagon is 161 centimeters. Find the length of each side of the decagon.

Find the perimeter of each figure.

21.

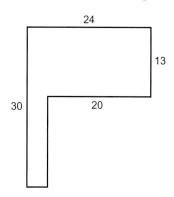

22.

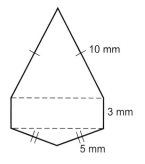

23.

24.

Write answers in complete sentences.

25. A farmer wants to build a fence around a grazing meadow. The meadow is shaped like a rectangle and is 110 meters long and 72 meters wide. How much fencing material must the farmer buy?

26. Kara glued 72 inches of yarn around a photo. What is the width of the photo if the length is 20 inches?

27. A sandbox is shaped like a regular hexagon with a side length of 8.5 meters. How far will a child walk if he walks along the entire border of the sandbox three times?

28. Find the perimeter of a rectangle whose vertices are located at $(-2, 5)$, $(1, 5)$, $(1, -3)$, and $(-2, -3)$.

*__29.__ **Challenge** Find the perimeter of a rectangle that has a width of 18 inches and a length of 2 feet.

*__30.__ **Challenge** The length of a rectangle is twice its width. Find the width if the perimeter is 66 centimeters.

Areas of Rectangles and Triangles

Every closed figure has an interior.

The interior of the rectangle is the space enclosed by the sides of the rectangle. The interior of this rectangle is shaded.

DEFINITION

The **area** of a figure is the number of square units in the interior of the figure.

THINK ABOUT IT

Area is expressed using square units, such as ft² (square feet). When no units are provided, we use "square units."

This rectangle has an area of 32 square units. Notice that 32 is the product of the number of rows, 4, and number of columns, 8.

Finding the Area of a Rectangle

AREA OF A RECTANGLE

The area of a rectangle with length *l* and width *w* is

$$A = lw.$$

Example 1 Find the area of the rectangle.

60 mm

11 mm

Solution Use the formula. The calculation may be performed with or without the units.

Method 1

$A = lw$

$\quad = 60 \cdot 11$ Substitute 60 for *l* and 11 for *w*.

$\quad = 660$ Multiply.

Method 2

$A = lw$

$\quad = (60 \text{ mm}) \cdot (11 \text{ mm})$

$\quad = 60 \cdot 11 \cdot \text{mm} \cdot \text{mm}$

$\quad = 660 \text{ mm}^2$

TIP

We generally use the first method because it is simpler.

The area is 660 square millimeters. ∎

Finding the Area of a Triangle

A triangle is half a rectangle, so the formula for the area of a triangle is half the formula for the rectangle.

The area of a triangle with base b and height h is

$$A = \frac{1}{2}bh.$$

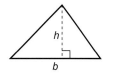

The base of a triangle always forms a right angle with the height of the triangle.

For acute triangles, the height is always shown inside the triangle. For obtuse triangles, it can be located in the exterior of the triangle. In a right triangle, the height can be one of the sides of the triangle.

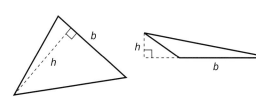

TIP

Any side can be used as the base. The height will change accordingly.

Example 2 Find the area of the triangle.

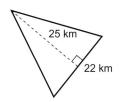

25 km
22 km

Solution Use the formula.

$A = \frac{1}{2}bh$

$\quad = \frac{1}{2} \cdot 22 \cdot 25 \qquad$ Substitute 22 for b and 25 for h.

$\quad = 11 \cdot 25 \qquad\qquad$ Multiply.

$\quad = 275 \qquad\qquad\quad$ Multiply.

The area is 275 square kilometers. ∎

TIP

The area can also be written as 275 km².

Finding Missing Lengths

Example 3

A The area of the triangle is 54 square centimeters. What is the height of the triangle?

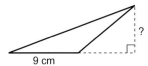

9 cm

Solution Substitute the known information into $A = \frac{1}{2}bh$. Solve for h.

$A = \frac{1}{2}bh$	Write the formula.
$54 = \frac{1}{2} \cdot 9 \cdot h$	Substitute 54 for A and 9 for b.
$54 = 4.5h$	Simplify.
$12 = h$	Divide both sides by 4.5.

The height is 12 centimeters. ∎

B The area of a rectangle is 231 square inches. What is the length of the rectangle if the width is 42 inches?

Solution Substitute the known information into $A = lw$. Solve for l.

$A = lw$	Write the formula.
$231 = l \cdot 42$	Substitute 231 for A and 42 for w.
$5.5 = l$	Divide both sides by 42.

The length is 5.5 inches. ∎

Finding Areas of Combination Figures

Example 4 Find the area of the figure.

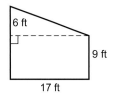

6 ft

9 ft

17 ft

Solution Add the area of the triangle to the area of the rectangle. The base of the right triangle is the length of the rectangle, 17 ft.

$A = \frac{1}{2}bh + lw$	Use the formulas for areas of a triangle and a rectangle.
$= \frac{1}{2} \cdot 17 \cdot 6 + 17 \cdot 9$	Substitute 17 for b and l, 6 for h, and 9 for w.
$= 51 + 153$	Multiply.
$= 204$	Add.

The area is 204 square feet. ∎

Finding the Difference of Areas

Example 5 Find the area of the shaded region.

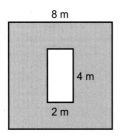

8 m

4 m

2 m

Solution Subtract the area of the rectangle from the area of the square.

$A = s^2 - lw$ Use the formulas for area of a square and area of a rectangle.

$= 8^2 - 2 \cdot 4$ Substitute 8 for s, 2 for l, and 4 for w.

$= 64 - 8$ Simplify.

$= 56$ Subtract.

The area of the shaded region is 56 square meters. ■

Problem Set

Find the area of each figure.

1.

18 m

8 m

2.

7 yd

8 yd

3.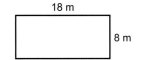

1.2 m

9 m

4.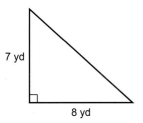

16 mm

13 mm

5.

18 cm

23 cm

6.

1 km

1 km

7.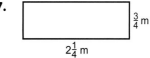

$\frac{3}{4}$ m

$2\frac{1}{4}$ m

8.

2

21

9.

$6\frac{1}{2}$ in.

4 in.

10.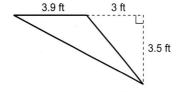

3.9 ft

3 ft

3.5 ft

Answer each question.

11. The area of the rectangle is 114 square units. What is the width of the rectangle?

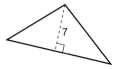

19

12. The area of the triangle is 52.5 square units. What is the base of the triangle?

7

13. The area of the triangle is 384 square inches. What is the height of the triangle?

40 in.

32 in.

14. What is the length of a rectangle if its width is 7 meters and its area is 63 square meters?

15. What is the height of a triangle if its area is 192 square feet and its base is 16 feet?

16. The area of a square is 9 square meters. What is the length of each side of the square?

17. The area of a square is 49 square meters. What is the perimeter of the square?

Find the area of each figure.

18.

15

7

18   12

19.

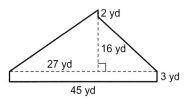

2 yd

16 yd

27 yd

3 yd

45 yd

20.

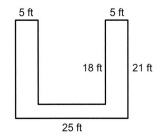

5 ft   5 ft

18 ft   21 ft

25 ft

21.

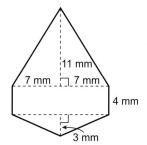

11 mm

7 mm   7 mm

4 mm

3 mm

22.

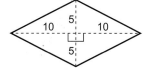

5

10   10

5

23.

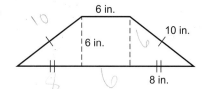

6 in.

10 in.

6 in.

8 in.

Find the area of the shaded region.

24.

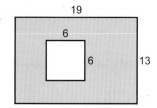

25.

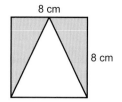

Write answers in complete sentences.

26. A basketball court is 94 feet long and 50 feet wide. What is the area of the basketball court?

27. Mr. Nunez has a back yard that is shaped like a right triangle with a base of 84 meters and a height of 60 meters. How much will it cost him to fertilize the yard if the cost is 3 cents per square meter?

*28. **Challenge** Show that the area of the triangle is the same regardless of which side is used as the base.

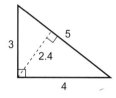

*29. **Challenge** Tell how the formula for the area of a triangle is related to the formula for the area of a rectangle.

*30. **Challenge** Find the area of a triangle whose length is 12 centimeters and whose width is 55 millimeters.

Special Quadrilaterals

A quadrilateral can have zero pairs, one pair, or two pairs of parallel sides.

TIP

Arrows are used to indicate parallel lines and segments.

DEFINITION

A **trapezoid** is a quadrilateral with exactly one pair of parallel sides.

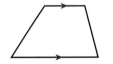

DEFINITION

A **parallelogram** is a quadrilateral with two pairs of parallel sides.

Parallelograms are further classified by their side and angle measures.

DEFINITION

A **rectangle** is a quadrilateral with four right angles.

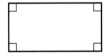

DEFINITION

A **rhombus** is a quadrilateral with four congruent sides.

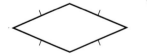

TIP

The plural of rhombus is rhombi.

A **square** is a quadrilateral with four congruent sides and four right angles.

All rectangles, rhombi, and squares are also parallelograms.

Classifying Quadrilaterals

Example 1 For each figure, write all names that apply: trapezoid, parallelogram, rectangle, rhombus, and square.

Solution Both pairs of sides are parallel, so the figure is a parallelogram. Because all the angles are right angles, it is also a rectangle. ■

Solution Only one pair of sides is parallel. The figure is a trapezoid. ■

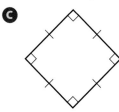

Solution All four angles are right angles and all four sides are congruent. The figure is a parallelogram, rectangle, rhombus, and square. ■

Classifiying Quadrilaterals

A chart can help you see how the special quadrilaterals are related.

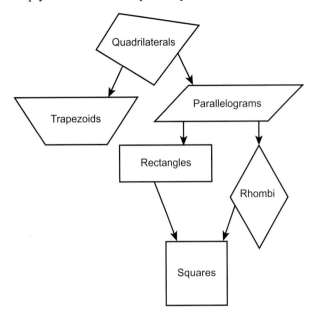

THINK ABOUT IT

A square can be defined as a rectangle with four congruent sides, or as a rhombus with four right angles.

A figure always belongs to a classification above it in the chart, provided they are connected. For example, all parallelograms are quadrilaterals.

A figure will sometimes belong to a classification below it, provided they are connected. For example, a quadrilateral is sometimes a parallelogram.

Figures that are not connected will never belong to the same classification. For example, a parallelogram is never a trapezoid.

Example 2   Tell if each statement is *always, sometimes,* or *never* true.

A A rectangle is a square.

Solution   Some rectangles are squares, but not all are. Only rectangles with all sides congruent are squares. The statement is *sometimes* true. ■

B A square is a rectangle.

Solution   Every square is a rectangle because all squares have four right angles. The statement is *always* true. ■

C A square is a parallelogram.

Solution   A square is always a parallelogram. Both pairs of sides are always parallel, so the statement is *always* true. ■

D A rhombus is a trapezoid.

Solution   A rhombus always has two pairs of parallel sides, while a trapezoid always has exactly one pair of parallel sides. The statement is *never* true. ■

Using Properties of Parallelograms

Parallelograms have properties that other quadrilaterals do not have.

The opposite sides of a parallelogram are congruent. The opposite angles of a parallelogram are congruent.

TIP

The opposite sides are the parallel sides. The opposite angles do not have a common side.

Example 3

A *AWRT* is a parallelogram. Which sides are congruent? Which angles are congruent?

Solution Opposite sides are congruent: $\overline{AT} \cong \overline{WR}$ and $\overline{WA} \cong \overline{RT}$.

Opposite angles are congruent: $\angle A \cong \angle R$ and $\angle W \cong \angle T$. ■

B Find the values of x and y in the parallelogram.

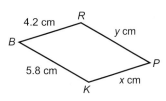

Solution Opposite sides of a parallelogram are congruent.

$\overline{BR} \cong \overline{KP}$, so $x = 4.2$.

$\overline{BK} \cong \overline{RP}$, so $y = 5.8$. ■

Identifying Quadrilaterals on a Coordinate Grid

Example 4 The set of points $(0, 4)$, $(3, 3)$, $(0, 2)$, $(-3, 3)$ identifies the vertices of a quadrilateral. Use the most specific description to tell which figure the points form.

Solution

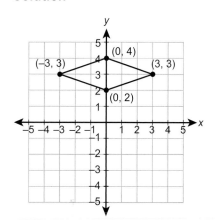

Plot and connect the points.

All 4 sides are congruent.

The quadrilateral is a rhombus. ■

TIP

You can measure to see that the sides have the same length.

Problem Set

For each figure, write all the names that apply: trapezoid, parallelogram, rectangle, rhombus, and square.

1.

2.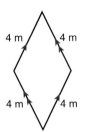

3.

4.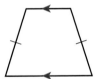

5.

6.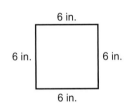

7.

8.

6 in.

6 in.   6 in.

6 in.

Tell if each statement is *always*, *sometimes*, or *never* true.

9. A square is a rhombus.

10. A rectangle is a trapezoid.

11. A quadrilateral is a square.

12. A square is a quadrilateral.

13. A rectangle is a rhombus.

14. A parallelogram is a square.

15. A rhombus is a parallelogram.

Draw each figure.

16. A rectangle that is a rhombus.

17. A rectangle that is not a rhombus.

18. A parallelogram that is not a rectangle.

19. A parallelogram that is not a rhombus.

20. A trapezoid with two right angles.

Each set of points identifies the vertices of a quadrilateral. Use the most specific description to tell which figure each set of points forms.

21. $(-4, 2), (1, 2), (1, -2), (-4, 0)$

22. $(4, -4), (5, -4), (5, -5), (4, -5)$

23. $(-6, -4), (-1, -4), (-2, -6), (-7, -6)$

24. $(4, 4), (5, 4), (5, 0), (4, 0)$

25. $(0, 6), (3, 5), (0, 4), (-3, 5)$

Find the values of x and y in each parallelogram.

26.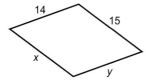

27.

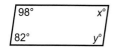

28.

29.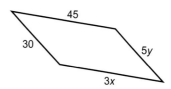

Answer the question.

*30. **Challenge** Use a Venn diagram to illustrate the relationships among the quadrilaterals.

Areas of Special Quadrilaterals

The formulas for the area of a parallelogram and for a trapezoid are similar to the area formula for a rectangle.

Parallelograms and trapezoids have bases and heights. A **base** is defined to be the bottom side of a geometric figure. The **height** is perpendicular to the base. It is the length of the segment that extends from the base to the opposite side.

Finding the Area of a Parallelogram

Every parallelogram has four bases; each side can be a base. The height depends on which side is used as the base. Heights are sometimes shown outside the parallelogram.

THINK ABOUT IT

Any side of a parallelogram can be the base because the parallelogram can be rotated so that any side is on the bottom.

AREA OF A PARALLELOGRAM

The area of a parallelogram with base b and height h is

$$A = bh.$$

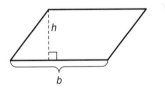

THINK ABOUT IT

When a parallelogram is a rectangle, the height is a side of the parallelogram and the terms length and width are used instead of base and height.

Example 1 Find the area of the parallelogram.

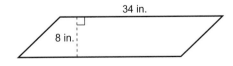

Solution

$$\begin{aligned} A &= bh & &\text{Write the formula.} \\ &= 34 \cdot 8 & &\text{Substitute 34 for } b \text{ and 8 for } h. \\ &= 272 & &\text{Multiply.} \end{aligned}$$

The area is 272 square inches. ■

Finding the Area of a Trapezoid

A trapezoid has two bases: b_1 and b_2. The parallel sides are always the bases. The height is the length of a segment that joins the bases and forms right angles with them.

The area of a trapezoid with bases b_1 and b_2 and height h is

$$A = \frac{1}{2}h(b_1 + b_2).$$

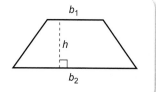

Example 2   Find the area of the trapezoid.

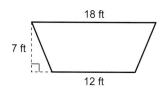

18 ft

7 ft

12 ft

Solution $A = \frac{1}{2}h(b_1 + b_2)$ Write the formula.

$= \frac{1}{2} \cdot 7 \cdot (18 + 12)$ Substitute 18 for b_1, 12 for b_2 and 7 for h.

$= \frac{1}{2} \cdot 7 \cdot 30$ Simplify inside the parentheses.

$= 105$ Multiply.

The area is 105 square feet.   ■

Finding Missing Lengths

With a known area and some algebra, you can find missing side lengths.

Example 3

A The area of a parallelogram is 675 square centimeters. What is the height of the parallelogram if its base is 45 centimeters long?

Solution   Substitute the known information into $A = bh$. Solve for h.

$A = bh$ Write the formula.

$675 = 45 \cdot h$ Substitute 675 for A and 45 for b.

$15 = h$ Divide both sides by 45.

The height is 15 centimeters.   ■

(continued)

B The area of the trapezoid is 54 meters. Find the unknown base length.

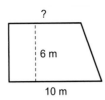

?

6 m

10 m

Solution $A = \frac{1}{2}h(b_1 + b_2)$ Write the formula.

$54 = \frac{1}{2} \cdot 6 \cdot (b_1 + 10)$ Substitute 54 for A, 6 for h, and 10 for one of the bases.

$54 = 3 \cdot (b_1 + 10)$ Multiply on the right.

$18 = b_1 + 10$ Divide both sides by 3.

$8 = b_1$ Subtract 10 from both sides.

The length of the unknown base is 8 meters.

Check $A = \frac{1}{2}h(b_1 + b_2) = \frac{1}{2} \cdot 6 \cdot (8 + 10) = 3 \cdot 18 = 54$ ∎

Application: Painting

Example 4   Each wall of a four-sided garden shed is 10 feet long and 8 feet high and has one rhombus-shaped window. The windows are congruent and each has a base of 2 feet and a height of 1.5 feet. The gardener wants to paint the inside of the walls. A can of the paint covers about 350 square feet per gallon. How many cans of paint will she need for two coats?

Solution   Find the area to be painted.

First, find the area that is covered with one coat.

$A = 4lw - 4bh$ Subtract the area of the windows from the area of the walls.

$= 4 \cdot 10 \cdot 8 - 4 \cdot 2 \cdot 1.5$ Substitute values for the variables.

$= 320 - 12$ Multiply.

$= 308$ Subtract.

She has to cover 308 square feet for one coat.

Next, double that amount to find the area covered in two coats.

$2 \times 308 = 616$ Multiply area of one coat by 2.

Divide by 350 to find how many cans of paint she needs.

$616 \div 350 = 1.76$ Divide by 350.

The gardener needs 2 cans of paint. ∎

> **THINK ABOUT IT**
>
> You can also use $A = 4(lw - bh)$.

Problem Set

Find the area of each figure.

1.

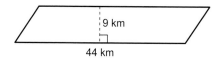

9 km
44 km

2.

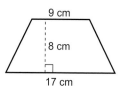

9 cm
8 cm
17 cm

3.

18
50
20

4.

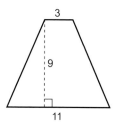

3
9
11

5.

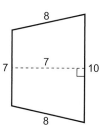

8
7
7
10
8

6.

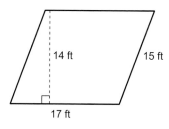

14 ft
15 ft
17 ft

7.

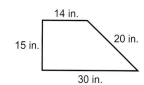

14 in.
15 in.
20 in.
30 in.

8.

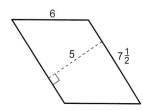

6
5
$7\frac{1}{2}$

9.

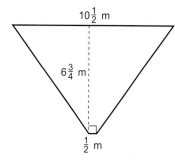

$10\frac{1}{2}$ m
$6\frac{3}{4}$ m
$\frac{1}{2}$ m

10.

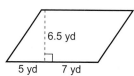

6.5 yd
5 yd   7 yd

11.

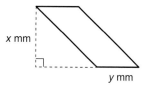

x mm
y mm

12.

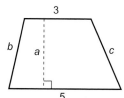

3
b   a   c
5

Answer each question.

13. The area of the parallelogram is 126 square units. What is the height of the parallelogram?

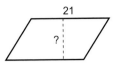

14. The area of the trapezoid is 56 square units. What is the height of the trapezoid?

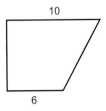

15. The area of the trapezoid is 114 square yards. Find the unknown base length.

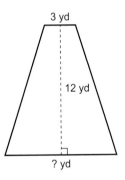

16. How long is the base of a parallelogram if its area is 100 square meters and its height is 5 meters?

17. What is the height of a parallelogram whose base length is 16 meters and whose area is 136 square meters?

18. What is the height of a trapezoid whose bases have lengths of 9 centimeters and 12 centimeters and whose area is 52.5 square centimeters?

19. The area of a trapezoid is 65 square feet. The height is 10 feet and the length of one of the bases is $9\frac{1}{2}$ feet. Find the length of the other base.

Find the area of each figure.

20.

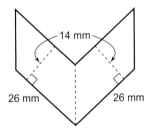

21.

22.

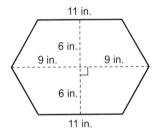

23.

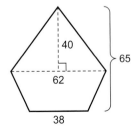

Answer each question.

24. Find the area of a parallelogram whose vertices are located at $(-1, 1)$, $(5, 1)$, $(3, -2)$, and $(-3, -2)$.

25. Find the area of a trapezoid whose vertices are located at $(0, 4)$, $(9, 4)$, $(5, 2)$, and $(2, 2)$.

26. Mia wants to apply two coats of paint to her deck. Her deck is shaped like a trapezoid with base lengths of 14 meters and 20 meters. The perpendicular distance between the bases measures 16 meters. If paint costs $22 per gallon and one gallon of paint covers about 350 square meters, how much will it cost Mia to paint her deck?

27. Joey will both mow and rake a yard for a fee of $0.05/square meter. How much will Joey charge to mow and rake a front yard that is shaped like a trapezoid with bases of 30 meters and 35 meters and with a height of 48 meters?

28. Lee is making a rock garden in the shape of a rhombus. He wants the area of the garden to be exactly 50 square feet. Give two possible sets of dimensions Lee could use.

*29. **Challenge** Find the area of a trapezoid whose base lengths are 1 foot and 2 yards, and whose height is 18 inches.

*30. **Challenge** Use diagrams to show why a rectangle with a length of 12 and a width of 6 has the same area as a parallelogram with a base length of 12 and a height of 6.

Circumference

The distance around a polygon is called its perimeter while the distance around a circle is called its circumference.

> **DEFINITION**
>
> The **circumference** of a circle is the distance around the circle.

Finding the Circumference of a Circle

Since ancient times, people have known that the ratio of the circumference to the diameter of any circle is a constant that is just a bit more than 3. This constant is called π (pi), which is a decimal number that never repeats and never ends. In calculations, it is often approximated as 3.14.

> **CIRCUMFERENCE OF A CIRCLE**
>
> The circumference of a circle with diameter d and radius r is
>
> $$C = \pi d \quad \text{or} \quad C = 2\pi r.$$

> **THINK ABOUT IT**
>
> In a given circle, the diameter is twice the radius, so
> $$C = \pi d = \pi 2r = 2\pi r.$$

Answers that are found by substituting 3.14 for π are estimates and should include *the approximately equal to* ($\approx$) symbol. Answers that use the symbol for π are exact answers.

Example 1 Find the circumference of each circle. Give both exact and approximate answers.

A circle A

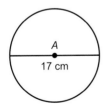

17 cm

Solution Because the diameter is given, use $C = \pi d$.

$C = \pi d$	Write the formula.
$= \pi \cdot 17$	Substitute 17 for d.
$\approx 3.14 \cdot 17$	Substitute 3.14 for π.
≈ 53.4	Multiply.

The circumference is exactly 17π centimeters or about 53.4 centimeters. ■

> **TIP**
>
> When using 3.14 for π, use three digits when writing the circumference.

B circle with radius of 5 meters

Solution Because the radius is given, use $C = 2\pi r$.

$C = 2\pi r$	Write the formula.
$= 2 \cdot \pi \cdot 5$	Substitute 5 for r.
$= 10\pi$	Multiply.
$\approx 10 \cdot 3.14$	Substitute 3.14 for π.
≈ 31.4	Multiply.

The circumference is exactly 10π meters or about 31.4 meters. ∎

> **TIP**
>
> Find the exact answer in terms of π first, and then substitute a value of π to find an approximation.

Finding Missing Lengths

Example 2

A The circumference of a circle is 18π feet. What is the radius?

Solution Substitute the known information into $C = 2\pi r$. Solve for r.

$C = 2\pi r$	Write the formula.
$18\pi = 2 \cdot \pi \cdot r$	Substitute 18π for C.
$18 = 2r$	Divide both sides by π.
$9 = r$	Divide both sides by 2.

The radius is 9 feet. ∎

B The circumference of a circle is 40 yards. What is the diameter?

Solution Substitute the known information into $C = \pi d$. Solve for d.

$C = \pi d$	Write the formula.
$40 = \pi d$	Substitute 40 for C.
$\dfrac{40}{\pi} = d$	Divide both sides by π.
$\dfrac{40}{3.14} \approx d$	Substitute 3.14 for π.
$12.7 \approx d$	Divide both sides by 3.14.

The diameter is about 12.7 yards. ∎

Finding Perimeters of Partial and Combination Figures

A *semicircle* is half a circle. To find the circumference of a semicircle, divide by 2: $C = \dfrac{\pi d}{2}$ or $C = \dfrac{\overset{1}{\cancel{2}}\pi r}{\cancel{2}_1} = \pi r$. A *quarter circle* is one-fourth of a

circle. To find the circumference of a quarter circle, divide by 4: $C = \dfrac{\pi d}{4}$

or $C = \dfrac{\overset{1}{\cancel{2}}\pi r}{\cancel{4}_2} = \dfrac{\pi r}{2}$.

(continued)

Example 3

(A) Find the exact circumference of a semicircle with radius 5 centimeters.

Solution Use the formula $C = \pi r$.

$C = \pi r$ Use the formula for circumference of a semicircle.

$C = \pi \cdot 5$ Substitute 5 for r.

$C = 5\pi$ Simplify.

The exact circumference is 5π centimeters. ■

(B) Find the circumference of a quarter circle with diameter 6 inches. Use 3.14 to approximate π.

Solution Use the formula $C = \dfrac{\pi d}{4}$.

$C = \dfrac{\pi \cdot 6}{4}$ Subtitute 6 for d.

$C = 1.5\pi$ Simplify.

$C \approx 1.5 \cdot 3.14$ Substitute 3.14 for π.

$C \approx 4.71$ Multiply.

The circumference is exactly 1.5π cm or about 4.71 cm. ■

Example 4

(A) The figure is made up of two semicircles and a rectangle. Find the perimeter of the figure.

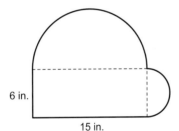

6 in.

15 in.

Solution

$P = \dfrac{\pi d_1}{2} + \dfrac{\pi d_2}{2} + 6 + 15$ Add the circumference of the semicircles to the two sides of the rectangle.

$= \dfrac{\pi \cdot 15}{2} + \dfrac{\pi \cdot 6}{2} + 6 + 15$ The diameters are 15 and 6.

$= 10.5\pi + 21$ Simplify.

$\approx 10.5 \cdot 3.14 + 21$ Substitute 3.14 for π.

≈ 54.0 Simplify.

The perimeter is about 54 inches. ■

B The figure is made up of two congruent squares and a quarter circle. Find the perimeter of the figure to the nearest tenth.

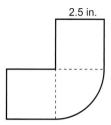

2.5 in.

Solution   The side of each square is the radius of the quarter circle.

$P = 6s + \dfrac{\pi r}{2}$ Add the six sides of the square to the circumference of the quarter circle.

$= 6 \cdot 2.5 + \dfrac{\pi \cdot 2.5}{2}$ Substitute 2.5 for s and r.

$= 15 + 1.25\pi$ Simplify.

$\approx 15 + 1.25 \cdot 3.14$ Substitute 3.14 for π.

$\approx 15 + 3.93$ Multiply.

≈ 18.9 Add.

The perimeter is about 18.9 inches. ∎

Application: Sports

Example 5   A bicycle wheel has a radius of 16 inches. It is rolled on the ground for one complete revolution. How far did the wheel travel?

Solution   The distance traveled equals the circumference of the wheel.

$C = 2\pi r$ Write the formula.

$= 2 \cdot \pi \cdot 16$ Substitute 16 for r.

$= 32\pi$ Multiply.

$\approx 32 \cdot 3.14$ Substitute 3.14 for π.

≈ 100 Multiply.

The wheel traveled about 100 inches. ∎

Problem Set

For problems 1–8, the center of each circle is shown. Find the circumference of each circle. Give both exact and approximate answers.

1.

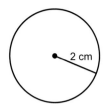

2 cm

2.

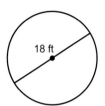

18 ft

3.

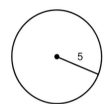

5

4.

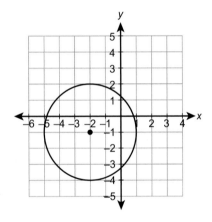

5.

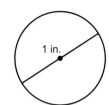

1 in.

6.

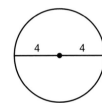

4   4

7.

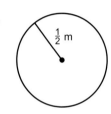

$\frac{1}{2}$ m

8.

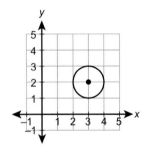

Answer each question.

9. The circumference of a circle is 19π inches. What is the radius of the circle?

10. The circumference of a circle is 76 centimeters. What is the diameter of the circle?

The value of π can be approximated by $\frac{22}{7}$. Estimate the circumference of each circle using $\frac{22}{7}$.

11.

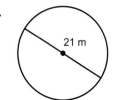

21 m

12.

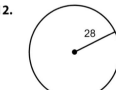

28

Find the perimeter of each figure.

13.

22 cm

14.

3 ft

15.
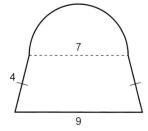
7
4
9

16.
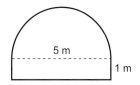
5 m
1 m

17.
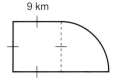
9 km

18.
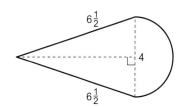
$6\frac{1}{2}$
4
$6\frac{1}{2}$

Answer each question.

19. What is the circumference of a swimming pool if its diameter is 8.5 cm?

20. The bottom of a lamp shade has a circumference of about 60 inches. Estimate the diameter to the nearest tenth.

21. A ring has a diameter of 1.6 cm. Estimate the circumference of the ring.

22. A tire has a radius of 15 inches. How far does it travel in 5 revolutions?

23. Joseph is making a plant holder so that the pot sits partly above and partly below a wooden board. To cut the hole in the board, he needs to know the diameter of the circle, but because a plant is already in the pot, he cannot measure it directly. Instead, he measures how much string can be wrapped around the pot at the desired height. What will be the diameter of the circle he cuts in the board if he used 35 millimeters of string?

24. A pitcher's mound on a baseball field has a diameter of 18 feet. What is its circumference?

25. A gardener has 48 kilometers of fencing material. If she makes a circular garden and uses all her fencing material, what will be the radius of her garden?

26. At the center of a basketball court, the inner circle has a radius of 2 feet and the outer circle has a radius of 6 feet. What is the difference in the circumferences of the circles?

27. Suri's ornament has a diameter of 2.75 inches and Ada's ornament has a diameter of 1.25 inches. How much greater is the circumference of Suri's ornament than Ada's ornament?

*28. Challenge A wheel has a diameter of 14 inches. How many revolutions will it make after rolling 20 feet?

Find the length of the darkened part of each circle.

*29. Challenge.
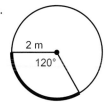
2 m
120°

*30. Challenge.
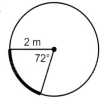
2 m
72°

Areas of Circles

In addition to its use in the formula for circumference, π can help you calculate the area of a circle.

Finding the Area of a Circle

AREA OF A CIRCLE

The area of a circle with radius r is

$$A = \pi r^2.$$

> **TIP**
>
> r^2 is read "r squared" and means $r \cdot r$.

Example 1 Find the area of each circle. Give both exact and approximate answers.

Ⓐ circle C

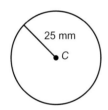

25 mm

C

Solution Use the formula with $r = 25$.

$A = \pi r^2$	Write the formula.
$\quad = \pi \cdot 25^2$	Substitute 25 for r.
$\quad = 625\pi$	$25^2 = 25 \cdot 25 = 625$
$\quad \approx 625 \cdot 3.14$	Substitute 3.14 for π.
$\quad \approx 1960$	Multiply.

> **TIP**
>
> In the area formula, the order of operations tells you that only the radius is squared. Do not square π.

The area is exactly 625π square millimeters or about 1960 square millimeters. ■

Ⓑ circle D

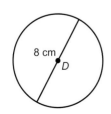

8 cm

D

Solution The diameter is given. Divide to find the radius: $8 \div 2 = 4$.

$A = \pi r^2$ Write the formula.

$= \pi \cdot 4^2$ Substitute 4 for r.

$= 16\pi$ Simplify.

$\approx 16 \cdot 3.14$ Substitute 3.14 for π.

≈ 50.2 Multiply.

The area is exactly 16π square centimeters or about 50.2 square centimeters. ■

Finding Missing Lengths

Example 2

Ⓐ The area of a circle is 100π square meters. What is the radius?

Solution Substitute the known information into $A = \pi r^2$. Solve for r.

$A = \pi r^2$ Write the formula.

$100\pi = \pi r^2$ Substitute 100π for A.

$100 = r^2$ Divide both sides by π.

$10 = r$ *Think:* What number times itself is 100?

The radius is 10 meters. ■

Ⓑ The area of a circle is 50 square inches. What is the diameter?

Solution After solving for r, multiply by 2 to find d.

$A = \pi r^2$ Write the formula.

$50 = \pi \cdot r^2$ Substitute 50 for A.

$\dfrac{50}{\pi} = r^2$ Divide both sides by π.

$\dfrac{50}{3.14} \approx r^2$ Substitute 3.14 for π.

$15.9 \approx r^2$ Divide.

$4 \approx r$ *Think:* $16 = 4 \cdot 4$.

The diameter is about 8 inches. ■

Finding Areas of Partial and Combination Figures

To find the area of a semicircle, divide by 2: $A = \dfrac{\pi r^2}{2}$. To find the area of a quarter circle, divide by 4: $A = \dfrac{\pi r^2}{4}$.

(continued)

Example 3 The radius of the semicircle and height of the triangle are shown. Find the area of the figure.

Solution

$$A = \frac{\pi r^2}{2} + \frac{1}{2}bh \qquad \text{Add the area of the semicircle to the area of the triangle.}$$

$$= \frac{\pi \cdot 11^2}{2} + \frac{1}{2} \cdot 22 \cdot 20 \qquad \text{The base of the triangle is } 11 + 11 = 22.$$

$$= 60.5\pi + 220 \qquad \text{Simplify.}$$

$$\approx 60.5 \cdot 3.14 + 220 \qquad \text{Substitute 3.14 for } \pi.$$

$$\approx 190 + 220 \qquad \text{Multiply.}$$

$$\approx 410 \qquad \text{Add.}$$

The area is about 410 square units. ∎

Application: Food

Example 4 A small pizza has a diameter of 10 inches, a medium pizza has a diameter of 13 inches, and a large pizza has a diameter of 16 inches.

Ⓐ Estimate the difference in the areas of a medium and large pizza.

Solution Find the area of each pizza.

Medium: $A = \pi r^2$

$\qquad = \pi \cdot 6.5^2$

$\qquad = \pi \cdot 42.25$

$\qquad \approx 3.14 \cdot 42.25$

$\qquad \approx 133$

Large: $A = \pi r^2$

$\qquad = \pi \cdot 8^2$

$\qquad = \pi \cdot 64$

$\qquad \approx 3.14 \cdot 64$

$\qquad \approx 201$

> **REMEMBER**
>
> Divide each diameter by 2 to find each radius.

Subtract to find the difference: $201 - 133 = 68$.

The difference is about 68 square inches. ∎

Ⓑ Angie ate one-fourth of a small pizza. About how many square inches of pizza did she eat?

Solution Find the area of a quarter circle with a radius of 5 inches.

$$A = \frac{\pi r^2}{4} \qquad \text{Write the formula.}$$

$$= \frac{\pi \cdot 5^2}{4} \qquad \text{Substitute 5 for } r.$$

$$= 6.25\pi \qquad \text{Simplify.}$$

$$\approx 6.25 \cdot 3.14 \qquad \text{Substitute 3.14 for } \pi.$$

$$\approx 19.6 \qquad \text{Multiply.}$$

Angie ate about 19.6 square inches of pizza. ∎

C A pizza with a 14-inch diameter costs $12.95 while a 12-inch pizza costs $10.95. Which pizza is a better deal?

Solution Find the unit price of each pizza by dividing the cost of the pizza by the area.

14 inch diameter

$$A = \pi r^2$$
$$= \pi \cdot 7^2$$
$$\approx 3.14 \cdot 7^2$$
$$\approx 154$$

Unit price $\approx \dfrac{\$12.95}{154 \text{ in}^2}$

$$\approx \$0.084 \text{ per square inch}$$

12 inch diameter

$$A = \pi r^2$$
$$= \pi \cdot 6^2$$
$$\approx 3.14 \cdot 6^2$$
$$\approx 113$$

Unit price $\approx \dfrac{\$10.95}{113 \text{ in}^2}$

$$\approx \$0.097 \text{ per square inch}$$

The 14-inch pizza is the better deal. ■

Finding Areas by Subtraction

Example 5 Find the area of the shaded region.

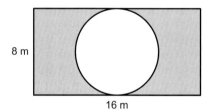

8 m

16 m

Solution

$A = lw - \pi r^2$	Subtract the area of the circle from the area of the rectangle.
$= 16 \cdot 8 - \pi \cdot 4^2$	Substitute 16 for l, 8 for w, and 4 for r.
$= 128 - 16\pi$	Simplify.
$\approx 128 - 16 \cdot 3.14$	Substitute 3.14 for π.
$\approx 128 - 50.2$	Multiply.
≈ 77.8	Subtract.

The area of the shaded region is about 77.8 square feet. ■

Problem Set

The center of each circle is shown. Find the area of each circle. Give both exact and approximate answers.

1.

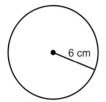
6 cm

2.

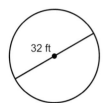
32 ft

3.

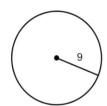
9

4.

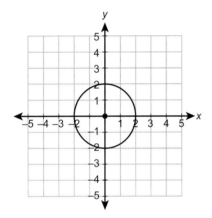

5.

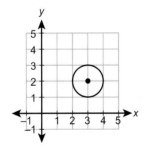

6.

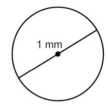
1 mm

7.

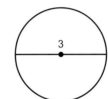
3

8.

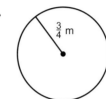
$\frac{3}{4}$ m

9.

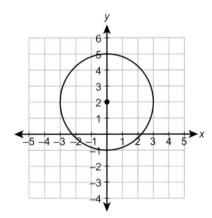

10.

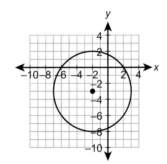

Answer each question.

11. The area of a circle is 16π square meters. What is the radius of the circle?

12. The area of a circle is 36π square feet. What is the diameter of the circle?

13. The area of a circle is 12.5 square centimeters. What is the diameter of the circle?

14. The area of a circle is 154 square millimeters. What is the radius of the circle?

Find the area of each figure.

15.

22 in.

16.

3 ft

17.

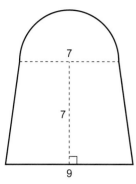

7

7

9

18.

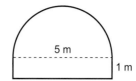

5 m

1 m

19.

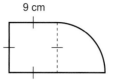

9 cm

20.

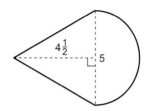

$4\frac{1}{2}$

5

Find the area of the shaded region.

21.

16 ft

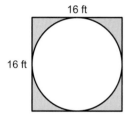

16 ft

22.

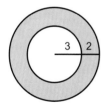

3   2

23.

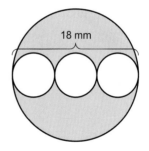

14 km

24.

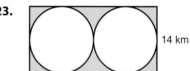

18 mm

Answer each question.

25. What is the area of a swimming pool if its diameter is 12 meters?

26. A pizza with a 14-inch diameter costs $12.99 while a 12-inch pizza costs $9.99. Which pizza is a better deal?

27. An 18-inch pizza costs $22.99 while a 16-inch pizza costs $18.99. Which pizza is a better deal?

28. The center circle on a soccer field has an area of 100π square meters. Find the circumference of the center circle.

29. Which area is greater: a circle with a diameter of 10 kilometers or a square with a side length of 10 kilometers?

30. Ms. Brady's old waffle maker made circular waffles with a diameter of 17 centimeters. Her new waffle maker makes rectangular waffles that are 22 centimeters long and 13 centimeters wide. Which makes waffles with a greater area? How much greater?

*31. **Challenge** Explain how you would find the area of a figure with this shape.

UNIT 11   Square Roots and Right Triangles

El Castillo at Chichen Itza is an ancient pyramid on the Yucatan peninsula in Mexico. The Mayans who built it probably used an understanding of the idea behind the Pythagorean theorem to create square bases for each tier.

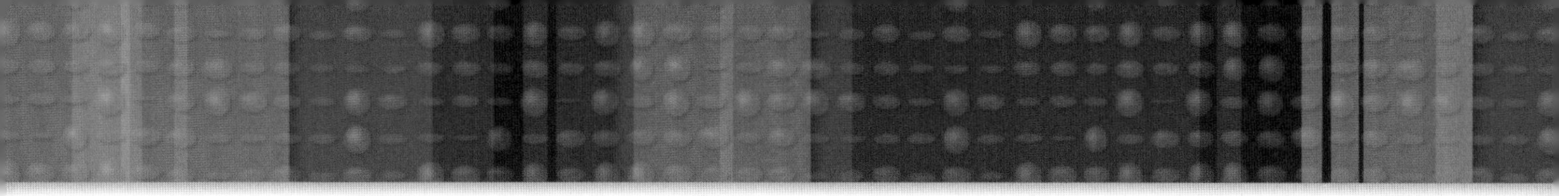

Since ancient times, people have used right triangles to survey land and build structures. Even before Pythagoras was born, the relationship between the side lengths of a right triangle has been essential to anyone building just about any structure, including pyramids, houses, skyscrapers, and bridges.

Big Ideas

▶ A number is any entity that obeys the laws of arithmetic; all numbers obey the laws of arithmetic. The laws of arithmetic can be used to simplify algebraic expressions.

▶ Many problems can be solved by using the properties of angles, triangles, and circles.

Unit Topics

▶ Rational Square Roots

▶ Irrational Square Roots

▶ The Pythagorean Theorem

▶ The Distance Formula

▶ Special Types of Triangles

▶ Trigonometric Ratios

Rational Square Roots

Taking a square root is the inverse operation of squaring a number.

A **square root** is a factor of a number that when multiplied by itself results in the number. If a square root of a number is a rational number, it is a **rational square root**.

Finding Positive and Negative Square Roots

The following table lists the squares for the whole numbers 1 through 15 and their opposites. You can use the table to find the positive and negative square roots of any number n^2 by looking at the values in the corresponding n column.

n	n^2		n	n^2		n	n^2
± 1	1		± 6	36		± 11	121
± 2	4		± 7	49		± 12	144
± 3	9		± 8	64		± 13	169
± 4	16		± 9	81		± 14	196
± 5	25		± 10	100		± 15	225

> **REMEMBER**
>
> A rational number is any number that can be expressed as a ratio $\left(\frac{a}{b}\right)$, where a and b are integers and $b \neq 0$.

> **TIP**
>
> The **plus-minus sign** ($\pm$) is convenient shorthand for a quantity with two possible values. For example, ± 7 means $+7$ or -7.

The square roots of 25 are 5 and -5 because $5 \cdot 5 = 5^2 = 25$ and $(-5) \cdot (-5) = (-5)^2 = 25$.

Example 1   Find all square roots of each number.

Ⓐ 81

Solution   Because $9 \cdot 9 = 81$, the positive square root of 81 is 9. Because $(-9) \cdot (-9) = 81$, the negative square root of 81 is -9. ■

Ⓑ $\frac{16}{9}$

Solution   Because $\frac{4}{3} \cdot \frac{4}{3} = \frac{16}{9}$, the positive square root of $\frac{16}{9}$ is $\frac{4}{3}$. Because $\left(-\frac{4}{3}\right) \cdot \left(-\frac{4}{3}\right) = \frac{16}{9}$, the negative square root of $\frac{16}{9}$ is $-\frac{4}{3}$. ■

Ⓒ -4

Solution   Whenever you multiply a number by itself, the product is positive. So, -4 has no real square roots. ■

The Principal Square Root

The symbol $\sqrt{}$ is called a radical sign. It is used to indicate a nonnegative square root, which is also called the **principal square root**.

The expression $\sqrt{25}$ indicates the principal square root of 25: $\sqrt{25} = 5$.

The expression $-\sqrt{25}$ indicates the negative square root of 25: $-\sqrt{25} = -5$.

Example 2   Evaluate.

Ⓐ $\sqrt{16}$

Solution   Think: $4 \cdot 4 = 16$. The principal square root of 16 is 4. So $\sqrt{16} = 4$. ∎

Ⓑ $-\sqrt{36}$

Solution   Think: $6 \cdot 6 = 36$. The principal square root of 36 is 6. Because the negative is in front of the radical sign, $-\sqrt{36} = -6$. ∎

Ⓒ $\sqrt{\dfrac{1}{49}}$

Solution   Think: $\dfrac{1}{7} \cdot \dfrac{1}{7} = \dfrac{1}{49}$. The principal square root of $\dfrac{1}{49}$ is $\dfrac{1}{7}$. So $\sqrt{\dfrac{1}{49}} = \dfrac{1}{7}$. ∎

> **TIP**
>
> For all positive real numbers a, $\sqrt{a}$ is the principal square root of a.

Solving Equations with Square Roots

When solving equations with square roots, you must note both the positive and the negative square roots of a number.

SQUARE ROOT PROPERTY

For nonnegative values of a:	**Examples**
if $x^2 = a$, then $x = \pm\sqrt{a}$.	If $x^2 = 49$, then $x = \pm 7$.
	If $x^2 = 100$, then $x = \pm 10$.

Example 3   Solve.

Ⓐ $x^2 = 121$

Solution

$x^2 = 121$	Write the equation.
$x = \pm\sqrt{121}$	Use the square root property.
$x = \pm 11$	Simplify.

Check

$11^2 = 121$ and $(-11)^2 = 121$ ∎

> **TIP**
>
> Check each answer by substituting it into the original equation.

B $m^2 = \dfrac{4}{9}$

Solution

$m^2 = \dfrac{4}{9}$ Write the equation.

$m = \pm\sqrt{\dfrac{4}{9}}$ Use the square root property.

$m = \pm\dfrac{2}{3}$ Simplify. ∎

C Solve $t^2 + 1 = 50$

Solution

$t^2 + 1 = 50$ Write the equation.

$t^2 = 49$ Subtract 1 from both sides.

$t = \pm\sqrt{49}$ Use the square root property.

$t = \pm 7$ Simplify. ∎

Application: Interior Design

Example 4   The area of a square rug is 36 ft². Write an equation to represent the area of the rug. What is the length of one side?

Solution   Because the rug is a square, you know that all four sides have the same measure. The area of a square with side length s is $A = s^2$.

$\text{Area} = s^2$ Write the formula for the area of a square.

$36 = s^2$ Substitute 36 for area.

$\pm\sqrt{36} = s$ Use the square root property.

$\pm 6 = s$ Simplify.

The solutions are $s = +6$ and $s = -6$. Because a measurement cannot be negative, choose the principal square root. The length of one side of the rug is 6 ft. ∎

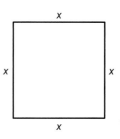

> **TIP**
>
> When solving a real-life problem, be sure to check if each solution makes sense.

Problem Set
· ·

Find the positive and negative square root of each number.

1. 49

2. 64

3. 100

4. 9

5. 16

6. $\dfrac{25}{36}$

7. $\dfrac{16}{81}$

8. $\dfrac{1}{64}$

9. $\dfrac{49}{100}$

10. $\dfrac{144}{25}$

Evaluate.

11. $\sqrt{4}$

12. $-\sqrt{1}$

13. $-\sqrt{100}$

14. $\sqrt{121}$

15. $-\sqrt{16}$

16. $\sqrt{\dfrac{4}{81}}$

17. $-\sqrt{\dfrac{1}{9}}$

18. $\sqrt{\dfrac{36}{49}}$

19. $\sqrt{0.25}$

20. $\sqrt{0.04}$

Solve.

21. $x^2 = 81$

22. $y^2 = 1$

23. $a^2 = 144$

24. $m^2 = 36$

25. $v^2 = \dfrac{49}{81}$

26. $b^2 = 25$

27. $x^2 = 9$

28. $u^2 = \dfrac{4}{25}$

29. $t^2 = \dfrac{1}{49}$

30. $d^2 = \dfrac{121}{9}$

31. $x^2 + 4 = 104$

32. $d^2 - 5 = 11$

33. $g^2 + 8 = 57$

34. $16 + c^2 = 25$

35. $c^2 - 30 = -26$

36. $u^2 - 20 = -4$

*37. Challenge $x^2 - \dfrac{2}{25} = \dfrac{14}{25}$

*38. Challenge $m^2 + \dfrac{2}{5} = \dfrac{89}{100}$

Solve each problem.

39. A checkerboard in the shape of a square has 64 squares. How many squares are on each side of the checkerboard?

40. A square garden has an area of 81 ft².
   A. What is the length of one side of the garden?

   B. What is the perimeter of the garden?

41. A parking lot is in the shape of a square. The area of the parking lot is 900 m². What is the length of one side of the parking lot?

*42. Challenge A large frame has an area of 98 cm². A smaller frame has an area equal to $\dfrac{1}{2}$ the larger frame. What is the length of one side of the smaller frame?

*43. Challenge A square napkin is divided into 4 equal squares. The area of one quarter section of the napkin is 225 cm².

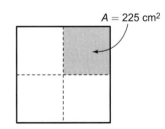
$A = 225$ cm²

   A. What is the area of the whole napkin?

   B. What is the side length of one side of the napkin?

   C. What is the perimeter of the napkin?

Irrational Square Roots

Not all square roots are rational numbers.

A **perfect square** is a whole number whose square root is an integer.

The numbers 100, 81, 25, and 225 are perfect squares because $\sqrt{100} = 10$, $\sqrt{81} = 9$, $\sqrt{25} = 5$, and $\sqrt{225} = 15$.

Because the square roots of perfect squares are whole numbers, a perfect square has *rational square roots*.

The number 16 is called a perfect square because 16 tiles form a square when arranged in rows and columns.

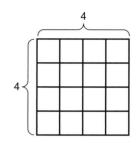

Identifying Irrational Square Roots

The numbers 20, 2, 35, and 88 are not perfect squares because they do not have integer square roots. The square roots of these numbers are irrational numbers.

Example 1   Identify whether each expression is rational or irrational.

A $\sqrt{49}$

Solution   The number 49 is a perfect square because $\sqrt{49} = 7$. The expression $\sqrt{49}$ is rational. ■

B $\sqrt{30}$

Solution   The number 30 is not a perfect square. The expression $\sqrt{30}$ is irrational. ■

Using Inequalities to Approximate Irrational Square Roots

You can use inequalities to approximate irrational square roots.

INEQUALITIES FOR IRRATIONAL SQUARE ROOTS

For nonnegative real numbers *a*, *b*, and *c*:	Example
if $a < b < c$, then $\sqrt{a} < \sqrt{b} < \sqrt{c}$.	Since $9 < 12 < 16$, $\sqrt{9} < \sqrt{12} < \sqrt{16}$.

Example 2 Between which two integers does $\sqrt{40}$ lie?

Solution The radicand 40 lies between the perfect squares 36 and 49, or in math language,

$$36 < 40 < 49, \text{ so}$$
$$\sqrt{36} < \sqrt{40} < \sqrt{49}$$
$$6 < \sqrt{40} < 7$$

So $\sqrt{40}$ lies between 6 and 7. ■

Approximating Square Roots on a Number Line

You can also use a number line to approximate square roots.
Use a number line to approximate $\sqrt{15}$. Find $\sqrt{15}$ on the number line.

REMEMBER

Any decimal form of the square root of a number that is not a perfect square is an approximation of the square root.

The expression $\sqrt{15}$ is between 3 and 4, but it is closer to 4. So we can approximate $\sqrt{15}$ as about 3.9. Check: $3.9^2 = 15.21 \approx 15$. ✓

Example 3 Use the number line to approximate $\sqrt{6}$ to the nearest tenth.

Solution The expression $\sqrt{6}$ is between $\sqrt{4}$ and $\sqrt{9}$ or between 2 and 3.

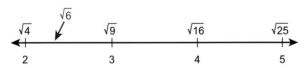

NOTATION

$\approx$ *is approximately equal to*

So $\sqrt{6} \approx 2.4$. Check: $2.4^2 = 5.76 \approx 6$. ✓ ■

Simplifying Radicals

You have seen that if a number is not a perfect square, any decimal form of its square is an approximation. However, it is possible to simplify radical numbers. A number in simplified radical form is exact.

To simplify radicals, use the product property of radicals.

PRODUCT PROPERTY OF RADICALS

For all nonnegative a, b, and c:

$$\sqrt{ab} = \sqrt{a} \cdot \sqrt{b}$$
$$\sqrt{a} \cdot \sqrt{b} = \sqrt{ab}$$

Examples

$$\sqrt{16 \cdot 2} = \sqrt{16} \cdot \sqrt{2}$$
$$\sqrt{12} \cdot \sqrt{3} = \sqrt{36}$$

Example 4   Simplify.

 $\sqrt{63}$

Solution

$\sqrt{63} = \sqrt{9 \cdot 7}$	Write 63 as a product of a perfect square and another factor.
$= \sqrt{9} \cdot \sqrt{7}$	Use the product property of radicals.
$= 3\sqrt{7}$	Simplify. ∎

B $\sqrt{32}$

Solution

$\sqrt{32} = \sqrt{16 \cdot 2}$	Write 32 as a product of a perfect square and another factor.
$= \sqrt{16} \cdot \sqrt{2}$	Use the product property of radicals.
$= 4\sqrt{2}$	Simplify. ∎

> **TIP**
>
> If a number in the radicand does not have a perfect square number as a factor, then it is already simplified.

Using a Calculator to Approximate Square Roots

You can use a calculator to find an approximate value of the square root:

$$\sqrt{20} \approx 4.472135955\ldots$$

Application: Construction

Example 5   A square parking lot has an area of 600 m². To the nearest tenth of a meter, what is the length of one side of the parking lot?

Solution   Squaring the length of one side will give the area.

$x^2 = 600$	Write an equation.
$x = \pm\sqrt{600}$	Use the square root property.
$x \approx \pm 24.5$	Use a calculator to approximate the square root.

The length has to be positive, so discard the negative answer. The parking lot has a side length of about 24.5 meters. ∎

Problem Set

· ·

Identify whether each expression is rational or irrational.

1. $\sqrt{20}$
2. $\sqrt{15}$
3. $\sqrt{25}$
4. $\sqrt{9}$
5. $\sqrt{45}$

6. $\sqrt{6}$
7. $\sqrt{81}$
8. $\sqrt{1}$
9. $\sqrt{49}$
10. $\sqrt{400}$

Name the consecutive integers between which each expression lies.

11. $\sqrt{30}$
12. $\sqrt{12}$
13. $\sqrt{95}$
14. $\sqrt{24}$
15. $\sqrt{50}$

16. $\sqrt{140}$
17. $\sqrt{19}$
18. $\sqrt{75}$
19. $\sqrt{190}$
20. $\sqrt{395}$

Approximate each expression to the nearest tenth.

21. $\sqrt{8}$
22. $\sqrt{27}$
23. $\sqrt{18}$
24. $\sqrt{35}$
25. $\sqrt{85}$

26. $\sqrt{2}$
27. $\sqrt{38}$
28. $\sqrt{130}$
29. $\sqrt{140}$
30. $\sqrt{68}$

Simplify.

31. $\sqrt{8}$
32. $\sqrt{48}$
33. $\sqrt{45}$
34. $\sqrt{54}$
35. $\sqrt{20}$

36. $\sqrt{125}$
37. $\sqrt{75}$
38. $\sqrt{162}$
39. $\sqrt{27}$
40. $\sqrt{72}$

Solve each problem.

41. An architect is designing a square window that has an area of 96 cm². To the nearest tenth of a centimeter, what is the length of each side?

42. A garden in the shape of a square has an area of 250 yd². To the nearest tenth of a yard, what is the length of one side of the garden?

43. A square tablecloth has an area of 8 m². To the nearest tenth of a meter, what is the length of one side of the tablecloth?

44. The bottom of a square cake pan has an area of 65 cm². To the nearest tenth of a centimeter, what is the length of one side of the bottom of the cake pan?

45. A square pool has an area of 105 ft². To the nearest tenth of a foot, what is the length of one side of the pool?

*46. **Challenge** A square frame has an area of 190 in².
   A. To the nearest tenth of an inch, what is the length of one side?
   B. What is the perimeter of the frame?

*47. **Challenge** A design consists of three squares placed next to each other as shown. The area of each square is 50 cm². To the nearest tenth of a centimeter, what is the perimeter of the design? Show how you got your answer.

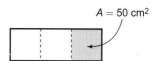

$A = 50 \text{ cm}^2$

The Pythagorean Theorem

The sides of a right triangle have a special relationship. To see this relationship, we give names to each side of a right triangle.

Identifying the Sides of a Right Triangle

The **hypotenuse** is the side opposite the right angle in a right triangle. The hypotenuse is red for each triangle below.

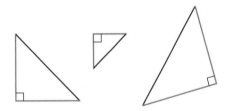

TIP

To find the hypotenuse, place your finger on the right angle. Then find the side that is not touching the right angle.

A **leg of a right triangle** is one of the two sides of a right triangle that form the right angle. Each right triangle has one hypotenuse and two legs. The legs are in blue for the triangles shown. The legs of a right triangle are always shorter than the hypotenuse.

Example 1 Identify the hypotenuse and the legs of each right triangle.

Ⓐ

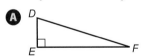

Solution The sides that make up the right angle are $\overline{DE}$ and $\overline{EF}$. So $\overline{DE}$ and $\overline{EF}$ are the legs of the right triangle. The side opposite the right angle is $\overline{DF}$. So $\overline{DF}$ is the hypotenuse. ■

Ⓑ

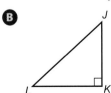

Solution The sides that make up the right angle are $\overline{JK}$ and $\overline{KL}$. So $\overline{JK}$ and $\overline{KL}$ are the legs of the right triangle. The side opposite the right angle is $\overline{JL}$. So $\overline{JL}$ is the hypotenuse. ■

The Pythagorean Theorem

The Pythagorean theorem shows a mathematical relationship between the sides of a right triangle.

In a right triangle, the sum of the squares of the lengths of the legs equals the square of the length of the hypotenuse.

$$a^2 + b^2 = c^2$$

Example

$$3^2 + 4^2 = 5^2$$
$$9 + 16 = 25$$
$$25 = 25$$

Example 2   Find the length of the hypotenuse for each figure.

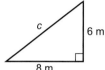

Solution   The legs are 6 and 8 so you can say $a = 6$ and $b = 8$.

$a^2 + b^2 = c^2$	Use the Pythagorean theorem.
$6^2 + 8^2 = c^2$	Substitute values into the Pythagorean theorem.
$36 + 64 = c^2$	Square terms.
$100 = c^2$	Add.
$\pm\sqrt{100} = c$	Use the square root property.
$\pm 10 = c$	Simplify.

Since length cannot be negative, disregard the negative square root. The hypotenuse measures 10 meters. ■

Solution   The legs are 5 and 7 so you can say $a = 5$ and $b = 7$.

$a^2 + b^2 = c^2$	Use the Pythagorean theorem.
$5^2 + 7^2 = c^2$	Substitute values into the Pythagorean theorem.
$25 + 49 = c^2$	Square terms.
$74 = c^2$	Add.
$\pm\sqrt{74} = c$	Use the square root property.
$\pm 8.6 \approx c$	Simplify.

Since length cannot be negative, disregard the negative square root. The hypotenuse measures exactly $\sqrt{74}$ feet or about 8.6 feet. ■

THINK ABOUT IT

When solving an equation with square roots, there is a positive answer and a negative answer. Because the measure of a side cannot be negative, use only the positive answer.

Finding the Missing Leg Length in a Right Triangle

When finding the missing leg length in a right triangle, substitute the values that are known. Then, solve for the missing length.

Example 3 Find the missing length in each triangle.

 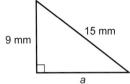

TIP

The missing leg can be called *a* or *b*.

Solution Let $b = 9$ and $c = 15$.

$a^2 + b^2 = c^2$	Use the Pythagorean theorem.
$a^2 + 9^2 = 15^2$	Substitute values into the Pythagorean theorem.
$a^2 + 81 = 225$	Square terms.
$a^2 = 144$	Subtract 81 from both sides.
$a = \pm\sqrt{144}$	Use the square root property.
$a = \pm 12$	Simplify.

Discard the negative solution. The length of the missing leg is 12 mm. ■

 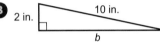

Solution Let $a = 2$ and $c = 10$.

$a^2 + b^2 = c^2$	Use the Pythagorean theorem.
$2^2 + b^2 = 10^2$	Substitute values into the Pythagorean theorem.
$4 + b^2 = 100$	Square terms.
$b^2 = 96$	Subtract 4 from both sides.
$b = \pm\sqrt{96}$	Use the square root property.
$b \approx \pm 9.8$	Simplify.

Discard the negative solution. The length of the missing leg is about 9.8 inches. ■

Pythagorean Triples

A Pythagorean triple is a set of three positive integers a, b, and c such that $a^2 + b^2 = c^2$.

For example, the set 3, 4, and 5 is a Pythagorean triple.

$$3^2 + 4^2 = 5^2$$
$$9 + 16 = 25$$
$$25 = 25$$

THINK ABOUT IT

Because 3, 4, 5 is a Pythagorean triple, any multiple of these numbers is also a Pythagorean triple. For example, 6, 8, and 10.

$$6^2 + 8^2 = 10^2$$
$$36 + 64 = 100$$
$$100 = 100$$

Example 4   State whether each set is a Pythagorean triple.

Ⓐ 8, 9, 10

Solution

$8^2 + 9^2 \stackrel{?}{=} 10^2$

$64 + 81 \stackrel{?}{=} 100$

$145 \neq 100$

Because $8^2 + 9^2 \neq 10^2$, the set 8, 9, and 10 is not a Pythagorean triple. ∎

Ⓑ 5, 12, 13

Solution

$5^2 + 12^2 \stackrel{?}{=} 13^2$

$25 + 144 \stackrel{?}{=} 169$

$169 = 169$ ✓

Because $5^2 + 12^2 = 13^2$, the set 5, 12, 13 is a Pythagorean triple. ∎

Application: Sports

Example 5   A bike ramp is in the shape of a right triangle. The length of the bottom of the ramp is 12 feet. The height is 2 feet. How long is the ramp?

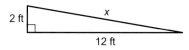

Solution   First, identify the side with the missing length. Because side x is opposite the right angle, it is the hypotenuse.

$a^2 + b^2 = c^2$	Use the Pythagorean theorem.
$2^2 + 12^2 = x^2$	Substitute the values and variable into the Pythagorean theorem.
$4 + 144 = x^2$	Square terms.
$148 = x^2$	Add.
$\pm\sqrt{148} = x$	Use the square root property.
$\pm 12.17 \approx x$	Simplify.

Discard the negative length. The length of the ramp is exactly $\sqrt{148}$ feet or about 12.17 feet. ∎

Problem Set

· ·

Identify the hypotenuse and legs of each right triangle.

1.
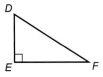

3.

2.
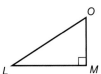

4.
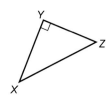

Find the length of the hypotenuse for each figure. Round to the nearest tenth, if needed.

5.
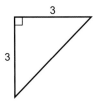

7.
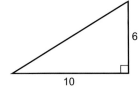

6.
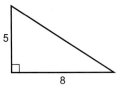

*8. Challenge
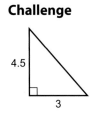

Find the missing length of the leg for each figure. Round to the nearest tenth, if needed.

9.
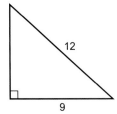

11.
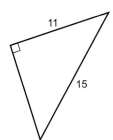

10.
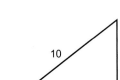

*12. Challenge
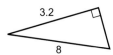

Let *a* and *b* represent the lengths of the legs of a right triangle. Let *c* represent the hypotenuse of the right triangle. Find the missing lengths. Round to the nearest tenth, if needed.

13. $a = 6, b = 10, c = ?$

14. $a = 5, b = ?, c = 13$

15. $a = ?, b = 6, c = 15$

16. $a = 8, b = 12, c = ?$

17. $a = 3, b = ?, c = 15$

***18. Challenge** $a = ?, b = 40, c = 41$

Solve each problem.

19. For problems 13−18, state which ones are Pythagorean triples.

20. A ladder extends from the top of a chimney to the ground. The measures are shown in the figure here. How tall is the chimney?

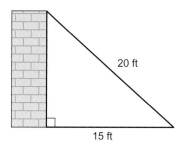

21. Streets on a street map form a right triangle. The measures are shown. What is the approximate measure of the missing length?

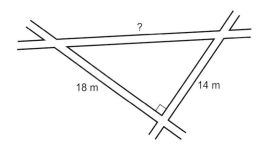

***22. Challenge** A ramp is in the shape of a right triangle. The measures are shown in the figure. What is the approximate height of the ramp?

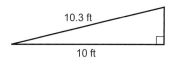

***23. Challenge** A garden in the shape of a right triangle has the measurements shown.

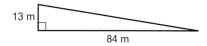

A. What is the perimeter of the garden?

B. Explain how you got your answer.

The Distance Formula

The Pythagorean theorem can be used to find the distance between two points on a coordinate plane.

In the graph shown, the distance between points A and B is horizontal. You can calculate this distance along a number line using $|x_2 - x_1|$ to find that the distance between points A and B is 4 units. The distance from points C to B is vertical. You can calculate that distance using the formula $|y_2 - y_1|$ to find that the distance between points C and B is 3 units. These distances form the legs of the right triangle.

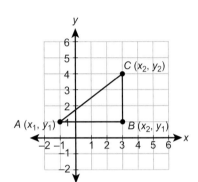

The distance between points C and A is the hypotenuse of the right triangle with legs of length 3 and 4 units.

$$3^2 + 4^2 = c^2$$

$$9 + 16 = c^2$$

$$25 = c^2$$

$$\pm 5 = c \qquad \text{Discard the negative value.}$$

The distance between C and A is 5 units.

Finding the Distance Between Two Points

As a direct result of the Pythagorean theorem you can find the distance d between any two points (x_1, y_1) and (x_2, y_2).

DISTANCE FORMULA

The distance between any two points (x_1, y_1) and (x_2, y_2) is given by the formula

$$d = \sqrt{(x_2 - x_1)^2 + (y_2 - y_1)^2}.$$

Example 1   Find the distance between each pair of points.

Ⓐ $(2, 8)$ and $(7, -4)$

Solution   Let $x_1 = 2$ and $y_1 = 8$. Then $x_2 = 7$ and $y_2 = -4$.

$d = \sqrt{(x_2 - x_1)^2 + (y_2 - y_1)^2}$ Write the distance formula.

$ = \sqrt{(7 - 2)^2 + (-4 - 8)^2}$ Substitute.

$ = \sqrt{5^2 + (-12)^2}$ Simplify within parentheses.

$ = \sqrt{25 + 144}$ Square terms.

$ = \sqrt{169}$ Add.

$ = 13$ Simplify. ∎

REMEMBER

Perform the operations inside the parentheses before squaring.

Ⓑ $(-3, 5)$ and $(-1, 2)$

Solution   Let $x_1 = -3$ and $y_1 = 5$. Then $x_2 = -1$ and $y_2 = 2$.

$d = \sqrt{(x_2 - x_1)^2 + (y_2 - y_1)^2}$ Write the distance formula.

$ = \sqrt{(-1 - (-3))^2 + (2 - 5)^2}$ Substitute.

$ = \sqrt{2^2 + (-3)^2}$ Simplify within parentheses.

$ = \sqrt{4 + 9}$ Square terms.

$ = \sqrt{13}$ Add.

$ \approx 3.6$ Simplify. ∎

Application: Tourism

Example 2   A map of a city is shown on the coordinate grid at right. Each unit is equal to 1 mile. Use the distance formula to find the distance between the museum and the park.

Solution   The museum is at $(0, 4)$ and the park is at $(5, -2)$. Let $x_1 = 5$ and $y_1 = -2$. Then $x_2 = 0$ and $y_2 = 4$.

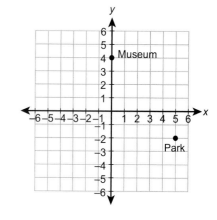

$d = \sqrt{(x_2 - x_1)^2 + (y_2 - y_1)^2}$ Write the distance formula.

$ = \sqrt{(0 - 5)^2 + (4 - (-2))^2}$ Substitute.

$ = \sqrt{(-5)^2 + 6^2}$ Simplify within parentheses.

$ = \sqrt{25 + 36}$ Square terms.

$ = \sqrt{61}$ Add.

$ \approx 7.8$ Simplify.

The museum is about 7.8 miles from the park. ∎

Problem Set

Find the distance between the points in each pair given. Round answers to the nearest tenth, if needed.

1. A and B

2. C and D

3. E and F

4. G and H

5. J and K

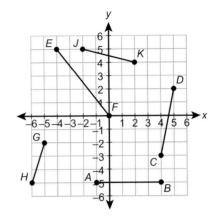

Find the distance between the given points. Round answers to the nearest tenth, if needed.

6. $(4, 8)$ and $(0, 5)$

7. $(0, 1)$ and $(6, 2)$

8. $(-5, 7)$ and $(-3, 2)$

9. $(2, -9)$ and $(-10, 4)$

10. $(4, 8)$ and $(-3, -8)$

11. $(-1, 10)$ and $(4, 1)$

12. $(3, 9)$ and $(4, 6)$

13. $(1, -3)$ and $(-6, 3)$

14. $(8, -8)$ and $(-1, 1)$

15. $(-4, 7)$ and $(10, 0)$

Use the distance formula to find the perimeter of each figure. Round answers to the nearest tenth.

*16. **Challenge** Triangle ABC

*17. **Challenge** Quadrilateral $DEFG$

*18. **Challenge** Triangle HIJ

*19. **Challenge** Pentagon $KLMNO$

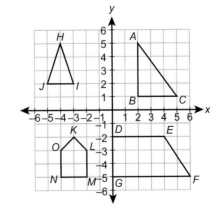

Solve each problem.

Use the grid for problems 20–29. For problems 20–27, find the distance between each of the following:

20. the bakery and the arcade

21. the bakery and the library

22. the school and the mall

23. the mall and the park

24. the school and the arcade

25. the park and the library

26. the school and the park

27. the bakery and the park

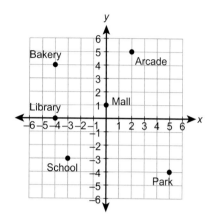

28. For problems 20–27, between which two places is the distance the shortest?

29. For problems 20–27, between which two places is the distance the greatest?

*30. **Challenge** A map shows a museum at $(-6, 6)$. City Hall is located at $(6, y)$. The distance between the museum and City Hall is 13 units. Use guess-and-check to find the location of City Hall.

Special Types of Triangles

Triangles are named based on the lengths of their sides.

An **isosceles triangle** is a triangle with at least two congruent sides.

Base angles of an isosceles triangle are congruent.

An **equilateral triangle** is a triangle with three congruent sides.

All three angles are congruent.

If an isosceles triangle must have *at least* two congruent sides, it can also have three congruent sides. Therefore, an equilateral triangle is also an isosceles triangle.

Finding Missing Side Lengths

If you know some side lengths, you can use algebra and properties of isosceles triangles to find missing lengths.

Example 1 Triangle LMN is an equilateral triangle. Expressions for the lengths of $\overline{LM}$ and $\overline{MN}$ are shown. What is the length of $\overline{LN}$?

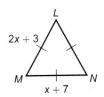

Solution Because the triangle is an equilateral triangle, all three sides are congruent. You are given two side lengths so you can set them equal to each other and solve for x.

$2x + 3 = x + 7$ Write an equation.

$x + 3 = 7$ Subtract x from both sides.

$x = 4$ Subtract 3 from both sides.

Substitute 4 back into either expression to find the length of one side.

$x + 7 = 4 + 7$

$= 11$

The length of $\overline{LN}$ is 11. ∎

45°- 45°- 90° Triangle

An isosceles triangle that has a right angle has angle measures 45°-45°-90°.

In a 45°-45°-90° triangle, the lengths of the legs are congruent. If the length of each leg is x, use the Pythagorean theorem to find the length of the hypotenuse.

$a^2 + b^2 = c^2$	Write the Pythagorean theorem.
$x^2 + x^2 = c^2$	Substitute.
$2x^2 = c^2$	Combine like terms.
$\sqrt{2x^2} = \sqrt{c^2}$	Use the square root property.
$x\sqrt{2} = c$	Simplify.

45°-45°-90° TRIANGLE

In a 45°-45°-90° triangle, the length of the hypotenuse is equal to $\sqrt{2}$ times the length of one of the legs.

Example

TIP

In a 45°-45°-90° triangle, the lengths of the legs are equal.

Example 2 Find the value of the variable.

Solution

$y = 7\sqrt{2}$	Multiply $\sqrt{2}$ by the length of one of the legs.
≈ 9.9	Approximate.

The value of y is $7\sqrt{2}$ or about 9.9. ∎

Solution

$x = \dfrac{15\sqrt{2}}{\sqrt{2}}$	Divide the length of the hypotenuse by $\sqrt{2}$.
$= 15$	Simplify.

The value of x is 15. ∎

30°-60°-90° Triangle

Because all angles in an equilateral triangle are congruent, each angle measures 60°.

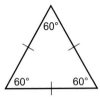

If an equilateral triangle is divided into two congruent triangles, each triangle has angle measures 30°-60°-90°. This is another special right triangle.

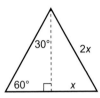

All sides of an equilateral triangle are congruent. When you divide an equilateral triangle into two congruent triangles, the length of one of the legs of the right triangle is equal to half the length of the hypotenuse. If the length of the shorter leg of the 30°-60°-90° triangle is x, then the length of the hypotenuse is $2x$. You can use the Pythagorean theorem to find the length of the longer leg.

$a^2 + b^2 = c^2$	Write the Pythagorean theorem.
$x^2 + b^2 = (2x)^2$	Substitute.
$x^2 + b^2 = 4x^2$	Square terms.
$b^2 = 3x^2$	Subtract x^2 from both sides.
$b = \pm\sqrt{3x^2}$	Use the square root property.
$b = x\sqrt{3}$	Simplify and discard the negative length.

30°-60°-90° TRIANGLE

In a 30°-60°-90° triangle, the length of the hypotenuse is 2 times the length of the shorter leg. The longer leg is equal to $\sqrt{3}$ times the length of the shorter leg.

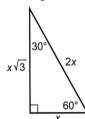

Example

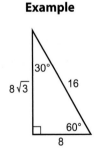

TIP

In a 30°-60°-90° triangle, the shorter leg is opposite the 30° angle. The longer leg is opposite the 60° angle.

Example 3   Find the value of each variable.

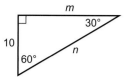

Solution

$m = 10\sqrt{3}$ The longer leg equals $\sqrt{3}$ times the shorter leg.

$n = 2 \cdot 10 = 20$ The hypotenuse equals 2 times the shorter leg. ■

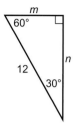

Solution

$m = \dfrac{12}{2} = 6$ The shorter leg equals $\dfrac{1}{2}$ times the hypotenuse.

$n = 6\sqrt{3}$ The longer leg equals $\sqrt{3}$ times the shorter leg. ■

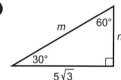

Solution

$n = \dfrac{5\sqrt{3}}{\sqrt{3}} = 5$ The shorter leg equals the longer leg divided by $\sqrt{3}$.

$m = 2 \cdot 5 = 10$ The hypotenuse equals 2 times the shorter leg. ■

Applications: Electronics and Traffic Signs

Example 4

A The screen on a music player is a square with a side length of 6 cm. What is the measure of the diagonal d of the screen to the nearest tenth of a centimeter?

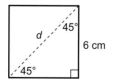

(continued)

Solution   Use the 45°-45°-90° property to find the length of the diagonal.

$d = 6\sqrt{2}$ The hypotenuse equals $\sqrt{2}$ times the length of one leg.

≈ 8.5 Approximate.

The diagonal of the screen measures about 8.5 cm. ■

B A standard yield sign is an equilateral triangle with a side length of 750 mm. What is the exact area of the standard yield sign?

750 mm

Solution   Use the 30°-60°-90° triangle property. Divide the equilateral triangle into two congruent triangles with angles that measure 30°, 60°, and 90°. The height of the triangle is equal to the length of the longer leg of the right triangle. Since the hypotenuse of each right triangle is 750 mm, the length of the longer leg is $750\sqrt{3}$ mm.

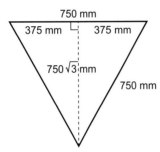

$A = \dfrac{1}{2}bh$ Write the formula for the area of a triangle.

$A = \dfrac{1}{2} \cdot 750 \cdot 750\sqrt{3}$ Substitute.

$A = 281{,}250\sqrt{3}$ Multiply.

The area of the standard yield sign is $281{,}250\sqrt{3}$ mm². ■

Problem Set

Find the value of x.

1.

2x + 6

3x + 4

2.

2x – 3

x – 7

Triangle *JKL* is an equilateral triangle.

3. What is the length of $\overline{JK}$?

*4. Challenge What is the perimeter of *JKL*?

J

2x + 5   3x

K   L

4x – 5

Triangle *PQR* is an isosceles triangle.

5. What is the length of $\overline{PQ}$?

*6. Challenge What is the perimeter of *PQR*?

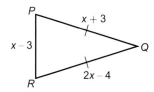

P

x + 3

x – 3

Q

2x – 4

R

Find the value of the variables.

7.

45°

9   y

45°

9

8.

m

30°

6

n

60°

9.

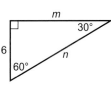

45°

x   5√2

45°

x

10.

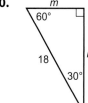

m

60°

18   n

30°

11.

45°

x   12√2

45°

x

12.

m

60°

n   4√3

30°

Solve each problem.

13. A pattern on a quilt consists of a triangle with sides measuring 8 inches, 8 inches, and $8\sqrt{2}$ inches. What are the angle measures of this triangle?

14. A triangular frame has sides measuring 10 centimeters, $10\sqrt{3}$ centimeters, and 20 centimeters. What are the angle measures of this triangle?

15. A design is in the shape of a square with side length 8 cm. What is the measure of the diagonal of the shape to the nearest tenth of a centimeter?

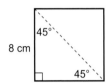

16. A garden is in the shape of an equilateral triangle. What is the area of the garden if the measure of each side is 6 meters?

17. An equilateral triangle has sides measuring $4x - 7$ and $2x + 4$. What is the perimeter of the triangle?

18. An equilateral triangle has sides measuring $x^2 + 9$ and 90. What is the value of x?

19. A square garden has a side length of 80 feet. A fence is built diagonally from one corner of the garden to the other. What is the length of the fence, to the nearest foot?

20. A ramp from a building is shown below. The ramp forms a 30° angle with the ground. The distance from the ground to where the ramp meets the building is 2 feet.

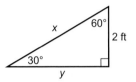

   A. What is the distance y from the bottom of the ramp to the building?

   B. What is the length x of the ramp?

21. A pattern contains a figure in the shape of a 30°–60°–90° triangle. The longer leg has a length of $7\sqrt{3}$. Find the length of the hypotenuse and the length of the shorter leg.

*22. **Challenge** The diagonal of a square frame measures $7\sqrt{2}$ centimeters.

   A. What is the measure of one side of the frame?

   B. What is the perimeter of the frame?

*23. **Challenge** The two congruent sides of an isosceles triangle have lengths x centimeters. The third side is half the length of one of the congruent sides. If the perimeter of the triangle is 80 centimeters, what are the lengths of the sides?

Trigonometric Ratios

Trigonometric ratios tell you about right triangles.

All similar triangles have congruent corresponding angles and proportional corresponding side lengths. Therefore, for any pair of similar triangles, the ratio of two side lengths will be constant. If you can find these ratios for one triangle, you know the ratio for all triangles that are similar to it. This can be helpful when solving problems involving right triangles.

Trigonometric ratios use the words *opposite*, *adjacent*, and *hypotenuse* to identify sides. Opposite and adjacent depend on the angle in question.

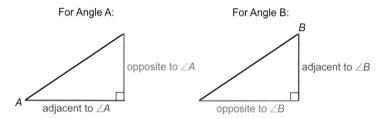

For Angle A: For Angle B:

> **TIP**
>
> Adjacent means "next to."

Sine, Cosine, and Tangent Ratios

$$\sin A = \frac{\text{opposite of } \angle A}{\text{hypotenuse}} = \frac{a}{c}$$

$$\cos A = \frac{\text{adjacent to } \angle A}{\text{hypotenuse}} = \frac{b}{c}$$

$$\tan A = \frac{\text{opposite of } \angle A}{\text{adjacent to } \angle A} = \frac{a}{b}$$

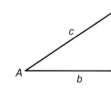

> **TIP**
>
> The trigonometric ratios are abbreviated as follows.
>
>   sine: sin
>   cosine: cos
>   tangent: tan

Example 1   Use the figure to find each ratio.

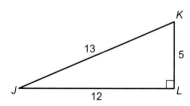

A $\sin J$

Solution $\sin J = \dfrac{\text{opp}}{\text{hyp}} = \dfrac{5}{13}$

B $\cos J$

Solution $\cos J = \dfrac{\text{adj}}{\text{hyp}} = \dfrac{12}{13}$

C $\tan J$

Solution $\tan J = \dfrac{\text{opp}}{\text{adj}} = \dfrac{5}{12}$

(continued)

D sin K

Solution $\sin K = \dfrac{\text{opp}}{\text{hyp}} = \dfrac{12}{13}$

E cos K

Solution $\cos K = \dfrac{\text{adj}}{\text{hyp}} = \dfrac{5}{13}$

F tan K

Solution $\tan K = \dfrac{\text{opp}}{\text{adj}} = \dfrac{12}{5}$ ■

Irrational Side Lengths

You can find the trigonometric ratios if the side lengths are irrational. Remember to simplify if possible.

Example 2 Use the figure to find each ratio.

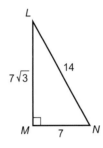

A sin N

Solution $\sin N = \dfrac{7\sqrt{3}}{14} = \dfrac{\sqrt{3}}{2}$

B cos N

Solution $\cos N = \dfrac{7}{14} = \dfrac{1}{2}$

C tan N

Solution $\tan N = \dfrac{7\sqrt{3}}{7} = \sqrt{3}$ ■

Using Trigonometric Ratios to Find Lengths

The sine of an angle is calculated by dividing the length of the opposite side by the length of the hypotenuse. Sometimes the sine is a rational number and sometimes it is irrational.

Example 3 The sine of C is 0.5. What is the length of $\overline{AB}$?

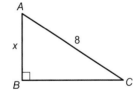

> **THINK ABOUT IT**
>
> Cosine and tangent can also be used to find a missing length.

Solution

$\sin C = \dfrac{\text{opp}}{\text{hyp}}$ \quad Write the trigonometric ratio.

$0.5 = \dfrac{x}{8}$ \quad Substitute the known values.

$0.5 \cdot 8 = \dfrac{x}{8} \cdot 8$ \quad Multiply both sides by 8.

$4 = x$ \quad Simplify.

The length of $\overline{AB}$ is 4 units.

Example 4

A The sine of A is 0.8. What is the value of x?

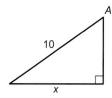

Solution

$\sin A = \dfrac{\text{opp}}{\text{hyp}}$	Write the trigonometric ratio.
$0.8 = \dfrac{x}{10}$	Substitute.
$0.8 \cdot 10 = \dfrac{x}{10} \cdot 10$	Multiply both sides by 10.
$8 = x$	Simplify.

The value of x is 8. ■

B The cosine of A is 0.9. What is the value of x?

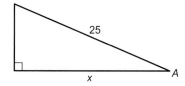

Solution

$\cos A = \dfrac{\text{adj}}{\text{hyp}}$	Write the trigonometric ratio.
$0.9 = \dfrac{x}{25}$	Substitute.
$0.9 \cdot 25 = \dfrac{x}{25} \cdot 25$	Multiply both sides by 25.
$22.5 = x$	Simplify.

The value of x is 22.5. ■

Application: Surveying

Example 5 A surveyor is determining the height of a building. The surveyor measures a distance of 38 feet from the base of the building. The tangent of the angle from the ground to the top of the building is 1.4. What is the height x of the building?

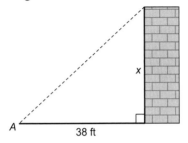

Solution

$\tan A = \dfrac{\text{opp}}{\text{adj}}$ Write a trigonometric ratio.

$1.4 = \dfrac{x}{38}$ Substitute.

$1.4 \cdot 38 = \dfrac{x}{38} \cdot 38$ Multiply both sides by 38.

$53.2 = x$ Simplify.

The building is 53.2 feet tall. ∎

Problem Set

Find each trigonometric ratio.

1. $\sin Q$
2. $\cos Q$
3. $\tan Q$

4. $\sin S$
5. $\cos S$
6. $\tan S$

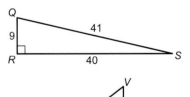

7. $\sin T$
8. $\cos T$
9. $\tan T$

10. $\sin V$
11. $\cos V$
12. $\tan V$

13. $\sin Y$
14. $\cos Y$
15. $\tan Y$

16. $\sin W$
17. $\cos W$
18. $\tan W$

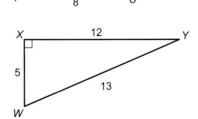

19. sin A

20. cos A

21. tan A

22. sin C

23. cos C

24. tan C

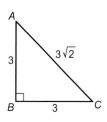

Find each length.

25. The cosine of E is $\dfrac{3}{10}$.

What is EF?

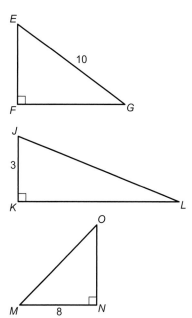

26. The sine of L is $\dfrac{3}{17}$.

What is JL?

27. The tangent of M is $\dfrac{\sqrt{41}}{8}$.

What is ON?

Solve each problem.

28. The height of a ramp is 3 feet. If the sine of the angle that the ramp makes with the ground is $\dfrac{1}{3}$, what is the length of the ramp to the nearest hundredth of a foot?

*29. Challenge A house is shown below. The sides of the roof meet at a right angle.

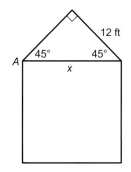

A. If the sine of 45° is about 0.7071, what is the length x to the nearest hundredth of a foot?

B. Use the properties of a 45°–45°–90° triangle to show that your answer to part A is correct.

*30. Challenge A building's brick wall forms a right angle with the ground. A surveyor stands 60 feet from the base of a building. The surveyor measures the angle from the ground to the top of the building to be 35°. If the tangent of 35° is about 0.7002, what is the height of the building to the nearest hundredth of a foot?

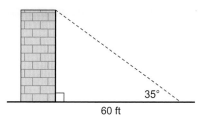

*31. Challenge A 45°–45°–90° right triangle has legs measuring 6 m. What is the decimal approximation for sin 45°, cos 45°, and tan 45°?

UNIT 12   Solid Figures

The volume of an engine's cylinders affects its power.

Gas-powered engines are driven by little explosions that move pistons up and down in cylinders. When you add up the volume of all the cylinders, you get the displacement of the engine. For instance, each cylinder in a four-cylinder, 1000 cc engine has a volume of 250 cubic centimeters. Engineers and mechanics must accurately compute volume when they build or maintain engines.

Big Idea

▶ Area is a measure of how much material is needed to cover a plane figure. Volume is a measure of the amount of space a figure occupies.

Unit Topics

▶ Volume and Capacity

▶ Volumes of Prisms and Cylinders

▶ Volumes of Pyramids and Cones

▶ Surface Area

▶ Surface Areas of Prisms and Cylinders

Volume and Capacity

Volume and capacity are two ways to measure a three-dimensional object.

A **cube** is a solid figure made up of six square faces that meet each other at right angles. A cube has eight vertices and 12 edges. The length, width, and height of a cube are equal.

cube

Finding the Volume of a Cube

The **volume** of a three-dimensional figure is a measure of the space inside the figure. You find volume by determining the number of cubes needed to fill a figure. Volume is measured in **cubic units**.

Example 1   Find the volume of the cube.

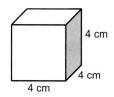

4 cm
4 cm
4 cm

Solution   Fill the cube with centimeter cubes.

Place 4 rows of 4 cubes on the bottom.

$4 \times 4 = 16$

The first layer holds 16 centimeter cubes.

Make 4 layers of 16 cubes.

$4 \times 16 = 64$

The figure holds 64 centimeter cubes.

The volume of the cube is 64 cubic centimeters or 64 cm³. ∎

The Formula for the Volume of a Cube

You can use a formula to find the volume of a cube.

The formula for the volume of a cube with side *s* is

$$V = s \cdot s \cdot s = s^3.$$

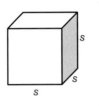

Example 2 Find the volume of each cube.

A

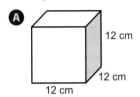

12 cm

12 cm

12 cm

Solution

$V = s^3$ Write the volume formula.

$= 12^3$ Substitute 12 for *s*.

$= 1728$ Evaluate the power.

The volume is 1728 cm³. ∎

B

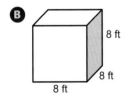

8 ft

8 ft

8 ft

Solution

$V = s^3$ Write the volume formula.

$= 8^3$ Substitute 8 for *s*.

$= 512$ Evaluate the power.

The volume is 512 ft³. ∎

TIP

You could also calculate the volume with the units:

$V = s^3$

$= (12 \text{ cm})^3$

$= 12^3 \cdot \text{cm}^3$

$= 1728 \text{ cm}^3$

It is simpler to calculate without the units, then add them in the final answer, but you can certainly include the units in your calculations. However you do it, be careful with your units.

Finding the Capacity of a Cube

Capacity is a measure of the amount a container can hold. In the U.S. customary system of measurement, tablespoons, quarts, and gallons are all units of capacity. In the metric system, capacity is most commonly measured using liters (L) or milliliters (mL).

You can find the capacity of a cube by finding its volume, then converting the measure of volume to a measure of capacity. To find a capacity in milliliters or liters, start by finding the volume in cubic centimeters. The unit "cubic centimeter" is abbreviated "cc."

METRIC VOLUME AND CAPACITY

$$1 \text{ cm}^3 = 1 \text{ cc} = 1 \text{ mL}$$
$$1000 \text{ mL} = 1 \text{ L}$$

THINK ABOUT IT

A cube that is 1 cm on each side holds one milliliter of water.

Example 3

A Find the capacity in milliliters and liters.

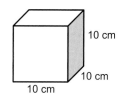

10 cm
10 cm
10 cm

Solution

$$V = s^3 \qquad \text{Write the volume formula.}$$

$$= 10 \text{ cm} \qquad \text{Substitute 10 cm for } s.$$

$$= 1000 \text{ cm}^3 \qquad \text{Find the volume in cm}^3.$$

$$\text{Capacity} = 1000 \text{ cm}^3 \cdot \frac{1 \text{ mL}}{\text{cm}^3} \qquad \text{Convert cm}^3 \text{ to mL.}$$

$$= 1000 \text{ mL}$$

$$= 1 \text{ L} \qquad \text{Convert mL to L.}$$

The capacity of the cube is 1000 milliliters or 1 liter. ■

REMEMBER

$1000 \text{ mL} = 1 \text{ L}$

B Find the capacity in mL and L to the nearest whole milliliter.

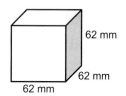

62 mm
62 mm
62 mm

Solution

$$s = 62 \text{ mm} = 6.2 \text{ cm} \qquad \text{Convert mm to cm.}$$

$$V = s^3 \qquad \text{Write the volume formula.}$$

$$= (6.2 \text{ cm})^3 \qquad \text{Substitute for } s.$$

$$\approx 238 \text{ cm}^3 \qquad \text{Find the volume in cm}^3.$$

$$\text{Capacity} = 238 \text{ cm}^3 \cdot \frac{1 \text{ mL}}{\text{cm}^3} \qquad \text{Convert cm}^3 \text{ to mL.}$$

$$= 238 \text{ mL} = 0.238 \text{ L}$$

The capacity of the cube is 238 mL or 0.238 L. ■

Application: Automotive Engineering

Example 4

One measure of the power of a car's engine is displacement, which measures the amount of air that is displaced when a piston moves up and down a cylinder. The amount of air displaced is the same as the capacity or volume of the cylinder.

Ron's car has 4 cylinders and each has displacement of 820 cc. He is looking at a new car with a 2.8L engine. Which car's engine has greater displacement?

Solution   Find the engine size for Ron's car. Then compare to the engine size of the new car.

4×820 cc $= 3280$ cc	Find the total displacement for all 4 cylinders.
$= 3280$ mL	Convert volume to capacity.
$= 3.28$ L	Convert mL to L.
2.8 L $<$ 3.28 L	Compare engine sizes.

The new car's engine has less displacement.   ■

Problem Set

Find the volume of the cube with the given side length.

1. $s = 4$ in.

2. $s = 8$ m

3. $s = 11$ ft

4. $s = 3.2$ cm

Find the volume of the cube.

5.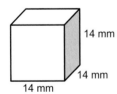
5 in. 5 in. 5 in.

6.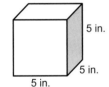
14 mm 14 mm 14 mm

7.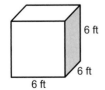
6 ft 6 ft 6 ft

8.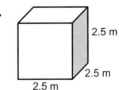
2.5 m 2.5 m 2.5 m

9.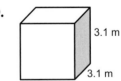
3.1 m 3.1 m 3.1 m

10.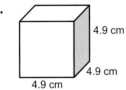
4.9 cm 4.9 cm 4.9 cm

Solve each problem.

11. A gift box has the shape of a cube. The box is 75 cm tall. What is the volume of the box?

12. Molly is filling a serving dish with sugar cubes. Each sugar cube measures 1 cm on each side. The serving dish has the shape of a cube and measures 8 cm on each side. What is the greatest number of sugar cubes Molly can fit in the serving dish?

*13. Challenge Each side of a cube is 2 feet long. What is the volume of the cube in cubic inches?

*14. Challenge The volume of a cube is 27 cm³. What is the length of each side of the cube?

Complete the conversion equation.

15. 1 cm³ = _____ mL

16. 1 cm³ = _____ cc

17. 4 cc = _____ mL

18. 15 mL = _____ cm³

19. 2000 mL = _____ L

20. 2 L = _____ cm³

Find the capacity of the cube.

A. in milliliters
B. in liters

21.

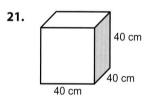

40 cm
40 cm
40 cm

22.

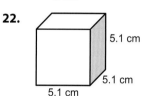

5.1 cm
5.1 cm
5.1 cm

23.

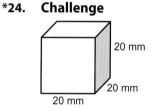

30 cm
30 cm
30 cm

*24. Challenge

20 mm
20 mm
20 mm

Compare. Use <, >, or =.

25. 2.5 L _____ 400 cc

26. 500 mL _____ 400 cm³

27. 1500 cc _____ 1.5 L

28. 250 cm³ _____ 2 L

Solve each problem.

29. A car with six cylinders has total displacement of 2993 cc. What is the displacement of each cylinder in liters?

*30. Challenge In the U.S. customary measurement system 1 gallon = 0.1337 ft³. What is the capacity in gallons of the tank shown?

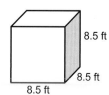

8.5 ft
8.5 ft
8.5 ft

Volumes of Prisms and Cylinders

Many food and drink containers have the shape of a prism or a cylinder.

Identifying Parts of Prisms

A **prism** is a solid figure with parallel congruent **bases** which are both polygons. The **lateral faces** are all rectangles. The name of that prism comes from the shape of its bases.

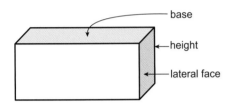

rectangular prism
2 rectangular bases
4 rectangular lateral faces

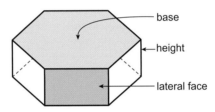

hexagonal prism
2 hexagonal bases
6 rectangular lateral faces

Example 1 Name the prism. Give the shape of its bases and the number of lateral faces.

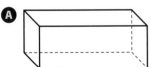
Ⓐ

Solution
The bases are rectangles.
There are 4 lateral faces.
The figure is a rectangular prism. ∎

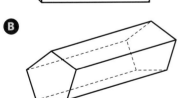
Ⓑ

Solution
The bases are pentagons.
There are 5 lateral faces.
The figure is a pentagonal prism. ∎

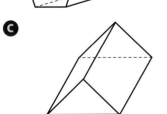
Ⓒ

Solution
The bases are triangles.
There are 3 lateral faces.
The figure is a triangular prism. ∎

TIP

Think of the bases of a prism as its floor and ceiling. Think of the lateral faces as walls. But watch out! A prism does not always sit on one of its bases. Sometimes it sits on a lateral face, like in Examples 1B and C.

The Volume of a Prism

The formula for the volume of a prism with base area B and height h is

$$V = Bh.$$

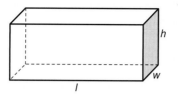

Example 2   Find the volume of the prism.

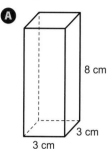

Solution   The figure is a square prism. The bases are squares. Use the formula $A = s^2$ to find B.

Step 1   Find B.

$B = s^2$ Write the area of a square formula.

$\quad = 3^2$ Substitute the side length of the square.

$\quad = 9$ Square the term.

The area B of the base of the square prism is 9 cm². ∎

Step 2   Find V.

The area of the base is 9 cm². Now use B in the formula $V = Bh$.

$V = Bh$ Write the volume formula.

$\quad = 9 \cdot 8$ Substitute the base area for B and the prism height for h.

$\quad = 72$ Multiply.

The volume of the triangular prism is 72 cm³. ∎

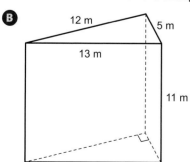

Solution   The figure is a triangular prism. The bases are triangles. Use the formula $A = \frac{1}{2}bh$ to find the area of base B.

> **THINK ABOUT IT**
>
> For a rectangular prism, $B = lw$, so $V = Bh = lwh$. Another way to find the volume is to use the formula $V = lwh$:
>
> $V = lwh$
>
> $\quad = 3 \times 3 \times 8$
>
> $\quad = 72$

> **TIP**
>
> Do a separate calculation to find B, using the appropriate area formula.

(continued)

Step 1 Find B

$B = \frac{1}{2}bh$ Write the area of a triangle formula.

$= \frac{1}{2} \cdot 5 \cdot 12$ Substitute the base and height of the triangle.

$= 30$ Multiply.

The area B of the base of the triangular prism is 30 m².

Step 2 Find V

Use the value for B in the formula $V = Bh$.

$V = Bh$ Write the volume formula.

$= 30 \cdot 11$ Substitute the base area for B and the prism height for h.

$= 330$ Multiply.

The volume of the triangular prism is 330 m³. ∎

Finding the Volume of a Cylinder

The bases of a **cylinder** are circles. A cylinder has one curved lateral surface.

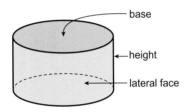

VOLUME OF A CYLINDER

The formula for the volume of a cylinder with base area B, height h, and radius r is

$$V = Bh \text{ or } V = \pi r^2 h.$$

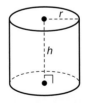

You can use 3.14 to approximate π. Or, you can use the symbol π to show an exact answer.

Example 3

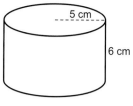

A Find the exact volume of the cylinder.

B Find the approximate volume of the cylinder.

Solution

A Leave your answer in terms of π.

$V = \pi r^2 h$ Write the volume formula.

$= \pi \cdot 5^2 \cdot 6$ Substitute for r and h.

$= 150\pi$ Simplify.

The volume of the cylinder is exactly 150π cm^3. ■

B Use 3.14 to approximate π.

$V = 150\pi$ Start with the exact volume.

$\approx 150 \cdot 3.14$ Use 3.14 for π.

≈ 471 Simplify.

The volume of the cylinder is approximately 471 cm^3. ■

Application: Beverage Packaging

Example 4   A case of juice contains 24 cans. The cans are packed in a box for shipping as shown in the diagram. Each can is a cylinder with radius 3.2 cm. If there are 9264 mL of juice in the entire case, what is the height of each can? Assume each can is completely full.

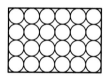

Solution   Use the total capacity to find the capacity of one can. Then convert capacity to volume and use the volume formula to find the height of a can.

9264 mL $\div$ 24 = 386 mL   Find the capacity of each can.

Each can contains 386 mL of juice. The volume of each can is 386 cm^3.

$V = \pi r^2 h$ Write the volume formula.

$386 = \pi \cdot 3.2^2 h$ Substitute for V and r.

$386 = 10.24\pi h$ Simplify.

$\dfrac{386}{10.24\pi} = h$ Divide both sides by 10.24π.

$\dfrac{386}{10.24 \cdot 3.14} \approx h$ Use 3.14 for π.

$12 \approx h$ Simplify.

The height of each can is about 12 cm. ■

Problem Set

Find the volume of the prism.

1. $B = 12$ in²
$h = 3$ in.

2. $B = 4$ mm²
$h = 3$ mm

3. $B = 200$ ft²
$h = 60$ ft

4. $B = 3.5$ cm²
$h = 2.5$ cm

Find the volume of the prism.

5.

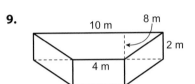

10 in.

6 in.

6 in.

6.

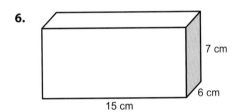

7 cm

6 cm

15 cm

7.

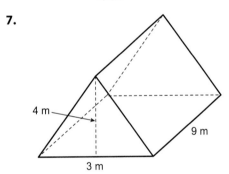

4 m

9 m

3 m

8.

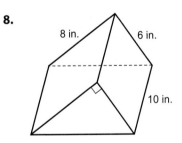

8 in.

6 in.

10 in.

9.

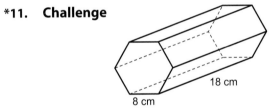

10 m

8 m

2 m

4 m

10.

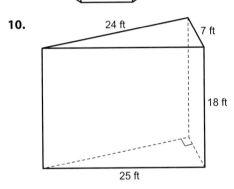

24 ft

7 ft

18 ft

25 ft

*11. **Challenge**

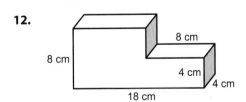

18 cm

8 cm

Hint: The area of a regular hexagon with side s is $\dfrac{3\sqrt{3}}{2}s^2$.

12.

8 cm

8 cm

8 cm

4 cm

4 cm

18 cm

For problems 13–24,

A. Find the exact volume.

B. Find the approximate volume. Use 3.14 to approximate π.
   Round your answer to three places.

13. $r = 7$ in.
   $h = 4$ in.

14. $r = 6$ m
   $h = 15$ m

15. $r = 5$ cm
   $h = 9$ cm

16. $r = 12$ ft
   $h = 50$ ft

17. $r = 8.3$ cm
   $h = 2$ cm

18. $r = 3.5$ ft
   $h = 3.2$ ft

*19. Challenge $d = 20$ cm
   $h = 50$ mm

*20. Challenge $r = 2\pi$ ft
   $h = \dfrac{\pi}{4}$ ft

21.

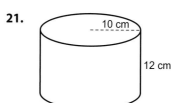
10 cm
12 cm

22.

9 ft
4 ft

23.

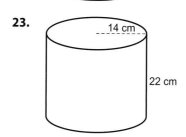
14 cm
22 cm

24.

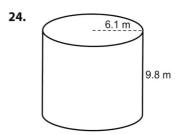
6.1 m
9.8 m

**Solve. Use 3.14 to approximate π. Round your answer to three places,
unless stated otherwise.**

25. A cylindrical can has radius 7.2 cm and height 32 cm. What is the volume of the can?

26. The volume of a cylinder is 48π m^3. The height of the cylinder is 3 m. What is the radius of the cylinder?

27. The volume of a cylinder is about 942 cubic inches. The radius of the cylinder is 5 inches. What is the height of the cylinder?

28. The radius of a cylinder is 9.1 cm and its height is 4.2 cm. What is the capacity of the cylinder in milliliters?

29. A car has an 8-cylinder engine. Each cylinder has radius 5.08 cm and height 9.2 cm. What is the total displacement (capacity) of the engine in liters? Round your answer to the nearest liter.

*30. Challenge One liter of a liquid chemical is divided equally into 40 identical cylindrical test tubes. Each test tube is completely filled. If each test tube has radius 0.7 cm, what is the height of each test tube?

Volumes of Pyramids and Cones

The Great Pyramid of Cholula is the world's largest pyramid with a volume estimated to be 4.45 million cubic meters.

Identifying Pyramids

A **pyramid** has one base that is a polygon and its triangular lateral faces meet at a single **vertex**. A pyramid is named by the shape of its base.

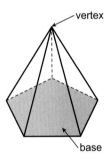

vertex

base

pentagonal pyramid

Example 1 Name the pyramid. Give the shape of its base and the number of lateral faces.

A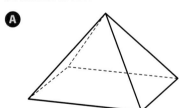

Solution
The base is a rectangle.
There are 4 lateral faces.
The figure is a rectangular pyramid. ■

B

Solution
The base is a triangle.
There are 3 lateral faces.
The figure is a triangular pyramid. ■

C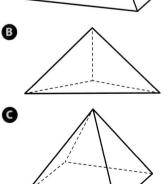

Solution
The base is a square.
There are 4 lateral faces.
The figure is a square pyramid. ■

The Volume of a Pyramid

The **height** of a pyramid is the distance from its base to its vertex along a line perpendicular to the base.

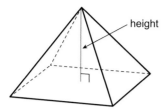

VOLUME OF A PYRAMID

The formula for the volume of a pyramid with base area B and height h is

$$V = \frac{1}{3}Bh.$$

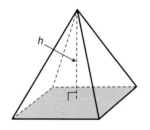

Example 2   Find the volume of the pyramid.

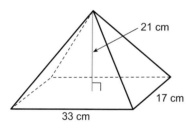

Solution   The figure is a rectangular pyramid. The base is a rectangle. Use the formula $A = lw$ to find B.

Step 1   Find B.

$B = lw$ Write the area of a rectangle formula.

$\quad = 33 \cdot 17$ Substitute the length and width of the rectangle.

$\quad = 561$ Multiply.

The area B of the base of the rectangular pyramid is 561 cm².

Step 2   Find V.

Use the value for B in the formula $V = \frac{1}{3}Bh$.

$V = \frac{1}{3}Bh$ Write the volume formula.

$\quad = \frac{1}{3} \cdot 561 \cdot 21$ Substitute the base area for B and the pyramid height for h.

$\quad = 3927$ Multiply.

The volume of the rectangular pyramid is 3927 cm³. ■

Finding the Volume of a Cone

The base of a **cone** is a circle. A cone has one curved lateral surface. Like a pyramid, a cone has a vertex. Its height is measured from the base to the vertex along a line perpendicular to the base.

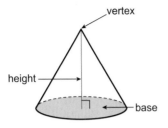

VOLUME OF A CONE

The formula for the volume of a cone with base area B, radius r, and height h is

$$V = \frac{1}{3}Bh \text{ or } V = \frac{1}{3}\pi r^2 h.$$

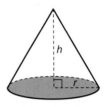

Example 3

A Find the exact volume of the cone.

B Find the approximate volume of the cone.

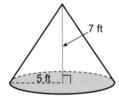

> **REMEMBER**
>
> You can use 3.14 to approximate π. Or, you can treat π as a numeral in your calculations.

Solution

A Leave your answer in terms of π.

$V = \frac{1}{3}\pi r^2 h$	Write the volume formula.
$= \frac{1}{3}\pi \cdot 5^2 \cdot 7$	Substitute for r and h.
$= \frac{1}{3} \cdot \pi \cdot 25 \cdot 7$	Evaluate the power.
$= \frac{175\pi}{3}$	Simplify.

The volume of the cone is exactly $\frac{175\pi}{3}$ ft³. ■

B Use 3.14 to approximate π. Round your answer to the hundredths place.

$V = \dfrac{175\pi}{3}$ Start with the exact volume.

$\approx \dfrac{175 \cdot 3.14}{3}$ Use 3.14 for π.

$\approx \dfrac{549.5}{3}$ Multiply.

≈ 183 Divide.

The volume of the cone is approximately 183 ft³. ■

Application: Public Safety

Example 4 A city sands its roads in icy weather. At the end of winter, the remaining sand is in a pile in the shape of a cone with diameter 50 feet and height 15 feet. Can all the sand be moved into a silo in the shape of a cylinder with radius 12 feet and height 18 feet for summer storage?

Solution Find the volume of sand in the cone. Compare it to the volume of the silo.

$V_{cone} = \dfrac{1}{3}\pi r^2 h$ Write the volume formula.

$= \dfrac{1}{3}\pi \cdot 25^2 \cdot 15$ If the diameter is 50 feet, then the radius is 25 feet. Substitute 25 for r and 15 for h.

$= 3125\pi$ Simplify to find the exact volume.

$\approx 3125 \cdot 3.14$ Use 3.14 for π.

≈ 9810 Multiply.

The volume of sand in the cone-shaped pile is about 9810 ft³.

$V_{silo} = \pi r^2 h$ Write the volume formula.

$= \pi \cdot 12^2 \cdot 18$ Substitute 12 for r and 18 for h.

$= 2592\pi$ Simplify to find the exact volume.

$\approx 2592 \cdot 3.14$ Use 3.14 for π.

≈ 8140 Multiply.

The volume of the silo is about 8140 ft³.

Since 9810 ft³ > 8140 ft³, all the remaining sand will *not* fit in the silo. ■

> **TIP**
>
> Using subscripts like in V_{cone} and V_{silo} helps you identify which figure you are working with in each part of the problem.

Problem Set

· ·

Find the volume of the pyramid with base area B and height h.

1. $B = 20$ ft^2
   $h = 16$ ft

2. $B = 4$ in^2
   $h = 8$ in.

3. $B = 12$ mm^2
   $h = 1.2$ mm

4. $B = 3.6$ cm^2
   $h = 2.5$ cm

Find the volume of the square pyramid. For each pyramid, s is the length of each side of the square base and h is the height of the pyramid.

5. $s = 4$ cm
   $h = 6$ cm

6. $s = 2$ in.
   $h = 8$ in.

7. $s = 20$ mm
   $h = 15$ mm

8. $s = 3.5$ ft
   $h = 4.5$ ft

Find the volume of the rectangular pyramid. For each pyramid, l and w are the length and width of the rectangular base and h is the height of the pyramid.

9. $l = 6$ cm
   $w = 2$ cm
   $h = 5$ cm

10. $l = 4$ in.
    $w = 9$ in.
    $h = 10$ in.

11. $l = 1.2$ m
    $w = 0.2$ m
    $h = 8$ m

12. $l = 3.1$ ft
    $w = 4.5$ ft
    $h = 6.2$ ft

Find the volume of the triangular pyramid. For each pyramid, b and h_{base} are the base and height of the triangular base and $h_{pyramid}$ is the height of the pyramid.

13. $b = 4$ in.
    $h_{base} = 12$ in.
    $h_{pyramid} = 6$ in.

14. $b = 10$ cm
    $h_{base} = 14$ cm
    $h_{pyramid} = 8$ cm

15. $b = 2.2$ m
    $h_{base} = 8$ m
    $h_{pyramid} = 4.2$ m

16. $b = 6.4$ mm
    $h_{base} = 3.2$ mm
    $h_{pyramid} = 5.7$ mm

Find the volume of the pyramid.

17.

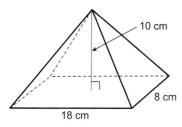

18.

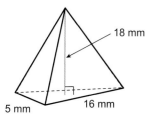

19.

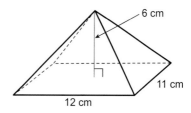

20.

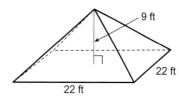

For each cone with radius *r* and height *h*,

A. Find the exact volume.
B. Find the approximate volume. Use 3.14 to approximate π.

21. $r = 9$ in.
$h = 3$ in.

22. $r = 15$ cm
$h = 3.5$ cm

23. $r = 7$ m
$h = 12$ m

*24. Challenge $r = \dfrac{3}{4}$ in.
$h = 1\dfrac{5}{8}$ in.

For each cone,

A. Find the exact volume.
B. Find the approximate volume. Use 3.14 to approximate π.

25.

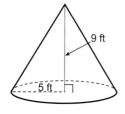

26.

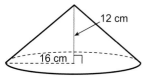

27.

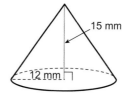

28.

Solve. Use 3.14 to approximate π.

29. An office water cooler has the shape of a cylinder with radius 8 in. and height 22 in. Water is dispensed into paper cups that have the shape of a cone with radius 1.75 in. and height 4 in. What is the greatest number of paper cups that can be completely filled from the water cooler?

*30. Challenge A store sells ice cream in sugar cones and waffle cones. A sugar cone costs $2.75 and has radius 1.25 in. and height 6 in. A waffle cone costs $4.00 and has radius 2 in. and height 7 in. If the store fills each cone exactly, which kind of cone is a better value?

Surface Area

The surface area of a figure is the sum of the areas of each of its faces (including bases).

Finding the Surface Area of a Cube

A cube has six congruent square faces. If each square face has side length s, then the area of each one is s^2. The surface area of a cube with side length s is $6 \cdot s^2$.

SURFACE AREA OF A CUBE

The formula for the surface area of a cube with side s is
$$SA = 6s^2.$$

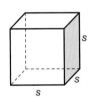

Example 1   Find the surface area of the cube.

3 mm

Solution   The length s of each side is 3 mm.

$SA = 6s^2$ Write the surface area formula.

$\quad = 6 \cdot 3^2$ Substitute for s.

$\quad = 6 \cdot 9$ Evaluate the power.

$\quad = 54$ Multiply.

The surface area of the cube is 54 mm². ■

REMEMBER

Area is measured in square units.

Finding the Lateral Area of a Prism

The **lateral area** of a figure is the sum of the areas of its lateral faces only. One way to find the lateral area is to find the area of each lateral face, then add. Or you can use a formula.

LATERAL AREA OF A PRISM

The formula for the lateral area of a prism with perimeter P and height h is

$$LA = Ph.$$

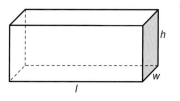

Example 2

A Find the lateral area of the rectangular prism by adding the areas of its lateral faces. Assume the figure is resting on its base.

12 in.   3 in.   2 in.

Solution   The four lateral faces are the front, right side, back, and left sides of the prism.

Area of front: $12 \times 3 = 36$ Area of back: $12 \times 3 = 36$

Area of right side: $2 \times 3 = 6$ Area of left side: $2 \times 3 = 6$

Lateral Area $= 36 \text{ in}^2 + 36 \text{ in}^2 + 6 \text{ in}^2 + 6 \text{ in}^2 = 84 \text{ in}^2$ ∎

B Find the lateral area of the rectangular prism using the formula. Assume the figure is resting on its base.

72 mm   6 mm   4 mm

Solution   First find the perimeter P of the base. Then, use P and h in the formula for lateral area.

$P = 2l + 2w$	Write the formula for perimeter of a rectangle.
$= 2 \cdot 72 + 2 \cdot 4$	Substitute 72 for l and 4 for w.
$= 144 + 8$	Multiply.
$= 152$	Add.
$LA = Ph$	Write the lateral area formula.
$= 152 \cdot 6$	Substitute for P and h.
$= 912$	Multiply.

The lateral area of the figure is 912 mm². ∎

(continued)

> **TIP**
>
> With a rectangular prism, any of the faces could be the base.

> **REMEMBER**
>
> The perimeter of a rectangle with length l and width w is $2l + 2w$.

One way to find the **surface area of a rectangular prism** is to find the lateral area and the area of each base, then add. Or you can use a formula.

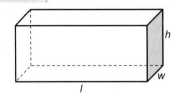
Finding the Surface Area of a Prism

Example 3

A Find the surface area of the rectangular prism by adding the areas of its lateral faces and bases.

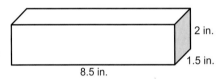

2 in.

1.5 in.

8.5 in.

Solution   The four lateral faces are the front, right side, back, and left side of the prism.

Area of front: $8.5 \times 2 = 17$ Area of back: $8.5 \times 2 = 17$

Area of right side: $1.5 \times 2 = 3$ Area of left side: $1.5 \times 2 = 3$

Area of top: $8.5 \times 1.5 = 12.75$ Area of bottom: $8.5 \times 1.5 = 12.75$

Surface Area $= 2 \cdot (17 \text{ in}^2) + 2 \cdot (3 \text{ in}^2) + 2 \cdot (12.75 \text{ in}^2)$

$= 34 \text{ in}^2 + 6 \text{ in}^2 + 25.5 \text{ in}^2 = 65.5 \text{ in}^2$ ■

B Find the surface area of the rectangular prism using the formula.

Solution   Use the formula. First, find B and P.

$B = lw$	Write the formula for the area of a rectangle.
$= 4 \cdot 6$	Substitute 4 for l and 6 for w.
$= 24$	Simplify.
$P = 2l + 2w$	Write the formula for perimeter of a rectangle.
$= 2 \cdot 4 + 2 \cdot 6$	Substitute 4 for l and 6 for w.
$= 8 + 12$	Multiply.
$= 20$	Add.
$SA = 2B + Ph$	Write the surface area formula.
$= 2 \cdot 24 + 20 \cdot 16$	Substitute for B, P, and h.
$= 48 + 320$	Multiply.
$= 368$	Add.

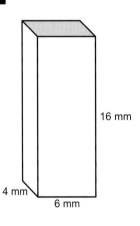

16 mm

4 mm

6 mm

> **TIP**
>
> Finding B, P, and h before substituting into the surface area formula can help you avoid mistakes.

The surface area of the figure is 368 mm². ■

Finding the Surface Area of a Complex Figure

Example 4 Find the surface area of the figure.

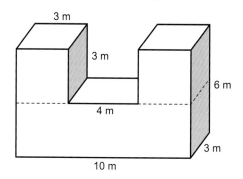

Solution The figure is a rectangular prism topped with two congruent cubes. Find the sum of the surface areas of the three figures, then subtract the area where the figures meet.

THINK ABOUT IT

You could also find the surface area of the figure by adding the areas of each face.

  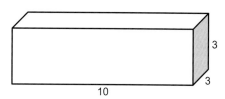

$SA = 6s^2$ $SA = 6s^2$ $SA = 2B + Ph$

$\quad = 6 \cdot 3^2$ $\quad = 6 \cdot 3^2$ $\quad = 2 \cdot (10 \cdot 3) + (2 \cdot 10 + 2 \cdot 3) \cdot 3$

$\quad = 6 \cdot 9$ $\quad = 6 \cdot 9$ $\quad = 2 \cdot 30 + 26 \cdot 3$

$\quad = 54$ $\quad = 54$ $\quad = 60 + 78$

$\quad\quad\quad\quad\quad\quad\quad\quad\quad = 138$

The total surface area of the figures is 54 m² + 54 m² + 138 m² = 246 m².

Now subtract the area of the bottom face of each cube and the areas on the top of the rectangular prism where the figures meet:

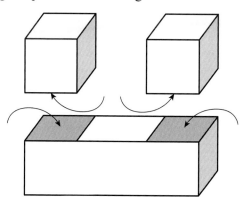

$246 - 4 \cdot 3^2 = 246 - 4 \cdot 9$ For each square surface, $s = 3$ m.

$\quad\quad\quad\quad = 246 - 36$ Multiply.

$\quad\quad\quad\quad = 210$ Subtract.

The surface area of the figure is 210 m². ∎

Problem Set

· ·

Find the surface area of the cube with the given side length.

1. $s = 2$ m

2. $s = 5$ cm

3. $s = 3.5$ mm

Find the surface area of the cube.

4.
7 m

5.
22 in.

6.
4.1 m

Find the lateral area of the rectangular prism.

7.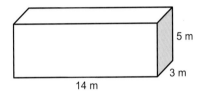
5 m
3 m
14 m

8.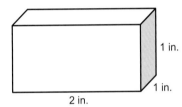
1 in.
1 in.
2 in.

9.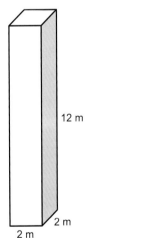
12 m
2 m
2 m

10.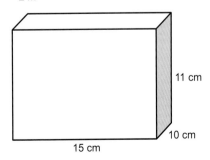
11 cm
10 cm
15 cm

11.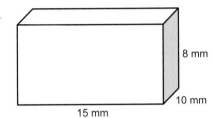
8 mm
10 mm
15 mm

12.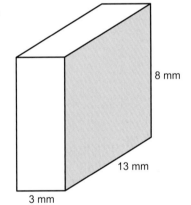
8 mm
13 mm
3 mm

13.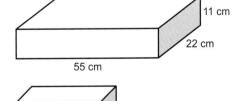
11 cm
22 cm
55 cm

14.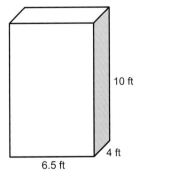
10 ft
4 ft
6.5 ft

Find the lateral area of the rectangular prism. For each figure, l and w are the length and width of the base and h is the height of the rectangular prism.

15. $l = 7$ m
$w = 12$ m
$h = 4$ m

16. $l = 3$ cm
$w = 6$ cm
$h = 12$ cm

17. $l = 15$ mm
$w = 22$ mm
$h = 48$ mm

18. $l = 5$ ft
$w = 2.5$ ft
$h = 7.5$ ft

Find the surface area of the rectangular prism.

19.
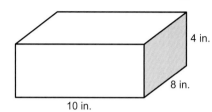
4 in.
8 in.
10 in.

20.
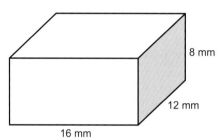
8 mm
12 mm
16 mm

21.
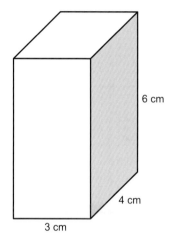
6 cm
4 cm
3 cm

22.
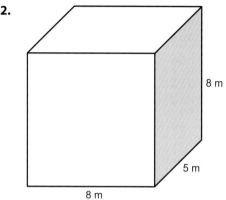
8 m
5 m
8 m

23.
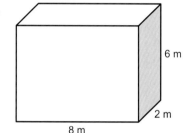
6 m
2 m
8 m

24.
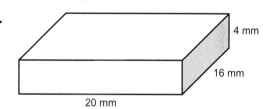
4 mm
16 mm
20 mm

Find the surface area of the figure.

25.

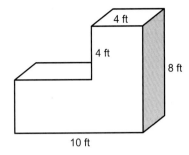

4 ft
4 ft
8 ft
10 ft

26.

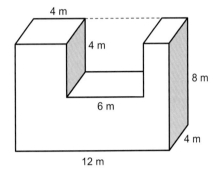

4 m
4 m
8 m
6 m
12 m
4 m

*27. Challenge

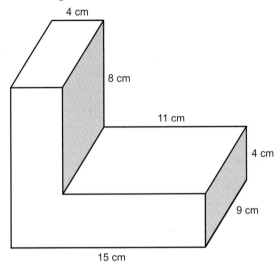

4 cm
8 cm
11 cm
4 cm
9 cm
15 cm

*28. Challenge

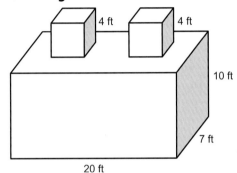

4 ft
4 ft
10 ft
7 ft
20 ft

Solve.

29. A single can of paint covers 350 ft². A room with 9-foot ceilings is 12 feet long and 14 feet wide. How many cans of paint are needed to cover the walls with two coats of paint?

*30. Challenge A packaging company needs to design a box with volume 432 in³. Find the dimensions of two boxes that have volume 432 in³. Then find the surface area of each box. Which box uses less material to make?

Surface Areas of Prisms and Cylinders

You can find the surface area of any prism using the same formula you used to find the surface area of a rectangular prism.

Finding the Surface Area of a Prism

SURFACE AREA OF A PRISM

The formula for the surface area of a prism with base area B, perimeter of the base P and height h is

$$SA = 2B + LA = 2B + Ph.$$

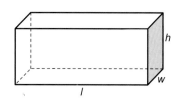

Example 1 Find the surface area of the triangular prism.

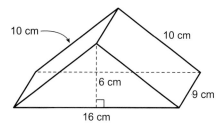

> **REMEMBER**
>
> The bases of the prism are the parallel triangles. The lateral faces are rectangles.

Solution The height h of the prism is 9 cm. Find B and P, then use B, P, and h in the surface area formula.

$$B = \frac{1}{2} bh_{triangle}$$ Write the formula for the area of a triangle.

$$= \frac{1}{2} \cdot 16 \cdot 6$$ Substitute 16 for b and 6 for $h_{triangle}$.

$$= 48$$ Multiply.

$$P = 10 + 10 + 16$$ Add the sides to find the perimeter of the base.

$$= 36$$ Add.

$$SA = 2B + Ph_{prism}$$ Write the surface area formula.

$$= 2 \cdot 48 + 36 \cdot 9$$ Substitute 48 for B, 36 for P, and 9 for h_{prism}.

$$= 96 + 324$$ Multiply.

$$= 420$$ Add.

> **TIP**
>
> Use subscripts to distinguish between the height of the triangle $h_{triangle}$ and the height of the prism h_{prism}.

The surface area of the triangular prism is 420 cm². ∎

Finding the Surface Area of a Cylinder

The formula for the surface area of a cylinder with radius r and height h is

$$SA = 2B + Ph \text{ or } SA = 2\pi r^2 + 2\pi rh.$$

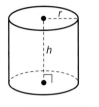

The area of a circle is πr^2. The circumference of a circle is $2\pi r$. So,

$$SA = \mathbf{2B} + \mathbf{Ph}$$
$$= \mathbf{2\pi r^2 + 2\pi rh}$$

Example 2

A Find the exact surface area of the cylinder.

B Find the approximate surface area of the cylinder.

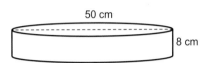

50 cm

8 cm

Solution

A The diameter is given. Find r by dividing the diameter by 2.

$r = d \div 2$	Find the radius.
$= 50 \div 2$	Substitute 50 for d.
$= 25$	Divide.
$SA = 2\pi r^2 + 2\pi rh$	Write the surface area formula.
$= 2\pi \cdot 25^2 + 2\pi \cdot 25 \cdot 8$	Substitute 25 for r and 8 for h.
$= 2\pi \cdot 625 + 2\pi \cdot 25 \cdot 8$	Evaluate the power.
$= 1250\pi + 400\pi$	Multiply.
$= 1650\pi$	Add.

The surface area of the cylinder is exactly 1650π cm². ∎

B

$SA = 1650\pi$	Start with the exact surface area.
$\approx 1650 \cdot 3.14$	Use 3.14 for π.
≈ 5180	Multiply.

The surface area of the cylinder is approximately 5180 cm². ∎

Using the Surface Area to Volume Ratio

Scientists and business people often need to figure out how an object's surface area compares to its volume. For instance, biologists study organisms that have more surface area to increase their drag in the water environment. Any business that needs to store or ship products cares about how surface area compares to the volume or capacity.

One way to compare the surface area of a figure to its volume is the **surface area to volume ratio**. This ratio can help you compare figures.

Example 3   Application: Product Packaging

A company is purchasing boxes to ship its product. The price of a box depends on the amount of material used to make it, and the company wants to pack as much product in the box as possible. So, the company wants to minimize surface area while maximizing volume. The company's suppliers have presented two options, shown below.

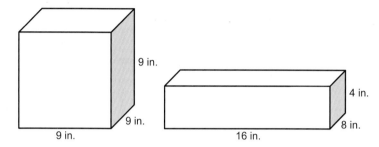

A Find the surface area to volume ratio for each figure.

B Analyze the ratios. Which package is the better choice?

Solution

A Calculate the surface area and volume for each figure.

$SA = 6s^2$	$V = s^3$	$B = 16 \cdot 8 = 128$	$V = Bh$
$= 6 \cdot 9^2$	$= 9^3$	$P = 2 \cdot 16 + 2 \cdot 8 = 48$	$= 128 \cdot 4$
$= 6 \cdot 81$	$= 729$	$SA = 2B + Ph$	$= 512$
$= 486$		$= 2 \cdot 128 + 48 \cdot 4$	
		$= 256 + 192$	
		$= 448$	
The surface area is 486 in².		The surface area is 448 in².	
The volume is 729 in³.		The volume is 512 in³.	

Find the surface area to volume ratios:

Cube: $\dfrac{486}{729} \approx \dfrac{0.67}{1}$ **Rectangular Prism:** $\dfrac{448}{512} = \dfrac{0.875}{1}$ ∎

B Compare the ratios $\dfrac{0.67}{1}$ and $\dfrac{0.875}{1}$. The second ratio shows a greater surface area to volume ratio. This means that the rectangular prism uses more material per unit of volume than the cube does. In order to save on materials, the company should choose the cube. ∎

Problem Set

. . . .

Find the surface area of the prism with area of the base *B*, perimeter of the base *P*, and height *h*.

1. $B = 8 \text{ m}^2$
    $P = 12 \text{ m}$
    $h = 3 \text{ m}$

2. $B = 20 \text{ ft}^2$
    $P = 18 \text{ ft}$
    $h = 2 \text{ ft}$

3. $B = 40 \text{ cm}^2$
    $P = 28 \text{ cm}$
    $h = 10 \text{ cm}$

4.
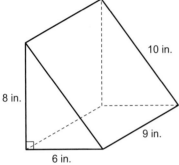

5.
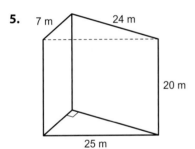

6. $B = 3\frac{2}{3} \text{ cm}^2$
    $P = 5\frac{1}{3} \text{ cm}$
    $h = 2 \text{ cm}$

7. $B = 48 \text{ in}^2$
    $P = 28 \text{ in.}$
    $h = 12.4 \text{ in.}$

*8. **Challenge** Find SA in cm².
    $B = 325 \text{ mm}$
    $P = 40 \text{ m}$
    $h = 120 \text{ cm}$

9.
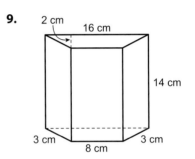

10.
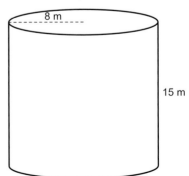

For problems 11 and 12,

A. **Find the exact surface area of the cylinder with radius *r* and height *h*.**

B. **Find the approximate surface area. Use 3.14 to approximate π.**

11. $r = 5 \text{ in.}$
     $h = 10 \text{ in.}$

12. $r = 42 \text{ mm}$
     $h = 37 \text{ mm}$

13.
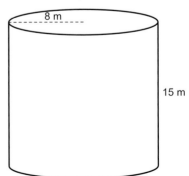

14.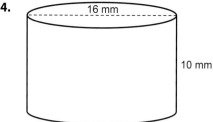

16 mm

10 mm

15. $r = 6$ m
$h = 3.2$ m

16. $r = 2.5$ cm
$h = 6.1$ cm

17. $r = 9\frac{1}{2}$ in.
$h = 8$ in.

18. $r = 4$ m
$h = 8.2$ m

19.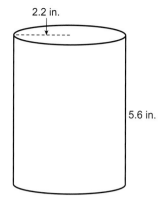

2.2 in.

5.6 in.

20.

$3\frac{1}{2}$ m

$2\frac{3}{4}$ m

*21. Challenge $r = 5.1$ cm
$h = 8r$

*22. Challenge $r = \pi$ mm
$h = 5\pi$ mm

Find the surface area to volume ratio for each figure. Use 3.14 to approximate π.

23. a cube with $s = 1$ cm

24. a cube with $s = 5$ cm

25. a cube with $s = 10$ cm

26. a rectangular prism with $l = 5$ cm, $w = 4$ cm, and $h = 2$ cm

27. a rectangular prism with $l = 1$ cm, $w = 5$ cm, and $h = 10$ cm

28. a cylinder with $r = 2.5$ cm and $h = 4$ cm

Solve.

*29. Challenge The Happy Apple juice company sells apple juice in cans of two different sizes. One can has radius 2.25 in. and height 9 in. The other can has radius 2.5 in. and height 8 in. Find the surface area to volume ratio for each can. Which can uses more material per unit of volume?

*30. Challenge What is the surface area to volume ratio for any cube? Give your answer in terms of s, the length of one side of the cube.

UNIT 13   Counting and Probability

An inspector can use counting and probability to determine how many apples are good.

How many apples have mass between 100 and 200 grams? How many are bruised? How many are not yet ripe? Checking every single apple would probably be pretty impractical, but if you understand probability and sampling, you could make a good estimate.

Big Idea

▶ Probability is a measure of how likely it is that some event will occur.

Topic Outline

▶ Counting Principles

▶ Permutations

▶ Combinations

▶ Probability

▶ Mutually Exclusive Events

▶ Samples and Prediction

Counting Principles

Use a counting principle to find the number of ways of doing more than one thing. A counting principle that involves addition and a counting principle that involves multiplication will help you. Both counting principles can best be understood by examples.

The Sum Counting Principle

If a task can be done two or more different ways, but the task cannot be broken down into separate stages, you can use addition to find the number of ways the task can be done.

Example 1

A How many ways are there to spin an odd number or a multiple of 4 on this spinner?

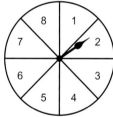

Solution There are 4 odd numbers: 1, 3, 5, and 7. There are 2 multiples of 4: 4 and 8. You cannot spin both an odd number and a multiple of 4, so add to find the number of ways.

$$\underbrace{1, 3, 5, 7}_{4} \quad \text{or} \quad \underbrace{4, 8}_{2} \quad = 6$$

There are 6 ways of spinning an odd number or a multiple of 4. ∎

B The integers 1–100 are written on 100 index cards, a different integer on each card, and placed into a hat. How many ways are there to choose an integer that is less than 10, a multiple of 30, or greater than 95?

(continued)

Solution   There are 9 integers less than 10: 1, 2, 3, 4, 5, 6, 7, 8, and 9. There are 3 multiples of 30: 30, 60, and 90. There are 5 integers greater than 95: 96, 97, 98, 99, and 100. Only one of the three conditions can be satisfied by choosing one integer, so add.

$$\underbrace{1, 2, 3, 4, 5, 6, 7, 8, 9}_{9} \quad \text{or} \quad \underbrace{30, 60, 90}_{3} \quad \text{or} \quad \underbrace{96, 97, 98, 99, 100}_{5}$$
$$9 \quad + \quad 3 \quad + \quad 5 \quad = 17$$

There are 17 ways to choose an integer that is less than 10, a multiple of 30, or greater than 95. ∎

PROPERTY

The **sum counting principle** states that if there are *m* ways of doing one thing and *n* ways of doing another thing, then there are *m* + *n* ways of doing one thing *or* the other.

TIP

The sum counting principal can be extended to three or more things.

The Product Counting Principle

When a task can be broken into stages, you can figure out the number of ways of doing the task by listing all the ways the task can de done, using a tree to see the ways, or multiplying.

Example 2

Ⓐ Ms. Gonzalez is buying a car. She can choose white, black, red, or silver for the paint color. She can choose cloth, leather, or synthetic leather for the seat fabric. How many different combinations of color and fabric can Ms. Gonzalez choose?

Solution   For each paint color choice, Ms. Gonzalez can choose any of the seat fabrics, so use a tree to see how multiplication can help.

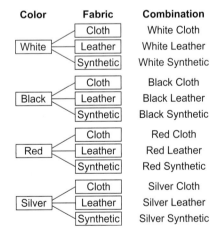

TIP

Drawing a tree diagram to solve a counting problem works well for a small number of choices, but is not always practical. For example, if there were 10 choices for colors and 7 choices for fabrics, the tree diagram would be very cumbersome.

For each of 4 paint color choices, Ms. Gonzalez can choose 3 fabrics, so there are 12 different combinations of color and fabric. ∎

B At a café, customers can choose one drink, one sandwich, and one side order for a lunch special. Use the table to determine how many different lunch specials are possible.

Drink	Sandwich	Side
Juice	Ham	Slaw
Soda	Turkey	Fruit
Iced Tea	Cheese	
	Veggie	

Solution For each drink, a customer can choose any of the sandwiches, and for each sandwich, any of the side orders. Use a tree diagram. There are 3 drinks, 4 sandwiches, and 2 side orders.

$$3 \cdot 4 \cdot 2 = 24$$

Drink	Sandwich	Side	Lunch Specials
	Ham	Slaw	Juice, Ham, Slaw
		Fruit	Juice, Ham, Fruit
	Turkey	Slaw	Juice, Turkey, Slaw
		Fruit	Juice, Turkey, Fruit
Juice	Cheese	Slaw	Juice, Cheese, Slaw
		Fruit	Juice, Cheese, Fruit
	Veggie	Slaw	Juice, Veggie, Slaw
		Fruit	Juice, Veggie, Fruit
	Ham	Slaw	Soda, Ham, Slaw
		Fruit	Soda, Ham, Fruit
	Turkey	Slaw	Soda, Turkey, Slaw
		Fruit	Soda, Turkey, Fruit
Soda	Cheese	Slaw	Soda, Cheese, Slaw
		Fruit	Soda, Cheese, Fruit
	Veggie	Slaw	Soda, Veggie, Slaw
		Fruit	Soda, Veggie, Fruit
	Ham	Slaw	Iced Tea, Ham, Slaw
		Fruit	Iced Tea, Ham, Fruit
	Turkey	Slaw	Iced Tea, Turkey, Slaw
		Fruit	Iced Tea, Turkey, Fruit
Iced Tea	Cheese	Slaw	Iced Tea, Cheese, Slaw
		Fruit	Iced Tea, Cheese, Fruit
	Veggie	Slaw	Iced Tea, Veggie, Slaw
		Fruit	Iced Tea, Veggie, Fruit

There are 24 different possible lunch specials. ∎

PROPERTY

The **product counting principle** states that if a task can be broken into two stages and there are m ways of doing the first stage and n ways of doing the second stage, then there are $m \cdot n$ ways of doing the task, that is, there are $m \cdot n$ ways of doing one thing *and* the other.

TIP

The product counting principle can be extended to three or more things.

Determining Which Counting Principle to Use

Example 3 Explain whether to use the sum or product counting principle. Then use the principle to answer the question.

A Ed has 6 shirts and 2 ties. How many ways can Ed choose one shirt and one tie?

Solution For each shirt, Ed can choose either tie, so use the product counting principle.

There are $6 \cdot 2 = 12$ ways to choose one shirt and one tie. ∎

B A box contains four $1-bills, three $5-bills, seven $10-bills, and six $20-bills. By choosing one bill, how many ways are there to get more than $8?

Solution You get more than $8 by choosing either a $10-bill or a $20-bill. You cannot choose both a $10-bill and a $20-bill, so use the sum counting principle. There are seven $10-bills and six $20-bills.

There are $7 + 6 = 13$ ways to get more than $8 with a single bill. ∎

Problem Set

Use the sum counting principle to answer the question.

1. Adriana has 12 paid sick days and 3 paid personal days to use throughout the year. When she takes a day off, she must use either a sick day or a personal day to get paid for that day. How many days with pay can Adriana take off?

2. Reggie is choosing a book from a shelf that has 9 fiction books and 12 nonfiction books. How many ways can Reggie choose a book?

3. Nina has 4 T-shirts and 3 sweaters in her luggage. How many different tops can she wear with one pair of jeans?

4. A new member at a fitness center is choosing an exercise class. How many options does she have if the fitness center offers 2 aqua classes, 4 cardio classes, and 3 cycle classes?

5. In deciding where to have lunch, a group of friends looks at the websites for 2 pizzerias, 3 drive-throughs, and 2 diners. How many choices are the friends considering?

Use the product counting principle to answer the question.

6. A restaurant offers 8 different appetizers, 15 different entrées, and 6 different desserts. A meal consists of an appetizer, an entrée, and a dessert. How many different meals can a customer order?

7. Natalie has 8 shirts and 3 pairs of pants in her luggage. How many different combinations of one shirt and one pair of pants can Natalie wear?

8. For her living room window, Mrs. Santiago can have the top curtain open or closed. She can also have the bottom curtain open or closed. How many ways can Mrs. Santiago arrange the curtains?

9. There are 5 pairs of gloves, 3 scarves, and 4 hats in Amy's closet. How many ways can Amy wear a pair of gloves, a scarf, and a hat?

10. On a washing machine, there are different load sizes: small, medium, large, and extra large. There are also different water temperatures: cold, warm, and hot. How many different combinations of load size and water temperature are available?

Explain whether to use the sum counting principle or the product counting principle. Then use the principle to answer the question.

11. When choosing a beverage, Tavon can order small, medium, or large. He can also order the beverage with or without ice. How many ways can Tavon order a beverage?

12. Helen can order her hotdog as regular or jumbo and with mustard, ketchup, or both. How many ways can Helen order her hotdog?

13. When a coin is tossed, it lands either heads up or tails up. Suppose a coin is tossed four times. How many outcomes are possible? (Hint: An example of an outcome is HTTH, where H represents heads and T represents tails.)

14. Cindy needs to buy a calculator. The store offers 3 different basic calculators, 6 different scientific calculators, and 4 different graphing calculators. How many ways can Cindy choose a calculator from this store?

15. Eli is ordering checks and is deciding on a background design. There are 4 traditional, 6 nature, 4 animal, 3 cartoon, and 3 sports designs. How many ways can Eli choose a design for his checks?

16. When ordering a sandwich, Tina can choose white, wheat, or rye bread. She can choose ham, turkey, or roast beef for the meat and American, Swiss, or cheddar for the cheese. She can also choose a 6-inch sandwich or a 12-inch sandwich. How many ways can Tina order a sandwich consisting of bread, meat, and cheese?

17. A customer can choose either a cup or a bowl of soup. He can choose the soup to be tomato, vegetable, or chicken. How many ways can the customer order soup?

18. Find the number of possible license plates for each of the following.
    A. A state that has license plates with one letter, followed by five digits.
    B. A state that has license plates with two letters, followed by four digits.
    C. A state that has license plates with three letters, followed by three digits.

19. All the letters in the alphabet, A through Z, and all the digits, 0 through 9, are written on slips of paper. Each slip of paper has exactly one character (letter or digit) on it.
    A. How many outcomes are possible if one slip of paper is chosen?
    B. How many outcomes are possible if one letter is chosen from the slips with letters on them and one digit is chosen from the slips with digits on them?

Follow the instructions for each problem. You may abbreviate when you write lists.

*20. **Challenge** A real-estate agent searches for property by choosing the type of property, the number of bedrooms, the number of bathrooms, and whether or not it has a garage. Use the table to determine the number of ways an agent can search for property.

Type	Bedrooms	Bathrooms	Garage
Condominium	1	1	Yes
Townhouse	2	1.5	No
Single Family	3	2	
Multifamily	4+	2.5	
		3+	

*21. **Challenge** For lunch, Fiona can have juice or milk for her beverage. She can have a burger, pizza, or a turkey sandwich for the meal. She can have an apple or raisins for dessert. List all the possible lunches Fiona can order.

*22. **Challenge** A woodworker makes 6-foot, 8-foot, and 12-foot long tables. Each table is oak, pine, or cedar. List all the possible tables that the woodworker can make.

*23. **Challenge** Paulo flips a coin, then rolls a die, and then rolls another die. List all the possible outcomes. (Hint: H52 can represent the outcome heads on the coin, 5 on the first die, and 2 on the second die.)

Permutations

You can count the number of ways items can be arranged.

Arranging 5 People in 5 Chairs

Example 1 Al, Brea, Carol, Dora, and Ernie are going to sit in five chairs that are along a wall. In how many ways can the people arrange themselves in the chairs?

Solution There are five people and five chairs. Any of the 5 people can sit in the first chair. Once that person is seated, there are 4 people who can sit in the second chair, 3 people in the third, 2 in the fourth, and 1 in the fifth.

$$5 \cdot 4 \cdot 3 \cdot 2 \cdot 1 = 120$$

Use the product counting principle. There are 120 ways 5 people can sit in 5 chairs. ∎

Calculating Factorials

Generalizing Example 1, if there are n people and n seats, there are $n \cdot (n - 1) \cdot (n - 2) \cdot \ldots \cdot 1$ ways to arrange the people. This product is a *factorial*.

FACTORIAL

The **factorial** (!) of a positive integer is the product of all the positive integers less than or equal to the integer.

$$n! = n \cdot (n - 1) \cdot (n - 2) \cdot \ldots \cdot 1$$

The factorial of 0 is defined to be 1.

$$0! = 1$$

Example

$$4! = 4 \cdot 3 \cdot 2 \cdot 1 = 24$$

Example 2 Find each value.

A 6!

Solution The expression is a factorial.

$6! = 6 \cdot 5 \cdot 4 \cdot 3 \cdot 2 \cdot 1$ Write out all the factors.

$= 720$ Multiply. ∎

B 5!2!

Solution The expression is the product of two factorials.

$5!2! = (5!) \cdot (2!)$

$= (5 \cdot 4 \cdot 3 \cdot 2 \cdot 1) \cdot (2 \cdot 1)$ Write each set of factors.

$= 120 \cdot 2$ Multiply within the parentheses.

$= 240$ Multiply. ∎

C

Solution The expression is the quotient of two factorials.

$\dfrac{4!}{2!} = \dfrac{4 \cdot 3 \cdot \cancel{2} \cdot \cancel{1}}{\cancel{2} \cdot \cancel{1}}$ Divide out the common factors.

$= 12$ Simplify. ∎

D $(8 - 5)!$

Solution The expression is the factorial of a difference.

$(8 - 5)! = 3!$ Evaluate inside parentheses.

$= 3 \cdot 2 \cdot 1$ Write the factors.

$= 6$ Multiply. ∎

THINK ABOUT IT
The value of $(8 - 5)!$ is not the same as $8! - 5!$.

Permutations

If you have n items being arranged in n places, you have $n!$ ways to arrange the items. A *permutation* is an arrangement of items.

DEFINITION

A **permutation** is an arrangement of items in which the order of the items is important.

Example 3

A Find the number of permutations of the 3 letters A, B, and C.

Solution

Method 1: List the permutations and then count them.

  ABC   ACB   BAC   BCA   CAB   CBA

Method 2: Use the product counting principle.

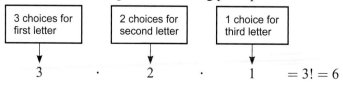

There are 6 permutations of the letters A, B, and C. ∎

THINK ABOUT IT
After the first letter is chosen, there are 2 remaining choices for the second letter.

After the second letter is chosen, there is 1 remaining choice for the third letter.

(continued)

B Leslie has 4 trophies, but only 2 trophies will fit in her display case. How many different ways can Leslie arrange her display case?

Solution

| 1st trophy | 2nd trophy | There are 2 spaces to fill. |

| 4 choices | | There are 4 ways to choose the first trophy. |
| 1st trophy | 2nd trophy | |

| 4 choices | 3 choices | There are 3 trophies left for the second space. |
| 1st trophy | 2nd trophy | |

$4 \cdot 3 = 12$ Use the product counting principle.

Leslie can arrange her display case in 12 different ways. ∎

Using a Formula to Calculate a Number of Permutations

You just learned two methods of calculating a number of permutations. A third method is to use a formula.

Example 4

A Find the value of $_5P_3$.

Solution

$_nP_r = {}_5P_3 = \dfrac{5!}{(5-3)!}$ Substitute 5 for *n* and 3 for *r*.

$= \dfrac{5!}{2!}$ Evaluate inside the parentheses.

$= \dfrac{5 \cdot 4 \cdot 3 \cdot \cancel{2 \cdot 1}}{\cancel{2 \cdot 1}}$ Write each factorial as a product and divide out common factors.

$= 60$ Simplify. ∎

B How many ways can you arrange 3 books in a row?

Solution   Find the number of permutations of 3 items taken 3 at a time.

$_nP_r = {}_3P_3 = \dfrac{3!}{(3-3)!}$ Substitute 3 for *n* and 3 for *r*.

$= \dfrac{3!}{0!}$ Simplify inside the parentheses.

$= \dfrac{3 \cdot 2 \cdot 1}{1}$ Write the factors.

$= 6$ Simplify.

There are 6 ways to arrange 3 books in a row. ∎

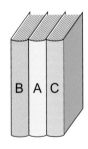

THINK ABOUT IT

Compare Example 3A and Example 4B. The number of permutations of 3 letters is the same as the number of ways to arrange 3 books in a row.

Application: Sports

Example 5   There are 9 runners in a race.

A How many ways can the runners finish?

Solution   Find the number of permutations of 9 items taken 9 at a time.

$$_nP_r = {_9}P_9 = \frac{9!}{(9-9)!}$$ Substitute 9 for n and 9 for r.

$$= \frac{9!}{0!}$$ Simplify inside the parentheses.

$$= \frac{9 \cdot 8 \cdot 7 \cdot 6 \cdot 5 \cdot 4 \cdot 3 \cdot 2 \cdot 1}{1}$$ Write the factors.

$$= 362{,}880$$ Multiply.

There are 362,880 ways the runners can finish. ∎

B How many ways can runners finish first, second, and third?

Solution   Find the number of permutations of 9 items taken 3 at a time.

$$_nP_r = {_9}P_3 = \frac{9!}{(9-3)!}$$ Substitute 9 for n and 3 for r.

$$= \frac{9!}{6!}$$ Simplify inside the parentheses.

$$= \frac{9 \cdot 8 \cdot 7 \cdot \cancel{6} \cdot \cancel{5} \cdot \cancel{4} \cdot \cancel{3} \cdot \cancel{2} \cdot \cancel{1}}{\cancel{6} \cdot \cancel{5} \cdot \cancel{4} \cdot \cancel{3} \cdot \cancel{2} \cdot \cancel{1}}$$ Divide out common factors.

$$= 504$$ Simplify.

There are 504 ways that runners can finish first, second, and third. ∎

> **THINK ABOUT IT**
>
> $$_nP_n = n!$$
>
> **Proof:**
>
> $$_nP_n = \frac{n!}{(n-n)!}$$
>
> $$= \frac{n!}{0!}$$
>
> $$= \frac{n!}{1}$$
>
> $$= n!$$

Application: Security

Example 6   Suppose you need to form a password using 5 different digits. How many passwords are possible?

Solution   There are 10 digits (0 through 9). Find the number of permutations of 10 items taken 5 at a time.

$$_nP_r = {_{10}}P_5 = \frac{10!}{(10-5)!}$$ Substitute 10 for n and 5 for r.

$$= \frac{10!}{5!}$$ Simplify inside the parentheses.

$$= \frac{10 \cdot 9 \cdot 8 \cdot 7 \cdot 6 \cdot \cancel{5} \cdot \cancel{4} \cdot \cancel{3} \cdot \cancel{2} \cdot \cancel{1}}{\cancel{5} \cdot \cancel{4} \cdot \cancel{3} \cdot \cancel{2} \cdot \cancel{1}}$$ Divide out common factors.

$$= 30{,}240$$ Simplify.

There are 30,240 possible passwords. ∎

> **THINK ABOUT IT**
>
> If digits can be repeated, there are 10^5, or 100,000 possible passwords.
>
> $$10 \cdot 10 \cdot 10 \cdot 10 \cdot 10 = 10^5$$

Problem Set

Find each value.

1. $1!$
2. $2!$
3. $4!$
4. $0!$
5. $8!$

6. $\dfrac{4!}{4!}$
7. $_3P_2$
8. $_4P_1$
9. $4!3!$

10. $(6-2)!$
11. $6!-2!$
12. $\dfrac{_5P_2}{2!}$
13. $\dfrac{9!}{8!}$

14. $_6P_3$
15. $_5P_5$
16. $\dfrac{_4P_3}{3!}$

Answer each question.

17. A chef has 8 jars of spice. How many ways can he line up the jars on his kitchen shelf?

18. Jonathan has 6 unread e-mails. If he chooses the order in which to read them randomly, how many ways can he choose to read the e-mails?

19. How many ways can 7 family members line up in a row for a photo?

20. A password must consist of exactly 5 letters. Julie decides to use every vowel (A, E, I, O, and U) in her password. How many different passwords can Julie make?

21. A chef has 10 jars of spice, but only 6 will fit on his spice rack. How many ways can the chef arrange 6 jars on his spice rack, choosing from 10 jars?

22. There are 4 empty seats in a row in a movie theater. A group of 6 friends just entered the theater, and they see that they will have to split up. How many ways can the friends in this group fill the 4 empty seats in that row?

23. Ten bicyclists are in a race. How many ways can first, second, and third places be awarded?

24. The manager of a baseball team is writing the 9-player batting order for a game.
    A. How many ways can he write the batting order if he has 9 players to choose from?
    B. How many ways can he write the batting order if he has 13 players to choose from?

25. There is a group of 7 children standing in a room.
    A. How many ways can children from the group sit in 6 chairs?
    B. How many ways can children from the group sit in 5 chairs?
    C. How many ways can children from the group sit in 3 chairs?

26. Yvette has 9 songs downloaded on her computer. She will transfer 5 of the songs from her computer to her music player.
    A. How many possible 5-song lists can Yvette put together, choosing from the 9 songs?
    B. How many possible 7-song lists can Yvette put together, choosing from the 9 songs?

27. Britney's password is a permutation of the 7 letters in her first name. If you try to guess her password by guessing all the possible permutations, what is the maximum number of passwords you need to check?

28. A restaurant has an opening for a waiter and an opening for a hostess. The manager received applications from 7 people qualified for either position. How many ways can he fill the positions?

29. There are 12 players on the red team and 11 players on the blue team. For a tug-of-war game, each team must pick 10 players.
    A. How many ways can the red team line up 10 players?
    B. How many ways can the blue team line up 10 players?

30. Explain how the product counting principle can be used to find the number of ways to arrange 3 books in a row, choosing from 5 books.

31. Write all the permutations of the letters in the word *cat*.

*32. Challenge Is $(n - r)!$ the same as $n! - r!$? Show why or why not.

*33. Challenge How does the number of permutations of all the letters in the word *dear* compare to the number of permutations of all the letters in the word *deer*? Explain.

*34. Challenge Show algebraically that $_nP_{(n-r)} = \dfrac{n!}{r!}$.

Combinations

Order is not always important when counting.

Determining if Order Matters

An arrangement can be a permutation or a combination, depending on whether order is important.

> **DEFINITION**
>
> A **combination** is an arrangement of items in which the order of the items is not important.

Example 1   Alex, Jorge, Emily, Lisa, and Tori are playing tennis. How many ways can you select 2 players to play tennis from a group of 5 players?

Solution   Use the permutation formula.

$$_nP_r = {_5P_2} = \frac{5!}{(5-2)!}$$ Substitute 5 for n and 2 for r.

$$= \frac{5!}{3!}$$ Evaluate inside parentheses.

$$= \frac{5 \cdot 4 \cdot \cancel{3} \cdot \cancel{2} \cdot \cancel{1}}{\cancel{3} \cdot \cancel{2} \cdot 1}$$ Write each factorial as a product and divide out common factors.

$$= 20$$ Simplify.

AJ AE AL AT JE JL JT EL ET LT

JA EA LA TA EJ LJ TJ LE TE TL

Make an ordered list of the 20 permutations using the first letter of each person's name to represent that person.

Order does not matter because Alex versus Jorge is the same as Jorge versus Alex, so you need to divide $_5P_2$ by 2.

$$_5P_2 \div 2 = 20 \div 2$$ Divide by 2.

$$= 10$$

There are 10 ways you can select 2 players to play tennis from a group of 5 players. ■

> **REMEMBER**
>
> A permutation is an arrangement of items in which the order of the items *is* important.

Using a Formula to Calculate a Number of Combinations

In general, if you want to find the number of ways of getting a group of r from a group of n, you have $_nP_r$ divided by $r!$.

$$_nC_r = \frac{_nP_r}{r!}$$

$$= \frac{\frac{n!}{(n-r)!}}{r!}$$

$$= \frac{\frac{n!}{(n-r)!}}{r!} \cdot \frac{\frac{1}{r!}}{\frac{1}{r!}}$$

$$= \frac{\frac{n!}{r!(n-r)!}}{1}$$

$$= \frac{n!}{r!(n-r)!}$$

The number of combinations of n items taken r at a time is

$$_nC_r = \frac{n!}{(n-r)!\,r!}.$$

TIP

$_nC_r$ is sometimes written as $C(n, r)$ or $\binom{n}{r}$.

Example 2 Find the value of $_5C_3$.

Solution

$$_nC_r = {}_5C_3 = \frac{5!}{(5-3)!\,3!}$$ Substitute 5 for n and 3 for r.

$$= \frac{5!}{2!\,3!}$$ Evaluate inside the parentheses.

$$= \frac{5 \cdot \overset{2}{\cancel{4}} \cdot \cancel{3 \cdot 2 \cdot 1}}{(\underset{1}{\cancel{2}} \cdot 1) \cdot (\cancel{3 \cdot 2 \cdot 1})} = 10$$ Write each factorial as a product and divide out common factors. ∎

Example 3 The Pleasing Pizza Pie Palace sells pizzas with 6 different possible toppings.

Ⓐ How many two-topping pizzas are possible?

Solution There are 6 items taken 2 at a time. Find $_6C_2$.

$$_nC_r = {}_6C_2 = \frac{6!}{(6-2)!\,2!}$$ Substitute 6 for n and 2 for r.

$$= \frac{6!}{4!\,2!}$$ Evaluate inside the parentheses.

$$= \frac{\overset{3}{\cancel{6}} \cdot 5 \cdot \cancel{4 \cdot 3 \cdot 2 \cdot 1}}{(\cancel{4 \cdot 3 \cdot 2 \cdot 1}) \cdot (\underset{1}{\cancel{2}} \cdot 1)}$$ List factors and divide out common factors.

$$= 15$$ Simplify.

There are 15 two-topping pizzas. ∎

THINK ABOUT IT

It does not matter which topping is listed first. A pizza with pepperoni and mushrooms is the same as a pizza with mushrooms and pepperoni.

B How many three-topping pizzas are possible?

Solution   There are 6 items taken 3 at a time. Find $_6C_3$.

$$_nC_r = {_6C_3} = \frac{6!}{(6-3)!\,3!}$$ Substitute 6 for n and 3 for r.

$$= \frac{6!}{3!\,3!}$$ Evaluate inside the parentheses.

$$= \frac{\overset{2}{\cancel{6}} \cdot 5 \cdot \overset{2}{\cancel{4}} \cdot \cancel{3} \cdot \cancel{2} \cdot \cancel{1}}{(\cancel{3} \cdot \cancel{2} \cdot \cancel{1}) \cdot (\cancel{3}_1 \cdot \cancel{2}_1 \cdot 1)}$$ List factors and divide out common factors.

$$= 20$$ Simplify.

There are 20 three-topping pizzas. ■

C How many four-topping pizzas are possible?

Solution   There are 6 items taken 4 at a time. Find $_6C_4$.

$$_nC_r = {_6C_4} = \frac{6!}{(6-4)!\,4!}$$ Substitute 6 for n and 4 for r.

$$= \frac{6!}{2!\,4!}$$ Evaluate inside the parentheses.

$$= \frac{\overset{3}{\cancel{6}} \cdot 5 \cdot \cancel{4} \cdot \cancel{3} \cdot \cancel{2} \cdot \cancel{1}}{(\cancel{2}_1 \cdot 1) \cdot (\cancel{4} \cdot \cancel{3} \cdot \cancel{2} \cdot \cancel{1})}$$ List factors and divide out common factors.

$$= 15$$ Simplify.

There are 15 possible four-topping pizzas. ■

D How many six-topping pizzas are possible?

Solution   There are 6 items taken 6 at a time. Find $_6C_6$.

$$_nC_r = {_6C_6} = \frac{6!}{(6-6)!\,6!}$$ Substitute 6 for n and 6 for r.

$$= \frac{6!}{0!\,6!}$$ Evaluate inside the parentheses.

$$= \frac{6!}{1 \cdot 6!}$$ $0! = 1$

$$= 1$$ Simplify.

There is 1 possible six-topping pizza. ■

THINK ABOUT IT

$_nC_n = 1$

Proof:

$$_nC_n = \frac{n!}{(n-n)!\,n!}$$

$$= \frac{n!}{0!\,n!}$$

$$= \frac{n!}{1 \cdot n!}$$

$$= 1$$

Distinguishing Between Permutations and Combinations

Example 4   For each situation, state whether permutations or combinations are indicated. Write an expression that represents the number of ways to do what is described.

A Select 6 CDs to take on a trip from a collection of 15 CDs.

Solution   Order does not matter when forming a group. Combinations are indicated. Use the expression $_{15}C_6$. ■

B Select a president, vice president, and treasurer from 30 students.

Solution Order matters because for any 3 students selected, there are different ways to fill the 3 positions with those students. Permutations are indicated. Use the expression $_{30}P_3$. ∎

C There are 40 tick marks on a lock, corresponding to the integers 0–39. Choose 3 integers to form a "combination" that unlocks the lock.

Solution Although it is customary to refer to this sort of lock as a "combination lock," these are really permutations because order matters. For example, 26-7-12 will not unlock the lock if 7-26-12 is required. So, permutations are indicated. Use the expression $_{40}P_3$. ∎

> **THINK ABOUT IT**
>
> A more accurate name for a "combination lock" is "permutation lock."

Problem Set

Find each value.

1. $_4C_2$

2. $_3C_2$

3. $_5C_5$

4. $_4C_3$

5. $_8C_4$

6. $_3C_3 \cdot _4C_4$

7. $C(5, 1)$

8. $\binom{6}{0}$

9. $_5P_2 - _5C_2$

For each situation,

A. State whether permutations or combinations are indicated.

B. Write an expression that represents the number of ways to do what is described.

10. Select the order in which to introduce 3 people to an audience.

11. Select a committee of 6 people from a group of 12 people.

12. Form a password with 8 different characters, selecting from the letters A−Z and the digits 0−9.

13. Select 12 of 20 flowers for a bouquet.

14. Select 2 quarters from the 4 quarters in your pocket for a parking meter.

15. Select 5 goldfish from 30 goldfish in a store aquarium.

Answer each question.

16. There are 8 types of wildflowers growing in a meadow. How many ways can a bouquet of 5 different flowers be made?

17. An art project requires the use of 2 different colored markers. How many sets of 2 colored markers can be chosen from a box of 10 markers if each marker is a different color?

18. There are 6 essay questions on a test. A student must answer any 2 of them. How many ways can the student choose 2 questions to answer?

19. A hiker has 5 different dried meals. He will take 2 of the meals on his hike. How many ways can he pick the 2 meals he will take?

20. There are 9 different throw pillows at a furniture store. A saleswoman will put 3 of them on the sofa in the display window. How many ways can she choose the pillows for the display window?

21. An employer is choosing 4 of his 12 employees to go with him on a trip. How many ways can he choose the employees that will go with him?

22. How many ways are there to select 8 dogs for a sled team from a group of 12 dogs?

23. An entertainer needs 2 people to come on the stage to help her. How many ways can she select her helpers from the 6 people in the audience who have volunteered?

24. A group of diners at a restaurant decide to order and share 5 different appetizers. How many ways can they pick the appetizers if there are 7 appetizers to choose from?

25. List all the 2-letter combinations that can be made from the letters in the word *math*.

26. Without doing any calculations, explain why the number of combinations of 5 items taken 3 at a time is less than the number of permutations of 5 items taken 3 at a time.

27. Why would it make more sense to call a combination lock a permutation lock?

*28. **Challenge** Show algebraically that $_nC_n = 1$ and $_nC_0 = 1$.

*29. **Challenge** Is $_nC_r = {_nC_{n-r}}$ true? Show why or why not.

*30. **Challenge** There are 8 old marbles and 5 new marbles in a bag. How many ways can 4 marbles be chosen so that 2 are old and 2 are new?

Probability

Probability is a measure of how likely it is that something will happen.

In the study of probability, some terms have different meanings from what you might be used to. For instance, you might think that an experiment is something that scientists do, an event is some sort of social gathering, and a trial involves a judge.

Understanding Basic Concepts of Probability

Examples

An **experiment** is any process or action that has a result.

Experiment: Roll a number cube.

A result is called an **outcome**.

A possible **outcome** is 4.

The set of all possible outcomes of an experiment is the **sample space**.

The **sample space** is {1, 2, 3, 4, 5, 6}.

An **event** is a set of one or more outcomes. An event is a subset of the sample space. Events are sometimes described as actions

Some **events** (described both as actions and as sets) are
- Roll a 4. {4}
- Roll an even number. {2, 4, 6}
- Roll a number less than 3. {1, 2}

If an experiment is performed more than once, each performance can be called a **trial**. For example, 100 rolls of a number cube can be described as 100 trials of an experiment.

Calculating Probability

PROBABILITY OF AN EVENT (THEORETICAL PROBABILITY)

The **probability** of an event E, written $P(E)$, is a number from 0 to 1 that describes how likely event E is to occur. If all outcomes in the sample space S are equally likely, then

$$P(E) = \frac{\text{number of outcomes in event } E}{\text{total number of outcomes in sample space } S} = \frac{n(E)}{n(S)}.$$

TIP

Unless otherwise noted, *probability* means *theoretical probability*. You will learn about experimental probability later in this topic.

(continued)

You can write a probability as a fraction, decimal, or percent.

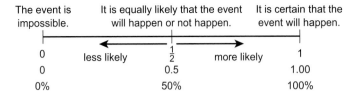

Example 1 A number cube is rolled.

(A) Find $n(S)$.

Solution The sample space S is $\{1, 2, 3, 4, 5, 6\}$, so there are 6 outcomes.

$n(S) = 6$ ∎

(B) Find $P(4)$.

Solution $P(4)$ represents the probability of rolling a 4. There is only one outcome that is a 4, so $n(4) = 1$.

$P(4) = \dfrac{n(4)}{n(S)} = \dfrac{1}{6} \approx 0.17$, or about 17% ∎

(C) Find $P(\text{odd number})$.

Solution The event "roll an odd number" contains 3 outcomes: 1, 3, and 5.

$P(\text{odd number}) = \dfrac{n(\text{odd number})}{n(S)} = \dfrac{3}{6} = \dfrac{1}{2} = 0.5 = 50\%$ ∎

Example 2 The integers 1 through 10 are written on 10 index cards, a different integer on each card. The cards are placed in a bag. One card is chosen without looking.

(A) Find $n(S)$.

Solution There are 10 cards, so $n(S) = 10$. ∎

(B) Find $P(\text{integer} > 7)$.

Solution $P(\text{integer} > 7)$ represents the probability of choosing an integer greater than 7. There are 3 outcomes in this event: 8, 9 and 10. So $n(\text{integer} > 7) = 3$.

$P(\text{integer} > 7) = \dfrac{n(\text{integer} > 7)}{n(S)} = \dfrac{3}{10} = 0.3 = 30\%$ ∎

(C) Find $P(12)$.

Solution There is no card with 12 written on it, so $n(12) = 0$.

$P(12) = \dfrac{n(12)}{n(S)} = \dfrac{0}{10} = 0 = 0\%$ ∎

(D) Find $P(\text{integer} < 12)$.

Solution Every integer in the bag is less than 12, so choosing an integer less than 12 is certain to happen.

$P(\text{integer} < 12) = 1 = 100\%$ ∎

Calculating Probability Involving Complementary Events

If one of two events must occur, but both cannot occur at the same time, then those events are **complementary**. When two events are complementary, the sum of their probabilities is 1.

Example 3 A bag contains 3 green marbles, 7 white marbles, and 5 red marbles (and no other marbles). One marble is chosen without looking.

Ⓐ Find $n(S)$.

Solution Since $3 + 7 + 5 = 15$, there are 15 outcomes in the sample space.

$n(S) = 15$ ∎

Ⓑ Find $P(\text{green})$.

Solution $P(\text{green})$ represents the probability of choosing a green marble. There are 3 outcomes in this event, so $n(\text{green}) = 3$.

$$P(\text{green}) = \frac{n(\text{green})}{n(S)} = \frac{3}{15} = \frac{1}{5} = 0.2 = 20\% \quad ∎$$

Ⓒ Find $P(\text{not green})$.

Solution

Method 1: The outcomes that are not green are the outcomes *white* and *red*, so $n(\text{not green}) = n(\text{white}) + n(\text{red}) = 7 + 5 = 12$.

$$P(\text{not green}) = \frac{n(\text{not green})}{n(S)} = \frac{n(\text{white}) + n(\text{red})}{n(S)} = \frac{12}{15} = \frac{4}{5} = 0.8 = 80\%$$

Method 2: The outcomes *green* and *not green* are complementary because one of them must occur, but both cannot occur at the same time.

$$P(\text{green}) + P(\text{not green}) = 1$$

$$\frac{1}{5} + P(\text{not green}) = 1$$

$$P(\text{not green}) = 1 - \frac{1}{5} = \frac{4}{5} = 0.8 = 80\% \quad ∎$$

> **TIP**
>
> If you think of only 3 outcomes (green, white, and red), then you are using outcomes that are not equally likely. The definition of probability requires that all outcomes in the sample space are equally likely, so think of each marble as an outcome, not each color.

Application: Weather

Example 4 A meteorologist forecasts that the probability of snow is 70%. What is the probability that it will not snow?

Solution The outcomes *snow* and *no snow* are complementary, so $P(\text{snow}) + P(\text{no snow}) = 100\%$.

$100\% - 70\% = 30\%$

The probability that it will not snow is 30%. ∎

Calculating Experimental Probability

Theoretical probability is based on the assumption that all outcomes in a sample space are equally likely. Experimental probability is based on actual observations or results of an experiment.

EXPERIMENTAL PROBABILITY OF AN EVENT

If n is the number of trials of an experiment or number of observations in a study, then the **experimental probability** of an event E is

$$P(E) = \frac{\text{number of times event } E \text{ has occurred}}{n}.$$

Example 5 Alicia rolls a number cube 50 times. The results are shown.

Outcome	1	2	3	4	5	6
Frequency	10	8	12	8	7	5

Based on the results, what is the experimental probability that the next roll will be a 3?

Solution The outcome 3 has occurred 12 times in 50 trials. Based on the results in the table, $P(3) = \frac{12}{50} = \frac{6}{25} = 0.24 = 24\%$.

Example 6 Ramon chooses a marble from a bag without looking and then replaces it. He does this 75 times. The results are shown.

Outcome	Red	White	Blue
Frequency	7	40	28

Based on the results, what is the experimental probability of choosing a red marble?

Solution The outcome *red* has occurred 7 times out of 75 trials. Based on the results in the table, $P(\text{red}) = \frac{7}{75} \approx 0.093$, which is 9.3%.

THINK ABOUT IT

Experimental probability might not equal theoretical probability. The theoretical probability of rolling a 3 is $\frac{1}{6}$, or about 17%.

THINK ABOUT IT

There is no way to calculate theoretical probability for the experiment in Example 6 because the contents of the bag are unknown.

Application: Surveys

Example 7 A survey shows that 171 out of 460 students play a team sport. Based on the survey, what is the probability that a student chosen at random plays a team sport?

Solution Based on the survey, the probability that a student chosen at random plays a team sport is $\frac{171}{460}$, or about 0.372, which is 37.2%.

Problem Set

List the sample space for each experiment.

1. Toss a coin.

2. Toss two coins.

3 Toss three coins.

4. Roll a die.

5. Toss a coin and then roll a die.

6. Spin the spinner once.

7. Spin the spinner twice.

Solve.

8. A die is rolled. Write each answer as a fraction, decimal, and percent.
   A. Find $P(2)$.
   B. Find P(number < 4).
   C. Find P(not 5).

9. A bag contains 7 white marbles, 3 blue marbles, and 15 red marbles (and no other marbles). One marble is chosen without looking.
   A. Find $n(S)$.
   B. Find P(white).
   C. Find P(red).
   D. Find P(green).
   E. Find P(not red).

10. The numbers 1 through 12 are written on 12 slips of paper, a different number on each paper slip, and placed in a bag. One slip of paper is chosen without looking.
    A. Find $n(S)$.
    B. Find $P(5)$.
    C. Find P(multiple of 4).
    D. Find P(multiple of 2).
    E. Find P(number < 13).

11. A coin is tossed and then a die is rolled.
    A. Find $n(S)$.
    B. Find P(heads *and* 4).
    C. Find P(tails *and* even number).
    D. Find P(heads *and* number > 2).

12. Denise rolled a die 10 times. The results are shown.

Outcome	1	2	3	4	5	6
Frequency	3	1	2	1	2	1

    Write each answer as a fraction, decimal, and percent.
    A. What is the experimental probability that the next roll will be a 6?
    B. What is the experimental probability that the next roll will be a 1?
    C. What is the experimental probability that the next roll will be a number greater than 3?

13. The letters A through M are written on slips of paper so that each letter is written once, and a different letter is on each paper slip. The slips of paper are placed in a bag and one slip of paper is chosen without looking.
    A. Find $n(S)$.
    B. Find P(vowel).
    C. Find P(consonant).

Answer each question.

14. A volunteer called 280 homes to ask questions about an upcoming election. Of these calls, 92 were not answered. Based on those results, what is the probability that the next call the volunteer makes is not answered?

15. Of the last 15 customers to enter a balloon shop, 6 ordered a single balloon. What is the experimental probability that the next customer will not order a single balloon?

*16. **Challenge** The odds in favor of an event is the ratio $n(E)$ to $n(\text{not } E)$. A die is rolled. Answer each question.

  A. Find the odds in favor of rolling a 2.

  B. Find the odds in favor of rolling an even number.

*17. **Challenge** Adam, Bob, Cathy, Dan, and Eric line up in a row for a photo. What is the probability that they line up in alphabetical order from left to right?

Mutually Exclusive Events

You can find the probability of two or more events.

Probabilities of Two Events

When finding the probability of two or more events, it helps to know whether the events can occur at the same time.

Example 1 A card is drawn from a standard deck. Determine if the following events can happen at the same time.

A Select an ace and select a red card.

Solution A card can be both an ace and a red card at the same time. ∎

B Select a jack and select a queen.

Solution A card cannot be a jack and a queen at the same time. ∎

C Select a heart and select a club.

Solution A card cannot be a heart and a club at the same time. ∎

D Select a diamond and select a card less than 5.

Solution There are three cards with diamonds numbered less than 5 ∎

TIP

Standard Deck

♠	♣	♥	♦
A	A	A	A
K	K	K	K
Q	Q	Q	Q
J	J	J	J
10	10	10	10
9	9	9	9
8	8	8	8
7	7	7	7
6	6	6	6
5	5	5	5
4	4	4	4
3	3	3	3
2	2	2	2

Determining if Events Are Mutually Exclusive

If two events cannot occur at the same time, the events are *mutually exclusive.*

DEFINITION

Events are **mutually exclusive** if they cannot happen at the same time.

Example 2 This spinner is spun one time. State whether or not the events are mutually exclusive.

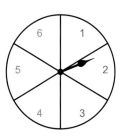

A Spin a 2 and spin a blue number.

Solution The number 2 is not a blue number, so you cannot spin a 2 and a blue number at the same time. The events are mutually exclusive. ∎

B Spin a 6 and spin a blue number.

Solution The number 6 is a blue number. Because both can happen at the same time, the events are not mutually exclusive. ∎

C Spin an even number and spin an odd number.

Solution A number cannot be both even and odd. The events are mutually exclusive. ∎

Finding Probabilities of Mutually Exclusive Events

For mutually exclusive events A and B,

$$P(A \text{ or } B) = P(A) + P(B).$$

The rule can extend to any number of mutually exclusive events.

If events A and B are mutually exclusive, $P(A \text{ and } B) = 0$.

Example 3 A card is randomly selected from a standard deck.

Ⓐ Find $P(\text{king } or \text{ queen})$.

Solution Out of the 52 cards in a standard deck, 4 are kings and 4 are queens.

$P(\text{king } or \text{ queen}) = P(\text{king}) + P(\text{queen})$

$$= \frac{4}{52} + \frac{4}{52}$$

$$= \frac{8}{52}$$

$$= \frac{2}{13} \approx 15.4\% \ \blacksquare$$

Ⓑ Find $P(\text{red } or \text{ spades})$.

Solution Each suit has 13 cards, so there are 13 diamonds (red), 13 hearts (red), and 13 spades.

$P(\text{red } or \text{ spades}) = P(\text{red}) + P(\text{spades})$

$$= \frac{26}{52} + \frac{13}{52}$$

$$= \frac{39}{52}$$

$$= \frac{3}{4} = 75\% \ \blacksquare$$

Ⓒ Find $P(2 \text{ of diamonds } or \text{ 3 of clubs } or \text{ 4})$.

Solution The rule can be extended to any number of mutually exclusive events.

$P(2 \text{ of diamonds } or \text{ 3 of clubs } or \text{ 4}) = P(2 \text{ of diamonds}) + P(3 \text{ of clubs}) + P(4)$

$$= \frac{1}{52} + \frac{1}{52} + \frac{4}{52}$$

$$= \frac{6}{52}$$

$$= \frac{3}{26} \approx 11.5\% \ \blacksquare$$

Example 4 The spinner is spun one time.

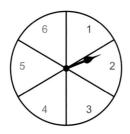

A Find $P(5 \text{ or red})$.

Solution

$P(5 \text{ or red}) = P(5) + P(\text{red})$

$= \dfrac{1}{6} + \dfrac{3}{6}$

$= \dfrac{4}{6}$

$= \dfrac{2}{3} \approx 66.7\%$ ∎

B Find $P(\text{red or blue})$.

Solution

$P(\text{red or blue}) = P(\text{red}) + P(\text{blue})$

$= \dfrac{3}{6} + \dfrac{3}{6}$

$= \dfrac{6}{6}$

$= 1 = 100\%$ ∎

Application: Entertainment

Example 5 To award a prize, a theater manager randomly selects one ticket from all the tickets sold over the two-day period indicated in the table.

	Saturday	Sunday
Child	1830	854
Adult	2722	1655
Senior	610	914

A Find the probability that the chosen ticket belongs to a child or senior.

Solution

number of child tickets sold: $1830 + 854 = 2684$

number of senior tickets sold: $610 + 914 = 1524$

total number of tickets sold:
$1830 + 854 + 2722 + 1655 + 610 + 914 = 8585$

$P(\text{child or senior}) = P(\text{child}) + P(\text{senior})$

$= \dfrac{2684}{8585} + \dfrac{1524}{8585}$

$= \dfrac{4208}{8585} \approx 49\%$ ∎

> **THINK ABOUT IT**
>
> The events are mutually exclusive; a person cannot be both a child and a senior.

B Find the probability that the chosen ticket belongs to an adult who went on Saturday or a senior who went on Sunday.

Solution Add each probability.

$P(\text{adult Saturday or senior Sunday}) = P(\text{adult Saturday}) + P(\text{senior Sunday})$

$= \dfrac{2722}{8585} + \dfrac{914}{8585}$

$= \dfrac{3636}{8585} \approx 42.4\%$ ∎

Problem Set

Solve.

1. For the experiment of drawing a card from a standard deck, state whether or not the events are mutually exclusive.

   A. Select a club and select a diamond.

   B. Select a heart and select a king.

   C. Select a black card and select a diamond.

   D. Select a black card and select a club.

2. For the experiment of rolling a die, state whether or not the events are mutually exclusive.

   A. Roll a 3 and roll an even number.

   B. Roll a 2 and roll an even number.

   C. Roll a 2 and roll a multiple of 3.

   D. Roll a 6 and roll a multiple of 3.

3. For the experiment of randomly selecting a letter from the alphabet, state whether or not the events are mutually exclusive.

   A. Select a vowel and select the letter P.

   B. Select a letter that is in the word MATH and select a letter that is in the word FUN.

   C. Select a letter that is in the word RAIN and select a letter that is in the word SNOW.

   D. Select a letter with a vertical line of symmetry and select a letter with a horizontal line of symmetry.

4. A card is randomly selected from a standard deck of cards.

   A. Find $P(4 \text{ or } 5 \text{ or } 6)$.

   B. Find $P(\text{red or black})$.

   C. Find $P(\text{heart or black } 10)$.

5. The spinner is spun one time.

   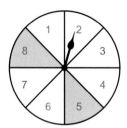

   A. Are the events "the spinner lands on a blue number" and "the spinner lands on a number with a yellow background" mutually exclusive? Explain.

   B. Are the events "the spinner lands on a red number" and "the spinner lands on a number with a yellow background" mutually exclusive? Explain.

   C. Find $P(\text{number in red or number with yellow background})$.

   D. Find $P(\text{blue number or } 7)$.

6. A bag contains 12 oranges, 8 nectarines, 7 red apples, and 3 green apples (and no other fruit). One fruit is chosen without looking.

   A. Are the events of getting a green apple and getting an apple mutually exclusive? Explain.

   B. Are the events of not getting a nectarine and getting an apple mutually exclusive? Explain.

   C. Find $P(\text{apple or nectarine})$.

   D. Find $P(\text{orange or red apple or grape})$.

7. A cooler contains 42 canned drinks: 10 lemonade, 3 diet cola, 8 regular cola, 12 diet tea, and 9 regular tea. One can is chosen without looking.

A. Are the events of getting a lemonade and getting a diet drink mutually exclusive? Explain.

B. Find P(tea *or* regular cola).

C. Find P(lemonade *or* diet cola *or* regular cola).

8. The table shows probabilities of drawing various colors of ribbons from a bag.

Red	Yellow	Green	Orange	Blue
0.35	0.25	0.2	0.1	0.1

One ribbon is chosen from the bag without looking.

A. Find P(red *or* green).

B. Find P(yellow *or* green *or* blue).

C. Find P(not blue *or* blue).

9. The table shows numbers of people who participated in a survey. Participants are randomly selected for further questioning.

Age	Male	Female
0–18	23	14
19–40	87	101
41–60	65	98
61+	33	52

A. Are the events of choosing a male and choosing a participant age 41 or older mutually exclusive? Explain.

B. Are the events of choosing a male age 0–18 and choosing a male age 19–40 mutually exclusive? Explain.

C. Find P(male *or* female 61+).

D. Find P(female 19–40 *or* male 19–40).

*E. **Challenge** To find $P(A \ or \ B)$ when A and B are not mutually exclusive, use $P(A \ or \ B) = P(A) + P(B) - P(A \ and \ B)$. Find P(female *or* participant 41–60).

Samples and Prediction

You can use information about part of a group to make predictions about the entire group. The way you choose a part of a group affects how useful your prediction about the whole group will be.

If a population is small, you can *survey*, or question, the entire population. However, if a population is large, such as every citizen in a certain state, it is more practical to survey a sample of the population.

> ### DEFINITIONS
>
> A **population** is a group of individuals or objects that you want information about. A **sample** is part of the population.

Identifying Bias and Possible Sources of Bias

For a sample to be useful, it must be *representative* of the population. A representative sample generally has the same characteristics as the population. For example, if most of a population is female, then most of the sample should be female.

> ### DEFINITIONS
>
> An **unbiased sample** is representative of the population. A **biased sample** is not representative of the population.

Example 1   State whether or not the sample is likely to be biased. Identify possible sources of bias.

A Claire wants to know if the people in her neighborhood think that the speed limit on their street should be reduced. She asks the parents of the children she babysits for.

Solution   It is unlikely that everyone in the neighborhood is a parent, so the sample is probably not representative of the population. Parents are likely to think of their children's safety and request lower speed limits. The sample is likely to be biased. ■

B A boss wants to know if his employees would be interested in a company picnic. He prints an alphabetical list of all the employee names and asks every 10th person on the list.

Solution This sample is likely to be representative of all the employees, so it is likely to be unbiased. ∎

C A reporter wants to know how many people in a town are interested in rock climbing. She goes to a sporting-goods store and asks every 10th person who exits.

Solution People who shop in a sporting-goods store are more likely to be interested in sports, such as rock climbing. The sample is likely to be biased. ∎

D On a TV news program, viewers are asked to go to the program's website and tell whether or not they are opposed to a recent tax increase.

Solution People opposed to the tax increase are more likely to make the effort to record their opinions than people who are not opposed. Also, not all viewers will have access to the Internet. For these reasons, the sample is likely to be biased. ∎

THINK ABOUT IT

Bias depends on the population you are working with. For instance, in Example 1C, if the reporter wanted to know how many patrons of that store are interested in rock climbing, this sampling method would not be bad.

Making Predictions About a Population

A prediction is an educated guess, or estimate. It is important to keep in mind the following points when making a prediction about a population.

- Estimates tend to become more accurate as the size of the sample increases. For example, an estimate based on a sample of 100 is likely to be better than an estimate based on a sample of 50.

- An estimate based on an unbiased sample is likely to be better than an estimate based on a biased sample.

REMEMBER

A biased sample does not represent the population well.

Example 2 In a sample of 100 people at a stadium, 72 preferred Brand A mustard to Brand B mustard. Predict about how many of the estimated 62,000 people in a baseball stadium would prefer Brand A mustard.

Solution Write and solve a proportion.

$$\frac{x}{62,000} = \frac{72}{100} \qquad \text{Write a proportion.}$$

$$100x = 4,464,000 \qquad \text{Cross multiply.}$$

$$x = 44,640 \qquad \text{Divide both sides by 100.}$$

Based on the sample, about 44,640 people in the stadium would prefer Brand A. ∎

TIP

In Example 2, you could simplify the fraction before cross multiplying.

Example 3 A study showed that 14% of the plants randomly sampled in a field were damaged by pests. Predict how many of the 750 plants from that field will show damage by pests.

Solution Find 14% of 750.

$$14\% \text{ of } 750 = 14\% \cdot 750 \qquad \text{The word } of \text{ indicates multiplication.}$$

$$= 0.14 \cdot 750 \qquad \text{Write the percent as a decimal.}$$

$$= 105 \qquad \text{Multiply.}$$

Based on the study, about 105 of the plants will show damage by pests. ∎

Problem Set

State whether the sample is likely to be biased. Identify possible sources of bias.

1. A magazine editor wants to know what percent of people ski. She chooses people randomly on a winter weekend and calls them at home to ask them.

2. To find out what percent of people approve of plans to convert a meadow into a shopping mall, a reporter goes to a nearby mall and asks every fifth person he sees.

3. An apartment manager is giving away coupons for $50 off a month's rent. He writes each apartment number on a slip of paper, puts the paper slips into a box, mixes them up, and picks 10 slips of paper without looking.

4. The question, "About how many hours per week do you spend on the Internet?" appears on a website. People respond by clicking on the link and typing their answer.

5. At a voting site, a surveyor asks every 15th voter who exits the building if they voted *yes* or *no* on a proposed bill.

6. To find out if people think a new traffic light is needed at a certain intersection in a small town, surveys are mailed to 100 homes distributed randomly throughout the town. People are requested to mark *yes* or *no* and send the survey back within one week.

7. At a baseball game, seat numbers are randomly chosen. People sitting in those seats are surveyed about raising ticket prices 10% to make improvements to the stadium.

8. At a soccer game, people sitting in the first 15 rows are surveyed about raising all ticket prices by $2 to make improvements to the stadium.

9. The manager at the new radio station in town wants to know what kind of music is popular in the area. She surveys people at random as they exit a supermarket between noon and 2 p.m. on a Monday.

10. A quality control worker needs to check samples of the items being produced on an assembly line to see if the machines are working properly. She checks the first 10 items produced on the assembly line every morning.

11. A quality control worker checks 5 randomly selected items produced during each hour on an assembly line.

12. To learn about opinions of people living in the United States, a reporter randomly chooses 10 cross-country airplane flights and questions people sitting in every tenth seat.

Solve.

13. In an unbiased sample of 320 state residents, 115 answered *yes* when asked if they like the current design on the state's license plate.
    A. Predict how many people in a town of 14,280 people in that state would like the current design on the license plate.
    B. Predict how many people in a city of 245,600 people in that state would not like the current design on the license plate.

14. A study showed that 3% of the potatoes randomly sampled did not meet standards for making potato chips. Any potato that does not meet standards will not be used.
    A. A load of potatoes contains approximately 1600 potatoes. About how many of those will not be used to make potato chips?
    B. A quality control manager discarded about 75 potatoes from a load. Predict how many potatoes were in the load.

15. In a survey, approximately 2 out of every 3 people said the current mayor was doing a good job.

   A. If 400 people were surveyed, about how many said the mayor was doing a good job?

   B. Predict how many of 2000 people would say the mayor is doing a good job.

16. A drink vendor at a flea market knows that about 20% of his customers in the past have preferred no ice in their drinks.

   A. On a certain weekend, about 15,000 customers are expected at the market. Past experience shows that about 8% of the customers will stop at the vendor's stall for a drink. About how many of those people will prefer ice in their drinks?

   B. The vendor uses about one-fifth pound of ice per drink. Use your answer for part A to find how many pounds of ice the vendor should have on hand that weekend.

*17. **Challenge** Identify a potential source of bias and suggest a change that can be made to minimize that bias.

   A. A restaurant owner wants to know what percent of her customers like a new hot and spicy sauce. One evening she asks all the customers who order entrées with that sauce.

   B. An insulation contractor wants to know how much energy is used by residents in a town. He selects random odd-numbered houses on random streets in the town to survey.

   C. A biologist collects samples of lake water by standing at one spot of the lake and filling test tubes.

*18. **Challenge** To estimate a population under certain conditions, you can use the proportion

$$\frac{\text{number tagged on 2nd visit}}{\text{number found on 2nd visit}} = \frac{\text{number tagged on 1st visit}}{\text{total number in population}}$$

   A. A biologist visits a lake and tags 45 fish. A week later, he visits the same lake and finds 30 fish. Twelve of them are tagged. Estimate the total number of fish in the lake.

   B. A researcher visits a park and tags 12 deer. Two weeks later, she visits the same park and finds 8 deer. Three of them are tagged. Estimate the number of deer in the park.

UNIT 14   Statistics

You can find lots of data in any group of people.

Data are everywhere. When you look at a group of people, you could use many numbers to describe them. How tall are they? How long is their hair? How old are they? What is their gender? What color are their eyes? Statistics helps you make sense of data.

Big Idea

▶ Statistics is a branch of mathematics concerned with collecting, analyzing, and making decisions or interpretations about data.

Unit Topics

- ▶ Graphs
- ▶ Measures of Center
- ▶ Stem-and-Leaf Plots
- ▶ Box-and-Whisker Plots
- ▶ Frequency Tables and Histograms

Graphs

Sometimes it's easier to understand a data set if it is presented in a picture. Graphs are used to show data in a picture appropriate to the given data.

Creating and Interpreting Bar Graphs

A **bar graph** compares two or more measurements of the same data. It can be used to show data arranged in categories. Make a bar graph by determining the scale, drawing the bars, and choosing a title.

Example 1   The table at right gives information on the types of songs being purchased for download from a music website. Use the information to create a bar graph.

Solution   The category with the greatest number is rock with 82 songs. You can make a vertical scale from 0 to 90.

Popular Songs	
Rock	82
Pop	28
Hip-Hop	41
Classical	15
Jazz	61

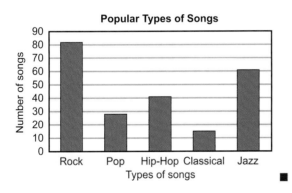

TIP

A bar graph can have vertical or horizontal bars.

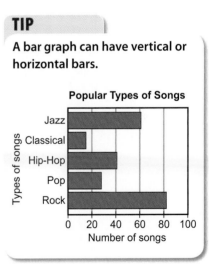

(continued)

Example 2   Use the graph to answer the questions.

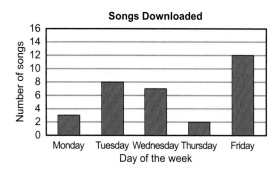

Songs Downloaded

A How many more songs were downloaded on Friday than on Monday?

Solution   There were 12 songs downloaded on Friday and 3 songs downloaded on Monday.

$12 - 3 = 9$ Subtract.

Nine more songs were downloaded on Friday than on Monday. ■

B How many total songs were downloaded?

Solution $3 + 8 + 7 + 2 + 12 = 32$ Add the values of each bar.

Thirty-two total songs were downloaded. ■

Creating and Interpreting Circle Graphs

Circle graphs show the relationship of each part to the whole. To make a circle graph, first determine the percent of each category. Multiply each percent by the number of degrees in a circle, 360°, to find the central angles of each category. Then, use a protractor to draw the angles and create the graph.

Example 3   The table at right gives information on the number of votes in an election. Make a circle graph for the data.

Number of Votes	
Landon	120
Maria	75
Bob	55

Solution

Step 1   The total number of votes in the table is $120 + 75 + 55 = 250$. Divide each category by the total to get the percent.

Landon: $\frac{120}{250} = 48\%$; Maria: $\frac{75}{250} = 30\%$; Bob: $\frac{55}{250} = 22\%$

Step 2   Calculate the angle measure for each category.

Landon: $0.48 \cdot 360° = 172.8°$; Maria $0.30 \cdot 360° = 108°$;
Bob: $0.22 \cdot 360° = 79.2°$

Step 3   Create the graph.

Number of Votes

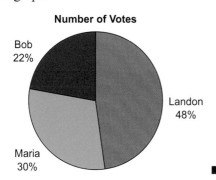

TIP

Ensure that a circle graph contains all its parts by adding the percents for each category, making sure they equal 100%.

22% + 30% + 48% = 100%

Example 4   Use the Favorite Color circle graph to answer each question.

A What percent of people chose green or blue as their favorite color?

Solution

$13\% + 25\% = 38\%$ Add the percents for each category.

Thirty-eight percent of people chose green or blue. ■

B If 200 people were surveyed, how many of them chose red?

Solution   Multipy the total number of people surveyed by the percent who chose red.

$0.18 \cdot 200 = 36$ Find 18% of 200.

Thirty-six people chose red. ■

Favorite Color

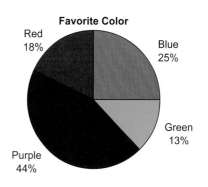

Broken-Line Graph

You can use a broken-line graph to show a change in data over time. To make a broken-line graph, determine the vertical and horizontal scales. Then, create a title and make the graph. In a broken-line graph, time is generally the independent variable, so it goes on the horizontal axis.

Example 5   Use the table at right to create a broken-line graph.

Solution   The greatest number of sweatshirts sold was 14 so a good vertical scale is 0 to 16. There are 4 weeks, so you can use each week as an interval.

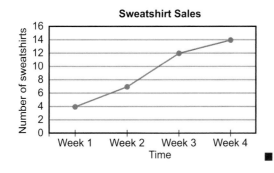

THINK ABOUT IT

This graph is referred to as a *broken-line* graph because it includes line segments.

Number of Sweatshirts Sold	
Week 1	4
Week 2	7
Week 3	12
Week 4	14

(continued)

Example 6 Use the broken-line graph to answer the questions.

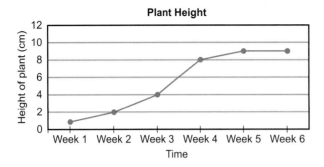

A Between which two consecutive weeks did the plant grow the most?

Solution The steepest line is between Week 3 and Week 4. The plant grew 4 cm. ■

B Between what two consecutive weeks did the plant grow the least?

Solution The flattest line is between Week 5 and Week 6. The difference in height is 0, which means the plant did not grow at all during that time. ■

Creating and Interpreting a Scatter Plot

You can use a scatter plot to determine if there is a relationship between two variables. For example, a teacher sometimes uses scatter plots to determine if there is a relationship between homework grades and test grades.

Example 7 The homework points and test grades for several students are shown in the table. Create a scatter plot for the data.

Solution The ordered pairs for the graph are (28, 48), (35, 54), (42, 60), (51, 83), (47, 66), (50, 87), (36, 50), (19, 23), (38, 68), (27, 41), (46, 73), (56, 95). The vertical scale is from 0 to 100. The horizontal scale is from 0 to 60.

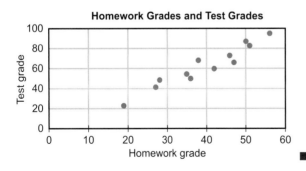

Homework Grades	Test Grades
28	48
35	54
42	60
51	83
47	66
50	87
36	50
19	23
38	68
27	41
46	73
56	95

The correlation between two variables describes the relationship of the two variables. A scatter plot can have a positive correlation, negative correlation, or no correlation.

CORRELATION

Positive Correlation
Two sets of data increase at the same time.

Negative Correlation
One set of data decreases as the other set increases.

No Correlation
No pattern of increase or decrease exists between the data sets.

Example 8 Describe the correlation between the data sets in the scatter plot in Example 7.

Solution It appears that as the homework grades increase, the test grades also increase. Therefore, this graph shows a positive correlation. ■

Problem Set

People were asked to choose their favorite gum flavor from a list of five flavors. Use the bar graph of the data to answer questions 1–7.

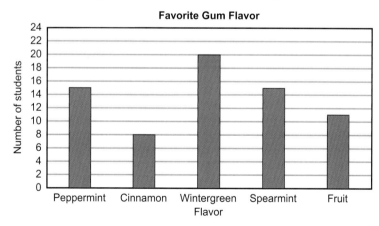

Favorite Gum Flavor

1. Which flavor of gum is the most popular?

2. Which flavor of gum is the least popular?

3. How many people chose Fruit?

4. How many more people chose Wintergreen than Peppermint?

5. How many people chose Spearmint or Cinnamon?

6. How many people were surveyed altogether?

*7. **Challenge** What percent of the people chose Wintergreen?

Mr. Arfur wanted to see if there was a correlation between his students math scores and reading scores. Use the scatter plot of the data to answer questions 8–11.

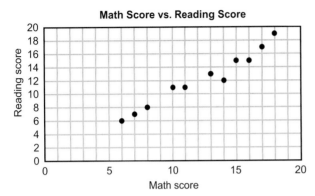

Math Score vs. Reading Score

8. **A.** What is the highest math score?

    B. What was the reading score of the person who got the highest math score?

9. **A.** What is the lowest math score?

    B. What was the reading score of the person who got the lowest math score?

10. As the math scores increase, what happens to the reading scores? Explain.

11. Describe the correlation between the math and reading scores.

Students were surveyed to see what sport they preferred. Use the circle graph of the data to answer questions 12–14.

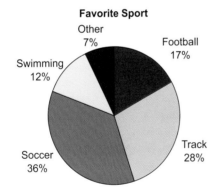

Favorite Sport

12. What percent of people chose football or track?

13. What is the difference (in percent) between the people who chose swimming and those who chose other?

14. If 200 people were surveyed, how many of them chose soccer?

The average monthly rainfall in centimeters for a city is shown in the broken-line graph. Use the graph to answer questions 15–19.

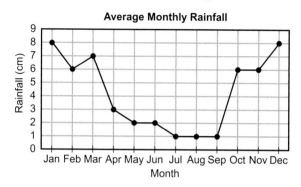

Average Monthly Rainfall

15. Which month or months had the highest average monthly rainfall?

16. Which month or months had the lowest average monthly rainfall?

17. What is the difference between the average rainfall for July and the average rainfall for December?

18. Between which two consecutive months was there the greatest change in average rainfall? State whether this was an increase or decrease.

19. State the consecutive months that had no change in average monthly rainfall.

Solve.

20. People were asked to state their favorite flower. Create a circle graph for the information in the table of favorite flowers.

Favorite Flower	
Daisy	28
Rose	12
Other	10

21. A store recorded sales of a certain book for four weeks. Create a broken-line graph for the information in the table of books sold.

Number of Books Sold			
Week 1	Week 2	Week 3	Week 4
60	75	50	40

22. A teacher kept track of the number of study hours and the test grade for each student. Create a scatter plot for the information in the table showing test grades and study hours.

Test Grades vs. Study Hours									
Study Hours	4	1	2	3	6	7	8	10	4	5
Test Grade	79	50	55	68	82	86	84	90	74	80

23. Describe the correlation between the study time and test grade data for problem 22.

Measures of Center

A measure of center is one number used to describe the typical value in a data set.

There are three types of measures of center: mean, median, and mode. Mean, median, and mode are called measures of center because they describe what the "center" or middle of the data looks like.

Mean

The **mean** is the average of the data. It is found by dividing the sum of the values by the number of values. The mean is often denoted by $\bar{x}$.

NOTATION

The symbol $\bar{x}$ is pronounced "x bar."

DEFINITION

The **mean** is the sum of the values in a data set divided by the number of values.

$$\bar{x} = \frac{x_1 + x_2 + \ldots + x_n}{n}$$

Example 1 Find the mean of each set of data. Round to the nearest tenth.

A 8, 9, 2, 3, 0, 6

Solution $\bar{x} = \dfrac{8 + 9 + 2 + 3 + 0 + 6}{6}$ Use the formula for mean.

$= \dfrac{28}{6} \approx 4.7$ Add the data values and divide by the number of data values.

The mean is about 4.7. ∎

THINK ABOUT IT

Although a value of 0 does not increase the sum of the values in the numerator, it is still counted as a data value in the denominator.

B 100, 125, 111, 132, 151

Solution $\bar{x} = \dfrac{100 + 125 + 111 + 132 + 151}{5}$ Use the formula for mean.

$= \dfrac{619}{5} = 123.8$ Add the data values and divide by the number of data values.

The mean is 123.8. ■

C −3, −3, −2, 0, 4, 6

Solution $\bar{x} = \dfrac{-3 + (-3) + (-2) + 0 + 4 + 6}{6}$ Use the formula for mean.

$= \dfrac{2}{6} \approx 0.33$ Add the data values and divide by the number of data values.

The mean is about 0.33. ■

Median

The **median** is the middle value of a data set after the values have been ordered from least to greatest.

In a set of data ordered from least to greatest with an odd number of values, the median is the center value.

In a set of data ordered from least to greatest with an even number of values, the median is the average of the two center values.

To find the median for an *odd* number of values, such as 22, 42, 13, 12, 8, do the following.

THINK ABOUT IT

Both the mean and the median can be values that do not appear in the data set.

Step 1 Arrange the data in order from least to greatest.

8, 12, ⑬ 22, 42

Step 2 Find the middle number.

The number 13 is in the middle.

The median is 13.

To find the median for an *even* number of values, such as 6, 2, 0, 4, 7, 12, do the following.

Step 1 Arrange the data in order from least to greatest.

0, 2, ④, ⑥ 7, 12

Step 2 Find the middle numbers.

Both 4 and 6 are in the middle.

Step 3 Find the mean of 4 and 6.

$\dfrac{4 + 6}{2} = \dfrac{10}{2} = 5$ The median is 5.

(continued)

Example 2   Find the median of each set of data.

Ⓐ Hourly wages: $8.50, $7.25, $6.75, $10.00, $9.80

Solution $6.75, $7.25, $8.50, $9.80, $10.00   Arrange the data in order. There are five values, so the median is the third one.

The median is $8.50. ∎

Ⓑ Height of plant after two weeks (in cm): 1.7, 1.0, 1.7, 2.4, 3.2, 1.8.

Solution   1.0, 1.7, 1.7, 1.8, 2.4, 3.2   Arrange the data in order.

$$\frac{1.7 + 1.8}{2} = 1.75$$ There are six values, so the median is the average of the third and fourth values.

The median is 1.75. ∎

Mode

> **DEFINITION**
>
> The **mode** is the data value that occurs the most. If all values occur the same number of times, there is no mode. If two values appear the same number of times, there are two modes.

Example 3

Ⓐ Find the mode of the values 7, 4, 2, 2, 4, 7, 9, 7.

Solution   The number 2 occurs twice, 4 occurs twice, 9 occurs once, and 7 occurs three times. The mode is 7. ∎

Ⓑ Test scores are 78, 65, 23, 78, and 42. What is the mode?

Solution   The value 78 occurs twice. All other values occur once. The mode is 78. ∎

Best Measure of Center

The mean, median, and mode can all be used to describe a data set. Sometimes one measure of center might be a better description than another. For example, the mean, median, and mode of 22, 31, 40, 210, and 31 are as follows:

The mean is 66.8.   The median is 31.   The mode is 31.

$$\frac{22 + 31 + 40 + 210 + 31}{5}$$ 22, 31, ⓐ31, 40, 210

$$= \frac{334}{5} = 66.8$$ The value 31 occurs twice.

Notice the mean is much different from the median and mode. When extreme values occur in a data set, they can affect the mean. An extreme value is called an outlier. An **outlier** is a value that is very small or very large compared to the rest of the data.

Example 4 Find the mean, median, and mode of the data set. State which measure or measures of center best represent the data.

$$2.8, 1.2, 1.5, 2.0, 2.4, 1.8$$

Solution Mean: $\dfrac{2.8 + 1.2 + 1.5 + 2.0 + 2.4 + 1.8}{6} = \dfrac{11.7}{6} = 1.95$

Median: $1.2, 1.5, \boxed{1.8, 2.0}\, 2.4, 2.8;\ \dfrac{1.8 + 2.0}{2} = 1.9$

Each value appears once. There is no mode.

The best measures of center are the mean and the median. ■

Application: Management

Example 5 A manager is writing a report describing the salaries of the workers at the store. The salaries are listed below.

$$\$20,000; \$35,000; \$28,000; \$180,000, \$20,000$$

Find the mean, median, and mode of the data. Which measure or measures best represent the data? Explain your reasoning.

Solution The mean is $\dfrac{\$283,000}{5} = \$56,600$.

The data in order are $20,000; $20,000; $28,000; $35,000; $180,000.

So the median is $28,000.

The mode is $20,000.

The measure that best represents the data is the median. The mean is not a good measure because the outlier of $180,000 makes the mean a much larger number than the median. The mode is not a good measure because it is the minimum value of the set. ■

Problem Set

Find the mean, median, and mode for each set of data.

1. 96, 84, 92, 96, 100

2. 74, 88, 79, 70, 74

3. 4, 8, 9, 2, 7, 2

4. 32, 29, 35, 25, 32, 22, 30

5. 106, 106, 92, 96, 92, 104

6. 50, 80, 60, 70, 60

7. 48, 46, 44, 40, 42, 50

8. 5, 3, 4, 2, 6

9. 102, 102, 100, 94, 102

10. $-6, -7, -2, -4, -1$

11. 1, 1, 0, 2, 1, 0

12. 1.4, 1.6, 1.0, 2.3, 1.4

13. $-5, -2, 3, 7, 2, -4, -1, 0$

14. 422, 350, 401, 376

*15. **Challenge** $\dfrac{1}{2}, \dfrac{1}{4}, \dfrac{3}{4}, \dfrac{5}{8}, \dfrac{1}{2}$

*16. **Challenge** $3\dfrac{1}{3}, 2\dfrac{1}{4}, \dfrac{5}{12}, 5\dfrac{1}{6}, 1\dfrac{1}{4}$

State the best measure or measures of center to use for each set of data. Explain your reasoning.

17. 4, 8, 6, 5, 32, 1

18. 1, 1, 3, 3, 4, 1, 3, 4

19. 22, 27, 32, 45, 36, 25

20. 102, 105, 233, 100, 110

21. 1, 1, 7, 1, 1, 1, 1, 1, 1

22. 14, 19, 20, 28, 13, 10, 25

23. 0, 0, 4, 2, 0, 1, 3, 2, 4

24. 2, 6, 1, 9, 11, 67

25. 5, 5, 15, 20, 14, 21

26. 62, 75, 53, 81

27. 5.6, 4.2, 3.1, 4.8, 4.2, 3.0

28. 2.3, 0.1, 3.8, 1.7, 2.9

Quiz scores for several classes are shown in the table at right. Use the information to answer questions 29–31.

29. Which class has the highest mean?

30. Which class has the highest median?

31. Which class has the highest mode?

Class A	Class B	Class C
15	10	13
18	15	14
19	19	20
16	19	19
16	20	12

Solve each problem.

32. A weather forecaster kept track of the low temperature for five consecutive days. The temperatures (in Celsius) are −5, 3, −3, 0, −1. What is the mean low temperature?

33. A biologist listed the weights of several beetles. The weights are shown in the table:

Weight (ounces)	2.1	2.8	1.7	1.5	3.0
	2.0	1.9	1.2	1.8	1.1

What is the median weight of the beetles?

34. The test scores for Class A have a mean of 85 and a median of 85. Class B test scores have a mean of 63 and a median of 85. Which class most likely has an outlier? Explain.

35. Students conducted a survey of the cost of shoes at different stores. They noticed that one pair of shoes cost a lot more than the other pairs. The data is shown below.

cost of shoes with outlier: $28, $30, $240, $27, $24

cost of shoes without outlier: $28, $30, $27, $24

A. Find the mean and median of the data for both sets of data.

B. For which set were the mean and median close together? For which set were the mean and median far apart?

C. What can be said if the mean and median of a set of data are far apart?

*36. Challenge Julie kept track of her test scores The first four tests had scores of 82, 95, 88, and 79. What was the score on the fifth test if Julie had a mean test score of 87?

*37. Challenge Write a set of 5 different numbers that have a mean and median of 3.

*38. Challenge John needs a mean test score of 90 or above to get an A in a class. There are 6 tests total. The maximum score on any test is 100. The scores on the first five tests are: 85, 100, 75, 82, and 90. Is it possible for John to get an A in the class? Show your work.

Stem-and-Leaf Plots

Stem-and-leaf plots are a type of graph used to organize large amounts of data.

The benefits of using these plots include showing the distribution of the data, or how the data are arranged, as well as the individual values.

Creating Stem-and-Leaf Plots

HOW TO CREATE A STEM-AND-LEAF PLOT

Step 1 Determine the stems and the leaves.

Step 2 Write the stems vertically beginning with the least and using equal intervals until you've reached the greatest.

Step 3 Write the leaves for each stem in order from least to greatest.

Step 4 Make a key.

Example 1 Create a stem-and-leaf plot for each set of data.

Ⓐ 87, 73, 80, 81, 104, 113, 108, 75, 78, 101, 87

Solution The stems will be the hundreds and tens digits and the leaves will be the ones digits. The lowest value is 73, which would have a stem of 7. The highest value is 113, which has a stem of 11. The stems will be 7, 8, 9, 10, and 11.

```
 7  | 3  5  8
 8  | 0  1  7  7
 9  |
10  | 1  4  8
11  | 3
```
Key: 8|1 means 81   ∎

> **TIP**
> Notice that stem 9 must be included even though there are no values in the 90s.

> **TIP**
> Because 87 is listed twice as a data value, there must be two 7s in the leaves for stem 8.

(continued)

B 0.7, 0.8, 3.2, 1.8, 1.9, 2.1, 0.4, 2.5, 2.7

Solution   The stems will be the ones digits and the leaves will be the tenths digits. The lowest value is 0.4 which will have a stem of 0. The highest value is 3.2 which will have a stem of 3. The stems will be 0, 1, 2, and 3.

```
0 | 4   7   8
1 | 8   9
2 | 1   5   7
3 | 2
Key: 0|4 means 0.4  ■
```

REMEMBER

Be sure to write the key to explain the values in a stem-and-leaf plot.

Finding Measures of Center in a Stem-and-Leaf Plot

Because the individual data values are shown in a stem-and-leaf plot, the mean, median, and mode can be found.

Example 2   Find the mean, median, and mode of the values in the stem-and-leaf plot.

```
0 | 1   4   4
1 | 1   2   7
2 | 0
3 | 5   5
4 | 8
Key: 3|5 means 35
```

Solution

Step 1   Find the mean.

$$\frac{1 + 4 + 4 + 11 + 12 + 17 + 20 + 35 + 35 + 48}{10} = \frac{187}{10}$$ Add the values.

$$= 18.7$$ Divide by the number of values.

The mean is 18.7.

Step 2   Find the median.

```
0 | 1   4   4
1 | 1   2   7
2 | 0
3 | 5   5
4 | 8
Key: 3|5 means 35
```

REMEMBER

If there are an even number of values, there will be two values in the middle. The mean of these two middle values is the median.

$$\frac{12 + 17}{2} = \frac{29}{2} = 14.5$$ There are 10 values. The median is the average of the fifth and sixth values.

The median is 14.5.

Step 3   Find the mode. There are two 4s with the 0 stem and there are two 5s with the 3 stem.

The modes are 4 and 35.   ■

Range and Quartiles

You can describe data by the measures of center and by its spread. To describe data by its spread means to find how far apart the values are from each other. A basic measure of spread is called the range.

> **DEFINITION**
>
> The **range** is the difference of the maximum and minimum values for a data set.
>
> Range = Maximum value − Minimum value

Another measure of spread is the quartiles.

> **DEFINITION**
>
> The **quartiles** divide data into quarters. To find the quartiles, first use the median to divide the data into halves. Then, the median of the bottom half is the first quartile and the median of the top half is the third quartile. The median itself is also referred to as the second quartile.

Finding the quartiles is similar to finding the median.

> **FINDING QUARTILES**
>
> **Step 1** Arrange the data in order from least to greatest.
>
> **Step 2** Find the median.
>
> **Step 3** Find the median of the lower half of the data. Do not include the median itself in the lower half. This is the first quartile or Q_1.
>
> **Step 4** Find the median of the upper half of the data. Do not include the median in the upper half. This is the third quartile or Q_3.

> **TIP**
>
> The quartiles are often abbreviated as follows.
>
> Q_1: first quartile
>
> Q_2: second quartile
>
> Q_3: third quartile

Example 3 Find the range, median, first quartile, and third quartile of the data values 7, 2, 4, 1, 0, 7, 8, and 8.

Solution 0, 1, 2, 4, 7, 7, 8, 8   Arrange the data in order.

range = 8 − 0 = 8   Maximum value − minimum value

median $= \dfrac{4+7}{2} = \dfrac{11}{2} = 5.5$ Find the average of the middle numbers.

The lower half of the data is 0, 1, 2, 4.

$Q_1 = \dfrac{1+2}{2} = \dfrac{3}{2} = 1.5$ Find the average of the middle numbers.

The upper half of the data is 7, 7, 8, 8.

$Q_2 = \dfrac{7+8}{2} = \dfrac{15}{2} = 7.5$ Find the average of the middle numbers. ∎

Finding Quartiles in a Stem-and-Leaf Plot

Because the values in a stem-and-leaf plot are already in order, you can find the median and quartiles by counting the values.

Example 4 Find the median, the first quartile, and the third quartile in the stem-and-leaf plot below.

```
2 │ 0  0  1  7
3 │ 2  3  4  9
4 │ 1  3  4  4  5  7
5 │ 2  2  5
6 │ 0  1
```
Key: 4│1 means 41

Solution There are 19 values, so the median is the tenth one, which is 43.

```
2 │ 0  0  1  7
3 │ 2  3  4  9          Q₁ = 32
4 │ 1  3  4  4  5  7    Med = 43
5 │ 2  2  5             Q₃ = 52
6 │ 0  1
```
Key: 4│1 means 41

To find the first quartile, count the number of values in the lower half. Remember to exclude the median.

There are 9 values in the lower half. So Q_1 is the fifth value. $Q_1 = 32$.

There are 9 values in the upper half. So Q_3 is the fifth value in the upper half. $Q_3 = 52$. ∎

Application: Education

Example 5 Test scores are given below. Arrange the data in a stem-and-leaf plot. Then find the mean, median, and mode.

100	95	78	84	67	88	81	79	100	91
68	70	80	99	100	94	72	81	86	85

Solution The lowest value is 67, which will have a stem of 6. The highest value is 100, which will have a stem of 10. So the stems are 6, 7, 8, 9, and 10.

```
 6 │ 7  8
 7 │ 0  2  8  9
 8 │ 0  1  1  4  5  6  8
 9 │ 1  4  5  9
10 │ 0  0  0
```
Key: 9│4 means 94

Write the stems and then fill in the leaves one stem at a time.

> **TIP**
> Count the leaves to be sure they match the number of data values given.

$$\text{mean} = \frac{1698}{20} = 84.9$$

Add the values. Divide by the number of values.

$$\text{median} = \frac{84 + 85}{2} = \frac{169}{2} = 84.5$$

There are 20 values, so the median is the average of the tenth and eleventh values.

The mode is 100. The 0 leaf is repeated three times with the 10 stem. ∎

Problem Set

....

Create a stem-and-leaf plot for each set of data.

1. 23, 27, 31, 17, 8, 4, 29, 35, 27

2. 16, 23, 38, 10, 4, 31, 11, 16, 1, 3, 17, 34, 26, 7

3. 3.2, 3.5, 4.2, 3.0, 5.9, 5.3, 4.7, 4.3, 3.1, 4.1, 4.0, 5.3, 3.5, 6.3

4. 99, 82, 74, 81, 86, 99, 73, 93, 88, 92, 77, 82

5. 2.3, 1.8, 0.0, 1.8, 1.3, 0.6, 2.3, 1.0, 0.8, 1.3, 0.7

6. 99, 126, 96, 101, 108, 137, 107, 146, 92, 102, 105, 101, 110, 98

7. 39, 65, 27, 36, 39, 57, 50, 35, 44, 65, 41, 22, 21, 44

8. 283, 287, 307, 319, 325, 305, 326, 293, 330, 295, 302, 294, 299, 294, 301, 309, 300

Find the mean, median, and mode for each stem-and-leaf plot.

9.
```
 8 | 0  0
 9 | 1  5  7
10 | 0  8
11 | 5
12 | 5
```
Key: 8|0 means 80

10.
```
3 | 1  7  8
4 | 0  5  5  9
5 | 2  9
6 | 0  7  8
7 | 1  4
```
Key: 5|2 means 5.2

11.
```
1 | 6
2 | 0  0  1
3 | 1  4  7
4 | 2
5 | 7
```
Key: 1|6 means 16

12.
```
11 | 9
12 | 0  2  2
13 | 1  3  4  5
14 | 4  9
15 | 1  2
```
Key: 11|9 means 11.9

Find the range, median, first quartile, and third quartile for each set of data.

13. 5, 9, 10, 3, 4, 2, 1

14. 22, 25, 20, 26, 32, 35, 21

15. 85, 87, 93, 88, 90, 85, 92, 86, 88

16. 1, 2, 0, 0, 1, 1, 1, 3, 1, 0

17. 130, 142, 150, 165, 158, 149, 135, 140

*18. **Challenge** −4.2, 5.0, −2.3, −1.9, 0.5, −3.1, 3.3, 4.7

Find the range, median, the first quartile, and the third quartile for each stem-and-leaf plot.

19.
```
 6 | 5
 7 | 1  5  6  7  8
 8 | 0  0  2  2  2
 9 | 1  8  8  9
10 | 0  0  0
```
Key: 9|1 means 91

20.
```
23 | 0
24 | 5  6
25 | 7  7  8  9
26 | 1  5  8
27 | 4
```
Key: 25|7 means 257

21.
```
3 | 1  3
4 | 2  3  5
5 | 0  5
6 | 4  8  9
7 | 1  4  9
```
Key: 3|1 means 31

22.
```
15 | 5
16 | 0  1
17 | 1  7  7
18 | 2  6  8
19 | 3  9
```
Key: 15|5 means 15.5

Solve each problem.

23. A coach kept track of the number of sit-ups each player could do in one minute. The information is shown in the stem-and-leaf plot at right.

```
3 | 0  3  4
4 | 6  8
5 | 6
6 |
7 |
8 | 2
```
Key: 5|6 means 56

  A. What are the mean, median, and mode?

  B. What are the range, first quartile, and third quartile?

  *C. Challenge Are there any potential outliers? Explain your reasoning.

24. The scores on a test are shown in the graph at right.

```
 6 | 7
 7 | 3  6  7
 8 | 3  5  5  8
 9 | 0  2  3
10 | 0  0
```
Key: 7|6 means 76

  A. What are the mean, median, and mode?

  B. What are the range, first quartile, and third quartile?

  *C. Challenge Are there any potential outliers? Explain your reasoning.

25. A biologist was comparing the leg spans in centimeters of several spiders. The data are shown below.

Leg Spans (in cm) of Spiders									
4.5	3.2	0.8	4.1	4.9	3.2	3.0	5.4	0.7	1.6
4.9	2.1	0.5	5.4	5.8	2.7	2.9	2.2	3.1	3.8

  A. Arrange the data in a stem-and-leaf plot.

  B. Find the mean, median, and mode.

26. The cost of several music players is shown in the table.

Cost (dollars) of Music Players				
106	110	118	137	127
140	125	142	189	125
150	160	154	122	138

  A. Arrange the data in a stem-and-leaf plot.

  B. Find the range, first quartile, median, and third quartile.

*27. Challenge Find a set of 7 whole numbers such that the first quartile is 5, the median is 9, the third quartile is 15, and the range is 20.

Box-and-Whisker Plots

A box-and-whisker plot shows the distribution or spread of data.

A box-and-whisker plot uses the minimum, maximum, median, first quartile, and third quartile values.

> **REMEMBER**
>
> The first quartile is the median of the lower half of the values. The third quartile is the median of the upper half.

Creating a Box-and-Whisker Plot

The "box" extends from Q_1 to Q_3. The median is on the vertical line in the box. The "whiskers" extend from the first quartile to the minimum and from the third quartile to the maximum.

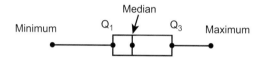

Example 1   Create a box-and-whisker plot for the data.

Scores from a quiz: 6, 3, 7, 2, 4, 9, 10, 8, 3, 10, 9, 10

Solution

Step 1   Find the median, the first quartile, and the third quartile.

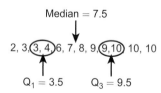

minimum: 2, Q_1: 3.5, median: 7.5, Q_3: 9.5, maximum: 10

Step 2   Plot the points above a number line. Then draw the box-and-whisker plot.

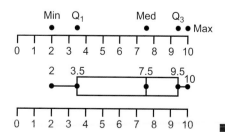

Interpreting a Box-and-Whisker Plot

A box-and-whisker plot separates data into four equal parts. Each part contains $\frac{1}{4}$ or 25% of the data.

TIP

Do not confuse the length of each quartile with the amount of data in each quartile. For example, if the lower whisker is the longest, it simply means 25% of the data is in a larger interval than others.

Example 2 The box-and-whisker plot represents quiz scores for a class of students. Use the graph to answer the following questions.

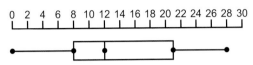

A What percent of the data fall between 8 and 12?

Solution The first quartile is 8 and the median is 12. So, 25% of the data fall between 8 and 12. ■

B What percent of the data fall between 8 and 28?

Solution The first quartile is 8 and the maximum is 28. This interval contains three quartiles or $\frac{3}{4}$ of the data. Therefore, 75% of the data fall between 8 and 28. ■

C If this graph represents 40 students, how many scored between 21 and 28 points?

Solution Twenty-five percent of the students scored between 21 and 28. The data are in one quartile.

$0.25 \cdot 40 = 10$ Multiply.

Ten students scored between 21 and 28 points. ■

Interquartile Range

Another measure that is used with the box-and-whisker plot is the interquartile range or IQR. The IQR is found by subtracting the value of the first quartile from the value of the third quartile.

$$IQR = Q_3 - Q_1$$

The IQR represents the middle 50% of the data. The IQR is useful when you have extreme values or outliers. By eliminating the extreme values from the calculations, it can give a better picture of the spread of the data than the range itself.

Example 3 Look at the box-and-whisker plot. Determine the range and the IQR.

A
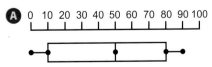

Solution The range is $90 - 0 = 90$. The IQR is $80 - 10 = 70$. So 100% of the data lies within a 90 point range and 50% of the data lies within a 70 point range. ■

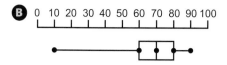

Solution The range is $90 - 10 = 80$. The IQR is $80 - 60 = 20$. So 100% of the data lie within an 80 point range and 50% of the data lie within a 20 point range. ■

Application: Consumer Economics

Example 4 A survey was conducted to determine the prices of a school backpack. The information is presented in the box-and-whisker plot below.

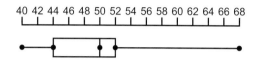

A What percent of prices are between $50 and $52?

Solution Twenty-five percent of the data lies between $50 and $52. ■

B If 150 backpacks were used in the survey, how many backpacks are between $40 and $50?

Solution This is 50% of the data. Minimum value is $40 and the median value is $50.

$0.50 \cdot 150 = 75$ Multiply. ■

C Find the range and the IQR.

Solution The range is $68 - \$40 = \$28$. The IQR is $\$52 - \$44 = \$8$. So 100% of the data lies within a $28 range and the middle 50% of the data lies within an $8 range. ■

Problem Set
· ·

Find the minimum, first quartile, median, third quartile, and maximum for each set of data. Then create a box-and-whisker plot.

1. 6, 2, 3, 9, 10, 4, 8, 7, 10

2. 6, 9, 2, 1, 1, 3, 1, 4, 7, 12, 6

3. 25, 27, 15, 29, 32

4. 65, 78, 99, 100, 75, 65, 82, 81, 80

5. 30, 25, 17, 18, 30, 0, 12, 5, 29, 22

6. 11, 22, 17, 19, 24, 29, 15, 35

7. 42, 58, 67, 48, 41, 52, 63, 42, 41, 48, 42

8. 0.9, 1.0, 0.5, 0.6, 0.2, 0.2, 0.7, 0.0, 0.1

Use the box-and-whisker plot to complete problems 9–13.

9. What percent of the data fall between 9 and 20?

10. What fraction of the data fall between 4 and 28?

11. What is the IQR?

12. What is the range?

13. If the graph represents 52 data points, how many values are between 20 and 28?

For each box-and-whisker plot, determine the range and the IQR.

14.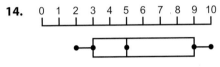

15.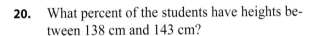

16.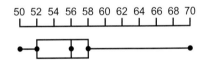

The recreation center charges a fee for classes. The box-and-whisker plot shows the distribution of the fees for the different classes. Use the plot to complete problems 17–19.

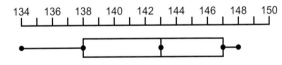

17. What percent of the classes lie between $52 and $70?

18. If the recreation center offers 20 classes, how many classes have a fee of $58 or less?

19. Find the range and the IQR.

The distribution of the heights of students (in centimeters) is shown on the box-and-whisker plot. Use the graph to complete problems 20–22.

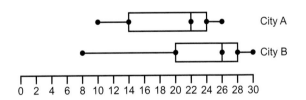

20. What percent of the students have heights between 138 cm and 143 cm?

21. If 72 students were measured, how many students have heights between 138 cm and 148 cm?

22. Find the range and the IQR.

A survey was conducted in two cities to find the average cost of a meal in a restaurant. The information is displayed in the parallel box-and-whisker plots to the right. Use the information to complete problems 23–25.

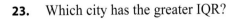

23. Which city has the greater IQR?

24. Which city has the lower median?

*25. **Challenge** Which city do you think has lower meal prices? Explain your reasoning.

Frequency Tables and Histograms

Frequency tables and histograms are used to show how often a number or a range of numbers appears in a data set. A histogram is the graphical representation of a frequency table.

Frequency Tables

A frequency table lists each data item with the number of times it occurs.

For example, a class of 33 students was surveyed to find the number of dogs owned by each student. Students either had no dogs, 1 dog, or 2 dogs. No student had 3 or more dogs. The results of the survey are shown in the frequency table below.

Number of Dogs	Tally	Frequency
0	卌 卌	10
1	卌 卌 卌	15
2	卌 III	8

Example 1 A survey was taken to find the number of books read by each student in one month. The data are shown below. Create a frequency table for the data.

8	7	6	7	6	6	7	8	5	8	7	6
7	6	8	7	5	8	7	5	5	7	7	8
6	7	8	5	8	6	6	7	7	5	6	6

Solution

Books	Tally	Frequency
5	卌 I	6
6	卌 卌	10
7	卌 卌 II	12
8	卌 III	8

There are four different values: 5, 6, 7, and 8. Create a table with these numbers in the left column. Then, count the number of times each value occurs. This count is the frequency. ∎

Finding Mean, Median, and Mode of Data in a Frequency Table

Step 1   To find the *mean* of the data above, multiply the number of books read by the frequency. Then, find the total of these products and divide by the total number of students.

Books	Tally	Frequency	Books · Frequency
5	卌 I	6	$5 \cdot 6 = 30$
6	卌 卌	10	$6 \cdot 10 = 60$
7	卌 卌 II	12	$7 \cdot 12 = 84$
8	卌 III	8	$8 \cdot 8 = 64$
Total		36	238

> **TIP**
>
> To help you understand why you sum the products of the number of books and their frequency, write out the sum $5 + 5 + 5 + 5 + 5 + 5 + 6 + 6 + \ldots + 8 + 8 = 238$. Notice this sum is the same as writing $5 \cdot 6 + 6 \cdot 10 + 7 \cdot 12 + 8 \cdot 8 = 238$.

$$\text{Mean} = \frac{238}{36} \approx 6.6$$

The mean is about 6.6.

Step 2   To find the *median* of the data in a frequency table, determine which values are the middle values. This data set has 36 values, so the median is the mean of the eighteenth and nineteenth numbers.

Number of Books Read	Frequency	
5	6	These are the first 16 values.
6	10	
7	12	← The eighteenth and nineteenth values are here.
8	8	
9	3	

> **TIP**
>
> To help visualize finding the median, begin writing out the data values: 5, 5, 5, 5, 5, 5, 6, 6, 6, 6, 6, 6, 6, 6, ….

The median is 7.

Step 3   To find the *mode*, use the frequency column to determine the value that occurs the most.

The mode is 7.

Example 2   Find the mean, median, and mode of the data summarized in the frequency table.

Cats	Frequency
0	3
1	5
2	2
3	1

Solution

Step 1 *Find the mean:*

Number of Cats	Frequency	Cats · Frequency
0	3	$0 \cdot 3 = 0$
1	5	$1 \cdot 5 = 5$
2	2	$2 \cdot 2 = 4$
3	1	$3 \cdot 1 = 3$
Total	11	12

$$\text{Mean} = \frac{12}{11} \approx 1.1$$

The mean is about 1.1.

Step 2 *Find the median.* There are 11 values. The median is the sixth value.

Number of Cats	Frequency
0	3
1	5
2	2
3	1

← The sixth value is here.

The median is 1.

Step 3 *Find the mode.* The value 1 occurs 5 times.

The mode is 1. ■

Histograms

A histogram is a bar graph that displays the frequencies for data within certain ranges or intervals. The height of each bar gives the frequency in the respective interval.

Example 3 The hourly wages of 24 students are shown below.

7.80	8.30	6.50	6.25	7.40	5.25	6.00	5.75
6.45	7.50	8.20	6.75	5.50	6.30	8.50	8.99
8.10	8.40	9.00	8.25	7.25	9.40	7.80	5.00

(continued)

Wages ($)	Frequency
5.00–5.99	4
6.00–6.99	6
7.00–7.99	5
8.00–8.99	7
9.00–9.99	2

Create a table with equal intervals for the wages. Then, find the frequency of each.

Make the histogram from the frequency table.

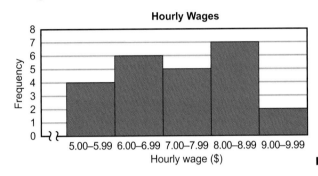

There are 9 people that have an hourly wage greater than or equal to $8.00. ∎

B How many people have an hourly wage less than $7.00?

Solution $4 + 6 = 10$ Add the bars for $5.00–$5.99 and $6.00–6.99.

There are 10 people that have an hourly wage less than $7.00. ∎

Interpreting a Histogram

You can use a data set's histogram to answer questions about the data.

Example 4   Use the histogram from Example 3 to answer the following questions.

A How many people have an hourly wage greater than or equal to $8.00?

Solution $7 + 2 = 9$ Add the bars for $8.00–$8.99 and $9.00–9.99.

There are 9 people that have an hourly wage greater than or equal to $8.00. ∎

B How many people have an hourly wage less than $7.00?

Solution $4 + 6 = 10$ Add the bars for $5.00–$5.99 and $6.00–6.99.

There are 10 people that have an hourly wage less than $7.00. ∎

Find the Median in a Histogram

You can determine the interval in which the median occurs.

Application: Biology

Example 5   The histogram shows the wingspan of certain butterflies. In which interval does the median wingspan occur?

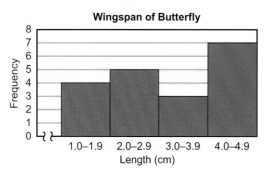

Wingspan of Butterfly

Solution

$4 + 5 + 3 + 7 = 19$ Add the frequency of each bar to determine the total number of butterflies.

The median is the tenth item, which is in the interval 3.0–3.9. ∎

Problem Set

Create a frequency table for the following data.

1.

10	14	12	12	13	11	11
11	12	11	14	10	15	14
10	12	11	14	15	15	10

2.

2	3	4	4	2	4	1	6	4
3	2	3	1	6	4	1	4	2
6	2	1	5	5	6	5	2	1

3.

81	82	81	80	83	83	82	85	80	85
82	80	82	84	83	81	84	83	81	81
83	80	83	81	83	83	84	83	83	84

4.

48	45	47	49	48	49	44	50	44	48
49	43	48	47	48	48	50	49	46	46
47	45	43	46	50	45	43	44	45	43

5.

100	103	102	103	100	106	102	101	104	105
103	101	106	103	106	101	100	101	103	101
106	105	103	103	106	106	104	104	102	104

Find the mean, median, and mode for each frequency table.

6.

Number of Cats	Tally	Frequency
0	JH IIII	9
1	JH I	6
2	JH II	7
3	IIII	4

8.

Number of Pages	Tally	Frequency
30	JH	5
31	JH II	7
32	IIII	4
33	JH I	6

7.

Number of Pencils	Tally	Frequency
12	II	2
13	JH II	7
14	JH JH	10
15	JH I	6
16	JH	5

*9. Challenge

Length	Tally	Frequency
1.0	JH JH I	11
1.2	JH JH	10
1.3	JH JH II	12
1.4	JH II	7
1.5	III	3

A ranger at a national park kept track of the ages of visitors entering the park for one hour. The information is displayed in the histogram below. Use the graph to answer questions 10–14.

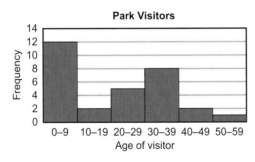

10. How many people entering the park were under 10 years of age?

11. How many people entering the park were aged 20 or older?

12. How many people entered the park in the hour?

13. In what interval is the median age? Explain.

*14. Challenge What percent of the people entering the park were less than 30 years of age?

The frequency table shows the number of times each student had seen a movie in the last month. Use the table to answer questions 15–17.

Number of Movies	Frequency
0	10
1	8
2	9
3	10
4	5

15. How many students saw 2 movies or fewer?

16. How many students saw more than 1 movie?

17. What are the mean, median and mode for the frequency table?

Solve each problem.

18. The table below shows the times, in seconds, for the 100-meter dash at a track meet.

100-Meter Dash Times (sec)									
14.47	12.04	13.59	12.26	12.12	12.02	10.32	12.60	12.37	11.68
13.14	12.01	12.45	10.62	12.08	11.10	11.31	13.82	12.69	10.81
14.23	12.50	14.35	12.15	13.83	10.64	12.28	14.53	13.95	12.03

A. Create a frequency table for the data. Use intervals of 10.00–10.99, 11.00–11.99, etc.

B. Create a histogram for the data.

19. A student kept track of the number of miles students lived from school. The information is shown in the table below.

Distance (miles) From School									
3.0	2.7	2.4	0.5	1.0	1.3	0.4	1.0	1.6	4.8
2.7	2.8	1.5	1.5	2.0	0.4	4.0	0.2	1.5	2.8
3.2	3.1	3.0	2.9	2.5	2.5	2.0	1.3	1.8	3.4
1.5	3.6	1.6	0.8	3.1	1.7	1.4	0.6	0.7	1.9

A. Create a frequency table for the data. Use intervals of 0.0–0.9, 1.0–1.9, 2.0–2.9, etc.

B. Create a histogram for the data.

Pronunciation Guide

The table below provides sample words to explain the sounds associated with specific letters and letter combinations used in the respellings in this book. For example, *a* represents the short "a" sound in *cat*, while *ay* represents the long "a" sound in *day*.

Letter combinations are used to approximate certain more complex sounds. For example, in the respelling of *trapezoid*—TRA-puh-zoyd—the letters *uh* represent the vowel sound you hear in *shut* and *other*.

Vowels

a	short a: apple, cat
ay	long a: cane, day
e, eh	short e: hen, bed
ee	long e: feed, team
i, ih	short i: lip, active
iy	long i: try, might
ah	short o: hot, father
oh	long o: home, throw
uh	short u: shut, other
yoo	long u: union, cute

Letter Combinations

ch	chin, ancient
sh	show, mission
zh	vision, azure
th	thin, health
th	then, heather
ur	bird, further, word
us	bus, crust
or	court, formal
ehr	error, care
oo	cool, true, rule
ow	now, out
ou	look, pull, would
oy	coin, toy
aw	saw, maul, fall
ng	song, finger
air	Aristotle, barrister
ahr	cart, martyr

Consonants

b	butter, baby
d	dog, cradle
f	fun, phone
g	grade, angle
h	hat, ahead
j	judge, gorge
k	kite, car, black
l	lily, mile
m	mom, camel
n	next, candid
p	price, copper
r	rubber, free
s	small, circle, hassle
t	ton, pottery
v	vase, vivid
w	wall, away
y	yellow, kayak
z	zebra, haze

Glossary

absolute value the positive number of any pair of opposite nonzero real numbers; the absolute value of a number is the distance of its graph from the origin; the absolute value of 0 is 0; the absolute value of a number a is denoted by $|a|$

acute angle an angle that measures less than 90°

acute triangle a triangle with three acute angles

additive identity a number such that the sum of it and any given number is the given number; the additive identity for the real numbers is 0

adjacent angles two angles in the same plane that have a common side and a common vertex but no common interior points

alternate exterior angles the outside angles on opposite sides of a transversal crossing two lines

alternate interior angles the inside angles on opposite sides of a transversal crossing two lines

angle a figure formed by two rays, called *sides* of the angle, that share the same endpoint

angle of rotation the number of degrees a figure is rotated; it can be any number of degrees from 0° to 360° (a full circle); figures can be rotated clockwise or counterclockwise

area the number of square units in the interior of a figure

bar graph a graph that uses bars to display and compare data

base (in a power) a number, variable, or expression that is a factor in a power; in the power a^n, the base is a

base of a cone the flat surface of the cone; the base of a cone is a circle

base of a cylinder one of the parallel, congruent faces of the cylinder; a base of a cylinder is a circle

base of a prism one of the parallel, congruent faces of the prism; a base of a prism is a polygon

biased sample a sample that is not representative of the population

box-and-whisker plot shows the distribution or spread of data; it uses the minimum, the maximum, and the three quartiles of the data

broken-line graph a graph in which points representing data are connected with line segments; a broken-line graph is also called a line graph

capacity a measure of the amount a container can hold

center of rotation the point about which a figure is rotated

chord a line segment that connects any two points on a circle

circle the set of all points in a plane that are equidistant from a given point in the plane called the *center*

circle graph a graph that uses sectors of a circle to display and compare data

circumference distance around a circle

coefficient the numerical factor of a term

combination a collection of items in which the order of the items is not important

common factor a factor shared by two or more terms

complementary events two events such that one must occur, but both cannot occur at the same time

composite number a natural number greater than 1 that has at least one positive factor other than 1 and itself

compound interest interest earned on both the principal and any interest that has already been earned

cone a three-dimensional figure with one base that is a circle, a curved lateral surface, and a point called a vertex

congruent figures figures that have the same size and shape

coordinate on a number line a number that gives the location of a point on the number line

coordinate plane a plane in which the coordinates of a point are its distances from two intersecting perpendicular lines called *axes*

coordinates in a coordinate plane the numbers in an ordered pair that give the location of a point in the coordinate plane

corresponding angles angles that lie in the same relative position or "match up" when a transversal crosses two lines

cosine for an acute angle in a right triangle, the ratio of the length of the adjacent side to the length of the hypotenuse; the abbreviation for cosine is *cos*

cube a solid figure made up of six square faces that meet at right angles

cubic unit a cube whose edges are each one unit long; a cubic unit is used to measure volume

cylinder a three-dimensional figure with two congruent, parallel bases that are circles and a curved lateral surface that joins them

dependent variable the output variable

diameter a chord that contains the center of the circle; the length of this chord is also called the diameter

difference the result of a subtraction

domain in a relation, the set of allowable inputs (the set of first elements of the ordered pairs in the relation)

element a member of a set

empty set the set with no members

equation a number sentence indicating that two expressions have the same value; an equation compares expressions using the $=$ symbol

equiangular polygon a polygon in which all angle measures are equal

equilateral polygon a polygon in which all side lengths are equal

equilateral triangle a triangle in which all three side lengths are equal

equivalent equations equations with the same solution set (same solution or solutions)

equivalent fractions fractions with the same value

equivalent inequalities inequalities with the same solution set

equivalent ratios ratios that describe the same numerical relationship

event a set of one or more outcomes; an event is a subset of the sample space

experiment any process or action that has a result

experimental probability probability based on actual observations or results of an experiment

exponent a number or variable that indicates how many times the base is used as a factor; in the power a^n, the exponent is n

expression a group of mathematical symbols that represents a numerical value; most expressions contain numerals as well as operation signs or grouping symbols or a combination of these elements; an expression containing one or more variables is called a *variable expression* or *algebraic expression*

extrapolation a process of inferring, estimating, or predicting an unknown value that is outside of known values

extremes in a proportion, the first and last numbers or variables; in $a : b = c : d$ or $\frac{a}{b} = \frac{c}{d}$, a and d are the extremes

factor a number, monomial, or polynomial used in an expression as a multiplicand

factor tree a diagram used to find a prime factorization

factorial the product of the whole numbers from 1 through the number; the symbol for factorial is ! for example, $4! = 4 \cdot 3 \cdot 2 \cdot 1 = 24$.

formula an equation that defines the relationship between two or more quantities

function a relation that assigns to each member of the domain exactly one member of the range

graph of a one-variable inequality the set of points on a number line that represent all the solutions of the inequality

graph of a two-variable equation all the points whose ordered pairs form the solution set of the equation

greatest common factor (GCF) the greatest integer that is a factor of two or more given integers

grouping symbols symbols such as parentheses, brackets, and fraction bars used to set apart an expression that should be simplified before other operations are performed

histogram a bar graph that displays the frequency of data values that occur within certain intervals; the height of each bar gives the frequency in the respective interval

hypotenuse (hiy-PAH-tn-oos) the side opposite the right angle in a right triangle

image in a transformation, the new figure that results from the transformation

improper fraction a fraction in which the numerator is greater than or equal to the denominator

independent variable the input variable

inequality a mathematical sentence that compares numbers or expressions using one of the symbols $<, >, \leq,$ or $\geq$

inputs the first elements of the ordered pairs in a relation

integers the set of whole numbers and their opposites, including zero; $\{\ldots, -3, -2, -1, 0, 1, 2, 3, \ldots\}$

interest the cost to borrow money or the amount earned by lending money

interest rate the percentage of the original amount of money that the interest is based on

interpolation the process of inferring, or estimating, an unknown value that is between known values

interquartile range found by subtracting the first quartile Q_1 from the third quartile Q_3; $IQR = Q_3 - Q_1$; interquartile range represents the middle half of the data

inverse operations operations that undo one another; for example, subtraction is the inverse operation of addition

isosceles triangle a triangle in which at least two of the side lengths are equal

lateral face of a prism a face that is not a base; in a *right prism*, the lateral faces are rectangles

lateral surface area the sum of the areas of all surfaces of a three-dimensional figure except the base(s)

least common denominator (LCD) the least common multiple of two or more denominators

least common multiple (LCM) the least multiple that is a common multiple of all the positive integers in a set

leg of a right triangle either of the two sides of a right triangle that form the right angle

like terms terms that contain the same variables raised to the same powers; constants are also like terms

line a collection of points arranged in a straight path that extends without end in both directions

line graph a graph in which points representing data are connected with line segments; a broken-line graph is also called a line graph

line of reflection the line that a figure is reflected across

line segment part of a line; a line segment includes two points on the line and all the points between those two points; also called *segment*

linear equation an equation whose graph is a line

literal equation an equation with two or more variables

lowest terms a fraction is in lowest terms when the numerator and denominator have no common factors other than 1

mean (average) the sum of the values in a data set divided by the number of values

means in a proportion, the second and third numbers or variables; in $a : b = c : d$ or $\frac{a}{c} = \frac{c}{d}$, b and c are the means

median for a data set with an odd number of values, the middle value after the values have been ordered from least to greatest; for a data set with an even number of values, the mean of the two middle values after the values have been ordered from least to greatest

mixed number a number consisting of both a whole number and a fraction or the opposite of such a number

mode the data value(s) that occurs most often in a data set

multiple (of a positive integer) the product of the positive integer and any other positive integer

multiplicative identity a number such that the product of it and any given number is the given number; the multiplicative identity for the real numbers is 1

mutually exclusive events events that cannot happen at the same time

natural numbers the set of counting numbers; $\{1, 2, 3, \ldots\}$

negative correlation a relationship between two sets of data in which the data values in one set generally increase as the data values in the other set decrease

number line a line that has equally spaced intervals labeled with coordinates

numerical expression an expression that names a particular number; for example, the numerical expression $10 + 2$ names the number 12

obtuse angle an angle that measures greater than 90° and less than 180°

obtuse triangle a triangle with an obtuse angle

open sentence an equation or inequality that contains one or more variables

opposites two numbers that are the same distance from zero on a number line but on opposite sides of zero; opposites are also called *additive inverses* because their sum is 0 (the additive identity)

order of magnitude an estimate of a number using the nearest power of 10

order of operations mathematical order that should be followed to simplify an expression when there is more than one operation

ordered pair a pair of numbers in which the first number is the x-coordinate and the second number is the y-coordinate of the location of a point

origin the point on a coordinate plane with coordinates $(0, 0)$ where the x-axis and y-axis intersect; on a number line, the point with coordinate 0

outlier a value that is unusually small or large compared to the rest of the data

outcome a result of an experiment

outputs second elements of the ordered pairs in a relation

parabola graph of a quadratic function

parallel lines coplanar lines that never intersect

parallelogram quadrilateral with two pairs of parallel sides

percent a ratio that compares a number to 100

percent of change ratio of the amount of change to the original amount, expressed in percent form

perfect square rational number whose square root is also rational

perimeter distance around a figure; the perimeter of a polygon is the sum of the lengths of all the sides

permutation an arrangement of items in which the order of the items is important

plane a flat surface with infinite length and width but no thickness

point a location in space with no length, width, or thickness

polygon a closed figure formed by three or more line segments in a plane such that each line segment intersects two other line segments at their endpoints only

population a group of individuals or objects about which information is wanted

power a type of product that is the result of repeated multiplication by the same factor; a power has a *base* and an *exponent*; in the power a^n, the base is a and the exponent is n (which indicates the number of times the base is repeatedly multiplied)

power of ten any number that can be written in the form 10^n, where n is an integer

preimage the original figure in a transformation

prime factorization shows a number written as the product of prime factors

prime number a natural number greater than 1 that has exactly two factors, the number itself and 1

principal money that earns interest at a given rate over time; the principal is the original amount of money that the interest is based on

principal square root the nonnegative square root, indicated by the $\sqrt{}$ symbol

prism a three-dimensional figure whose surfaces, called *faces*, are polygons; at least two faces are parallel and congruent and are called *bases* and all other faces are parallelograms (in a right prism, all other faces are rectangles)

probability a number from 0 to 1 that describes how likely an event is to occur

product the result of a multiplication; the numbers multiplied are factors

proportion an equation stating that two ratios are equal

pyramid a three-dimensional figure with one base that is a polygon and all other faces (called lateral faces) are triangles that meet at a single *vertex*

Pythagorean (puh-tha-guh-REE-uhn) triple a set of three positive integers a, b, and c such that $a^2 + b^2 = c^2$

quadrant one of the four regions into which the coordinate axes separate the coordinate plane

quartile one of three values that separate an ordered data set into four equal parts; the second quartile Q_2 is the median of the data set; the first quartile Q_1 is the median of the lower

half of the data set; the third quartile Q_3 is the median of the upper half of the data set

quotient the result of a division

radius a segment that connects the center of a circle to a point on the circle; the length of that segment is also called the radius

range in a relation the set of possible outputs (the set of second elements of the ordered pairs in the relation)

range of a data set the difference of the maximum and minimum values in the data set

rate a ratio of quantities that have different units

ratio a comparison of two quantities using division

rational number any number that can be expressed as a ratio $\left(\dfrac{a}{b}\right)$ where a and b are integers and $b \neq 0$; the set of rational numbers is represented by $\mathbb{Q}$.

rational square root a square root that is a rational number

ray part of a line; it begins at an endpoint and extends infinitely in one direction

reciprocal a number that when multiplied by a given number gives the multiplicative identity 1; reciprocals are also called *multiplicative inverses*

rectangle a quadrilateral with four right angles

reflection a transformation of a figure by flipping it across a line or line segment, creating a mirror image of the figure

regular polygon a polygon that is both equiangular and equilateral

relation any set of ordered pairs

relatively prime having no common factors other than 1

replacement set a set of values allowable as solutions of an open sentence

rhombus a quadrilateral with four congruent sides

right angle an angle that measures 90°

right triangle a triangle with a right angle

rise the change in the y-coordinates (the vertical change) when moving from one point on a line to another point on the line

rotation a transformation of a figure by turning it about a given point

run the change in the x-coordinates (the horizontal change) when moving from one point on a line to another point on the line

sample part of a population

sample space the set of all possible outcomes of an experiment

scale factor a ratio of one measure to another, where both measures are in the same unit of measure

scalene triangle a triangle in which none of the side lengths are equal

scatter plot a graph that displays two sets of data as points; scatter-plot points represent ordered pairs

scientific notation a representation of a number as the product of a number that is greater than or equal to 1 but less than 10 and an integer power of ten

semicircle half of a circle

set a collection of objects

sides of a polygon the line segments that form the polygon

similar figures figures that have the same shape but not necessarily the same size

simple interest interest earned or paid only on the principal, or initial deposit

simplify a numerical expression find its value

sine for an acute angle in a right triangle, the ratio of the length of the opposite side to the length of the hypotenuse; the abbreviation for sine is *sin*

slope a number that describes the steepness of a line, computed as the ratio of the change in the y-coordinates to the change in the x-coordinates (the ratio of rise to run) when moving from one point on the line to another point on the line

solution of an open sentence a value of the variable or variables that makes the open sentence a true statement

solution of a system of linear equations in two variables an ordered pair that is a solution of each equation in the system

solution set the set of all solutions of an open sentence

square a quadrilateral with four congruent sides and four right angles

square root a factor of a number that when multiplied by itself results in the number; the nonnegative square root is called the *principal square root* and is indicated by the $\sqrt{}$ symbol

standard form of a linear equation an equation of the form $Ax + By = C$, where A, B, and C are integers and A and B are not both zero

stem-and-leaf plot a graph used to organize and display data; its benefits include showing the distribution of the data as well as the individual values

sum the result of an addition; the numbers added are *addends*

surface area the sum of the areas of all surfaces of a three-dimensional figure

system of linear equations two or more linear equations with the same variables

tangent for an acute angle in a right triangle, the ratio of the length of the opposite side to the length of the adjacent side; the abbreviation for tangent is *tan*

transformation a change in the position, orientation, shape, or size of a figure

translation a transformation of a figure by sliding it in a straight path without rotation or reflection

transversal a line that intersects two or more lines in a plane

trapezoid a quadrilateral with exactly one pair of parallel sides

trial a performance of an experiment

triangle a polygon with 3 sides

unbiased sample a sample that is representative of the population

unit rate a rate that has a denominator of 1

variable a symbol that represents a value

variable expression a group of one or more variables, one or more operations, and possibly one or more numbers; also called an *algebraic expression*

vertex a point common to two sides of an angle or polygon; the plural of vertex is *vertices*

volume a measure of the space inside (or the space occupied by) a three-dimensional figure

whole numbers the set of counting numbers and zero; $\{0, 1, 2, 3, \ldots\}$

x-axis the horizontal number line in the coordinate plane

x-coordinate the first number in an ordered pair of numbers that designates the location of a point in the coordinate plane; also called *abscissa* (ab-SIH-suh)

x-intercept the x-coordinate of the point where a graph intersects the x-axis

y-axis the vertical number line in the coordinate plane

y-coordinate the second number in an ordered pair of numbers that designates the location of a point in the coordinate plane; also called *ordinate* (OR-duh-nuht)

y-intercept the y-coordinate of the point where a graph intersects the y-axis

Symbols

$\|$	such that	$\{\ldots\}$	description or list of all elements in a set; roster notation
$\in$	is an element of	%	percent
$\varnothing$ or $\{\ \}$	null or empty set	$\pm$	plus or minus
$\sqrt{a}$	principal square root of a	$a : b$	ratio of a to b
π	pi	$^{\circ}$	degree or degrees
$(\ )$	parentheses	$_{n}P_{r}$	number of permutations of n objects taken r at a time
$[\ ]$	brackets	$_{n}C_{r}$	number of combinations of n objects taken r at a time
$\{\ \}$	braces	$\overline{AB}$	line segment AB
$\approx$	is approximately equal to	AB	length of line segment AB
$=$	is equal to	$\overrightarrow{AB}$	ray AB
$\neq$	is not equal to	$\overleftrightarrow{AB}$	line AB
$\cong$	is congruent to	$\triangle ABC$	triangle ABC
$\sim$	is similar to	$\angle ABC$	angle ABC
$<$	is less than	$m\angle ABC$	measure of angle ABC
$>$	is greater than	$\llcorner$	right angle
$\leq$	is less than or equal to	$\parallel$	parallel
$\geq$	is greater than or equal to	$\perp$	perpendicular
$f(x)$	f of x; f is a function of x		
$\|x\|$	absolute value of x		
$-a$	the opposite of a		
a^{n}	a to the nth power		

Properties

Real Number Properties

Let a, b, and c be any real numbers.

Addition Property of Equality	If $a = b$, then $a + c = b + c$ and $c + a = c + b$.
Addition Property: Addends with Like Signs	For all $a > 0$ and $b > 0$, $a + b = |a| + |b|$. For all $a < 0$ and $b < 0$, $a + b = -(|a| + |b|)$.
Addition Property: Addends with Unlike Signs	For all $a > 0$ and $b < 0$, If $|a| > |b|$, then $a + b = |a| - |b|$. If $|a| < |b|$, then $a + b = -(|b| - |a|)$.
Subtraction Property of Equality	If $a = b$, then $a - c = b - c$.
Substitution Property of Equality	If $a = b$, then a may be replaced with b in any expression or equation.
Multiplication Property of Equality	If $a = b$, then $c \cdot a = c \cdot b$ and $a \cdot c = b \cdot c$.
Division Property of Equality	If $a = b$ and $c \neq 0$ then $\dfrac{a}{c} = \dfrac{b}{c}$.

	Addition	Multiplication
Commutative Properties	$a + b = b + a$	$a \cdot b = b \cdot a$
Associative Properties	$(a + b) + c = a + (b + c)$	$(a \cdot b) \cdot c = a \cdot (b \cdot c)$
Inverse Properties	$a + (-a) = 0$ and $(-a) + a = 0$	$a \cdot \dfrac{1}{a} = 1$ and $\dfrac{1}{a} \cdot a = 1, a \neq 0$
Identity Properties	$a + 0 = a$ and $0 + a = a$	$a \cdot 1 = a$ and $1 \cdot a = a$
Distributive Property	$a(b + c) = ab + ac$	

Absolute Value Equations

If $|x| = a$ for some positive number a, then $x = a$ or $x = -a$.

Properties of Exponents

Let a and b be nonzero real numbers. Let m and n be integers.

If n is a positive integer, $a^n = a \cdot a \cdot a \cdot ... \cdot a$ (n factors).

Zero Exponent Property	$a^0 = 1, a \neq 0$
Negative Exponent Property	$a^{-m} = \dfrac{1}{a^m}, a \neq 0$
Product of Powers Property	$a^m \cdot a^n = a^{m+n}$

Square Root Properties

For nonnegative values of m, n, and p, if $m < n < p$, then $\sqrt{m} < \sqrt{n} < \sqrt{p}$.

Product Property	For real numbers a and b, $\sqrt{ab} = \sqrt{a} \cdot \sqrt{b}$ and $\sqrt{a} \cdot \sqrt{b} = \sqrt{ab}$
Quotient Property	For real numbers a and b with b $\neq 0$, $\sqrt{\dfrac{a}{b}} = \dfrac{\sqrt{a}}{\sqrt{b}}$.

Reciprocal Properties

Reciprocal Property of Multiplication   For any nonzero real number a,

$a \cdot \dfrac{1}{a} = 1$.

For all nonzero real numbers a and b, the reciprocal of $\dfrac{a}{b}$ is $\dfrac{b}{a}$.

For any nonzero real number a, $\dfrac{1}{-a} = \dfrac{-1}{a} = -\dfrac{1}{a}$.

For all nonzero real numbers a and b, $\dfrac{1}{ab} = \dfrac{1}{a} \cdot \dfrac{1}{b}$.

Division Properties

For any real number a and nonzero real number b, $a \div b = a \cdot \dfrac{1}{b}$.

For all real numbers a and b and nonzero real number c, $\dfrac{a+b}{c} = \dfrac{a}{c} + \dfrac{b}{c}$.

For all $a > 0$ and $b > 0$, $a \div b > 0$.

For all $a < 0$ and $b < 0$, $a \div b > 0$.

For all $a < 0$ and $b > 0$, $a \div b < 0$.

Properties of Order

Comparison Property of Order	If $a > b$, then $b < a$. If $a < b$, then $b > a$.
Transitive Property of Order	If $a > b$ and $b > c$, then $a > c$. If $a < b$ and $b < c$, then $a < c$.
Addition Property of Order	If $a > b$, then $a + c > b + c$. If $a < b$, then $a + c < b + c$.
Subtraction Property of Order	If $a > b$, then $a - c > b - c$. If $a < b$, then $a - c < b - c$.
Multiplication Property of Order, Positive Multiplier	If $a > b$ and $c > 0$, then $ca > cb$ and $ac > bc$. If $a < b$ and $c > 0$, then $ca < cb$ and $ac < bc$.
Multiplication Property of Order, Negative Multiplier	If $a > b$ and $c < 0$, then $ca < cb$ and $ac < bc$. If $a < b$ and $c < 0$, then $ca > cb$ and $ac > bc$.
Division Property of Order, Positive Multiplier	If $a > b$ and $c > 0$, then $\dfrac{a}{c} > \dfrac{b}{c}$. If $a < b$ and $c > 0$, then $\dfrac{a}{c} < \dfrac{b}{c}$.
Division Property of Order, Negative Multiplier	If $a > b$ and $c < 0$, then $\dfrac{a}{c} < \dfrac{b}{c}$. If $a < b$ and $c < 0$, then $\dfrac{a}{c} > \dfrac{b}{c}$.

Comparison Property of Rational Numbers

For nonzero integers a and c and positive integers b and d.

$$\frac{a}{b} > \frac{c}{d} \text{ if and only if } ad > bc$$

$$\frac{a}{b} < \frac{c}{d} \text{ if and only if } ad < bc$$

Properties of Proportions

Let a, b, c, and d be real numbers.

Means-Extremes Product Property	$\dfrac{a}{b} = \dfrac{c}{d}$ if and only if $ad = bc$, given that b and d are not 0.
Reciprocal Property	If $\dfrac{a}{b} = \dfrac{c}{d}$, then $\dfrac{b}{a} = \dfrac{d}{c}$, given that a, b, c, and d are all nonzero.

Formulary

Geometric Formulas

Circle

Circumference $C = \pi d = 2\pi r$

Area $A = \pi r^2$

Cone

Volume $V = \frac{1}{3}Bh = \frac{1}{3}\pi r^2 h$

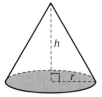

Cylinder

Volume $V = Bh = \pi r^2 h$

Surface Area $S = 2\pi r^2 + 2\pi rh$

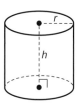

Parallelogram

Area $A = bh$

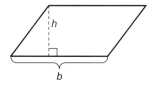

Prism: Cube

Volume $V = s^3$

Surface Area $S = 6s^2$

Prism: Rectangular

Volume $V = lwh$

Surface Area $S = 2lw + 2lh + 2wh$

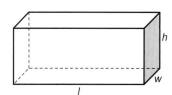

Pyramid

Volume $V = \frac{1}{3}Bh$

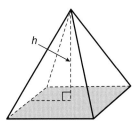

Trigonometry

$\sin A = \dfrac{\text{opposite of } \angle A}{\text{hypotenuse}} = \dfrac{a}{c}$

$\cos A = \dfrac{\text{adjacent to } \angle A}{\text{hypotenuse}} = \dfrac{b}{c}$

$\tan A = \dfrac{\text{opposite of } \angle A}{\text{adjacent to } \angle A} = \dfrac{a}{b}$

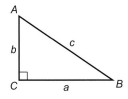

Rectangle

Area $A = lw$

Perimeter $P = 2l + 2w$

Square

Area $A = s^2$

Perimeter $P = 4s$

Trapezoid

Area $A = \frac{1}{2}h(b_1 + b_2)$

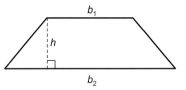

Triangle: General

Area $A = \frac{1}{2}bh$

Perimeter $P = a + b + c$

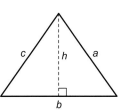

Triangle: Right

Pythagorean Theorem $a^2 + b^2 = c^2$

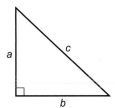

Analytic Geometry

Line

Standard form of equation: $Ax + By = C$

Distance formula: $d = \sqrt{(x_2 - x_1)^2 + (y_2 - y_1)^2}$

Slope

$m = \dfrac{\text{rise}}{\text{run}} = \dfrac{\text{vertical change}}{\text{horizontal change}} = \dfrac{y_2 - y_1}{x_2 - x_1}$

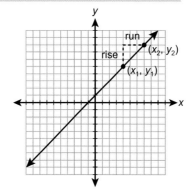

Other Formulas

Percent of Change

$\text{percent of change} = \dfrac{\text{amount of change}}{\text{original amount}} \cdot 100\%$

Simple Interest

$I = Prt$, where I is the amount of interest, P is the principal, r is the annual interest rate, and t is the time in years.

Factorial

$n! = n \cdot (n - 1) \cdot (n - 2) \cdot \ldots \cdot 1 \quad (n \text{ factors})$

$0! = 1$

Permutations

$_nP_r = P(n, r) = \dfrac{n!}{(n - r)!}$

Combinations

$_nC_r = C(n, r) = \binom{n}{r} = \dfrac{n!}{r!\,(n - r)!}$

Mean

$\bar{x} = \dfrac{x_1 + x_2 + \ldots + x_n}{n}$

Median

Arrange the values in order from least to greatest. For an

Odd number of values: The middle value

Even number of values: The average of the middle two values

Mode

The value that occurs most often in a set of data. If no one value occurs most often, then there is no mode for the set.

Simple Theoretical Probability

$$P(E) = \frac{\text{number of outcomes in event } E}{\text{total number of outcomes in sample space } S} = \frac{n(E)}{n(S)}$$

Probability of Mutually Exclusive Events

$$P(A \text{ or } B) = P(A) + P(B)$$

Conversion for Volume/Capacity

$1 \text{ cm}^3 = 1 \text{ cc} = 1 \text{ mL}$

$1000 \text{ mL} = 1\text{L}$

Sample Graphs

Linear Function

$f(x) = x$

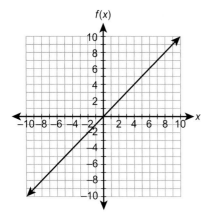

Quadratic Function

$f(x) = x^2$

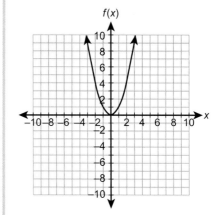

Absolute Value Function

$f(x) = |x|$

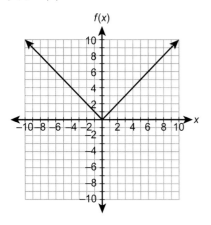

Box-and-Whisker Plot

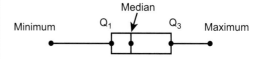

Range = Maximum − Minimum

Interquartile Range = $Q_3 - Q_1$

Stem-and-Leaf Plot

```
0 | 1   4   4
1 | 1   2   7
2 | 0
3 | 5   5
4 | 8
```

Key: 3|5 means 35

Histogram

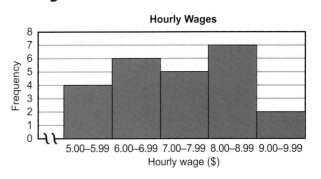

Broken Line Graph

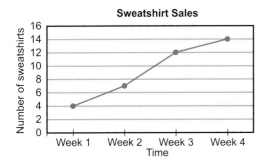

Circle Graph

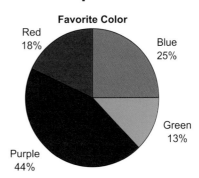

Selected Answers

Unit 1 The Basics

Pages 8–9

1. A. 6 **B.** 1 **3. A.** 78 **B.** 3 **5.** 11 **7.** 5 **9.** 1 **11.** 158
13. 5 **15.** 34 **17.** 4 **19.** 4 **21.** $23 + 3 \cdot (5 - 1)$
23. $(9 + 3) \cdot 5 \div (2 + 4)$ **25.** $(17 - 5) \div (1 + 3)$
27. $6 + 2 \cdot 4 = 14$; The height is 14 inches. **29.** $400 - (12 \cdot 20) = 160$; There are 160 gallons of water in the tank.
31. $(2 \cdot 14) - (3 \cdot 9) = 1$; Jamal read one more page.

Pages 12–13

1. 67 **3.** 7 **5.** 12 **7.** 25 **9.** 24 **11.** 30 **13.** 6 **15.** 45
17. 3 **19.** 17 **21.** 8 **23.** 144 square inches **25. A.** 3 **B.** 3
C. No reason for concern **27.** 561 cubic inches
29. 2048 cubic centimeters

Pages 16–17

1. $n - 15$ **3.** $n \div 7$ **5.** $25 - (6 + n)$ **7.** $6n$ **9.** $3 - 2n$
11. $\dfrac{3 + n}{n}$ **13.** $22 - x$ **15.** $5 \cdot [2 \cdot (n - 1)]$ **17.** Answers
will vary. Sample answer: twice the difference of 3 and x
19. Answers will vary. Sample answer: three times the product of m and n **21.** Answers will vary. Sample answer: the quotient of 2 and the sum of n and 3 **23.** Answers will vary. Sample answer: the difference of the sum of a and b and the sum of twice c and d **25.** $p + (p + 1) + (p + 2) + (p + 3)$
27. Isaiah: $2j - 3$, Kaleb: $4 \cdot (2j - 3)$ **29.** $0.05b + 0.05c$ or $0.05(b + c)$ **31.** $0.05x, x + 0.05x$

Pages 20–21

1. $13 > 11$ **3.** $6 > 4$ **5.** $6 = 6$ **7.** $5 < 12$ **9.** $42 = 42$
11. $25 < 36$ **13.** $4 = 4$ **15.** No **17.** Yes **19.** Yes **21.** Yes
23. Yes **25.** Yes **27.** No **29.** Hae Sung traveled the greatest distance **31.** The amount of money Shaelun has is equal to the amount of money Kirby has. **33.** Ms. Fields, Mr. Reese, Ms. Silva

Pages 24–25

1. $\{3\}$ **3.** $\{6\}$ **5.** $\{5\}$ **7.** $\{10\}$ **9.** $\{6\}$ **11.** $\{4\}$
13. $\{0, 1, 2\}$ **15.** $\{0, 1\}$ **17.** $\{2, 3, 4\}$ **19.** 37 **21.** 8
23. $\{4, 35, 196\}$ **25.** $\{8, 10, 12, 14, 16\}$ **27.** $59°F$ **29.** The test scores 82 and 83 will enable Tabitha to get a B for the course.

Pages 28–29

1. $11 + 7 = 18, 11 = 18 - 7, 7 = 18 - 11$ **3.** $3 \cdot 4 = 12,$
$3 = \dfrac{12}{4}, 4 = \dfrac{12}{3}$ **5.** $35 = 7k, 7 = \dfrac{35}{k}, k = \dfrac{35}{7}$ **7.** $\dfrac{r}{5} = 4,$
$r = 5 \cdot 4, \dfrac{r}{4} = 5$ **9.** $6 + h = 13, 6 = 13 - h, h = 13 - 6$
11. $n + 16 = 28, n = 28 - 16, 16 = 28 - n$ **13.** $m = 1.8 + 0.2, m - 1.8 = 0.2, m - 0.2 = 1.8$ **15.** $g + \dfrac{1}{2} = 5\dfrac{1}{2}, g = 5\dfrac{1}{2} - \dfrac{1}{2}, \dfrac{1}{2} = 5\dfrac{1}{2} - g$ **17.** $\dfrac{75}{w} = 15, 15w = 75, w = \dfrac{75}{15}$
19. $b \cdot 10 = 35, b = \dfrac{35}{10}, 10 = \dfrac{35}{b}$ **21.** $n + 19 = 25,$
$n = 25 - 19, 19 = 25 - n$ **23.** $b = 27 - 14, b = 13$
25. $n = \dfrac{84}{4}, n = 21$ **27.** $r = 81 - 21, r = 60$ **29.** $n = \dfrac{39}{3},$
$n = 13$ **31.** $192 - x = 51, 141 = x$ **33.** $\dfrac{c}{3} = 16; c = 16 \cdot 3;$
The child had 48 crayons.

Page 32

1. $n + 2 = 7$ **3.** $2n = n - 3$ **5.** $22 = 3n + 7$ **7.** $5n - 6 = 24$ **9.** $2n + (n - 1) = 14$ **11.** Answers will vary. Sample answer: The difference of 8 and a number is 3. **13.** Answers will vary. Sample answer: Five times a number is the quotient of 30 times the number and 6. **15.** Answers will vary. Sample answer: The quotient of twice a number and 5 is 14. **17.** $15 + n = 27, n = 12$ **19.** $21 = 3n, n = 7$
21. $3n - 1 = 26, n = 9$ **23.** $3 \cdot (n + 12) = 45, n = 3,$
25. $7 + n = 3n + 5, n = 1$ **27.** $I = Prt$ **29.** $m = \dfrac{180 \cdot (n - 2)}{n}$

Page 35

1. 20 monkeys **3.** 625 words **5.** 15, 16, 17, 18 inches
7. 56 miles per hour **9.** 14,780 feet and 44,340 feet
11. 10 years old **13.** 16 children; 3 fewer children
15. 12, 13, or 14 years old

Unit 2 Addition and Subtraction

Pages 43–44

1. -9 **3.** -1
5.

7.

9. $3 > -1$ **11.** $-5 < 0$ **13. A.** $|n| = 10$ **B.** $-n = -10$
15. A. $|n| = 4$ **B.** $-n = 4$ **17.** $|-4| = 4$ **19.** $-6 < |-10|$
21. $x = 5$ and $x = -5$ **23.** $r = -5, -4, -3, -2, -1, 0, 1, 2, 3, 4, 5$ **25.** no solution **27.** $x = -2, -1, 0, 1, 2$
29. Haley, Buan, Trent, Jared, Alana **31.** Max, Olivia, Leticia, Ramon, Emilio

Pages 48–49

1. -9 **3.** -4 **5.** 5 **7.** -96 **9.** -40 **11.** -4 **13.** -13
15. $>$ **17.** $=$ **19.** 7 **21.** 0 **23.** 39 **25.** 5 **27.** 20
29. A. Yes. **B.** The students will have \$72 left over. **C.** Since 72 is a positive number, they will have money left over.

Page 52

1. 1 **3.** 20 **5.** 13 **7.** 6 **9.** -10 **11.** -10 **13.** -8 **15.** 31
17. 7 **19.** 25 **21.** 8 **23.** -4 **25.** -3 **27.** $x = -17$ **29.** $178°F$

Pages 56–57

1. -1.6 **3.** 0.2 **5.** -2.6 **7.** 0.2 **9.** -33.8 **11.** -32.6
13.

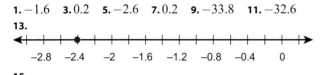

15.

17.

19. $<$ **21.** $>$ **23.** $>$ **25.** $-1.4, -0.3, 0.9, 1.3$ **27.** $-1.9,$
$-0.5, 0.03, 1.7$ **29.** College City, Green Valley, Snow Town, Oak Park; $-1.6, -1.45, -1.4, 0.2$

Page 61

1. -1.6 **3.** -1.1 **5.** -1.9 **7.** -22.23 **9.** -0.52 **11.** 8.4
13. 13.123 **15.** -0.88 **17.** 34.977 **19.** -27.5 **21.** -7.1
23. -1.46 **25.** 8.455 **27.** $a = 4.8$ **29.** $z = 6.6$ **31.** $a = -2.5$
33. 327.82

Page 65

1. 2.6 **3.** 14.4 **5.** 18.3 **7.** -1.28 **9.** -27.04 **11.** -4.42
13. -0.02 **15.** -194.27 **17.** 138.1 **19.** 419.77 **21.** -9.8
23. -6.1 **25.** 5.953 **27.** $m = 24.9$ **29.** $c = 0.9$ **31.** $d = 0$
33. $3.75°C$

Pages 69–70

1. opposite of a sum **3.** associative property of addition
5. opposite of a sum **7.** 54 **9.** 3 **11.** -49 **13.** 87 **15.** 3
17. 14.32 **19.** 21.8 **21.** $m = -5$ **23.** $c = -6$ **25.** $y = 3$
27. $x = 12$ **29.** \$33 **31.** 26

Pages 74–75

1. $x = -20$ **3.** $y = 17$ **5.** $k = -17$ **7.** $a = -16$ **9.** $x = -7$
11. $x = 19$ **13.** $z = -14$ **15.** $a = 6.8$ **17.** $k = -9$ **19.** $z = 8.0$ **21.** $m = -3.0$ **23.** $a = 9$ **25.** $z = 2$ **27.** $b = 18$
29. A. $x + 14 = -26$ **B.** -40 **C.** The number is -40.
31. A. $c + 275 = 325$ **B.** $c = 50$ **C.** Maggie needs to buy 50 cards. **33. A.** $8.39 - c = 7.14$ **B.** $c = 1.25$ **C.** The coupon was worth \$1.25.

Pages 79–81

1. $-2538, -411, -156, -86, -40, -28, -12$ **3.** 128 m
5. 9261 m **7.** $-44, -30, -22, -7, 23$ **9.** $45°F$ **11.** $x -(-30) = 23; x = -7;$ Philadelphia **13.** $x = -405.99;$ withdrawal **15.** 219 feet **17.** $214°F$ **19.** Sam: $+9$, Ella: -1, Anju: -3, Ben: -11 **21.** 20 points

Unit 3   Multiplication and Division

Page 88

1. 36 **3.** -30 **5.** 120 **7.** 72 **9.** 219 **11.** 4.2 **13.** 7.68
15. -9.1 **17.** 48 **19.** -15 **21.** -70 **23.** negative
25. positive **27.** 8 **29.** -20 **31.** 8 **33.** 8.2 **35.** -3 **37.** 40

Page 91

1. -7 **3.** -5 **5.** 9 **7.** -4 **9.** 0.9 **11.** 8 **13.** -1 **15.** 0.7
17. -30 **19.** 3 **21.** -5 **23.** -5 **25.** 12 **27.** -2 **29.** 1.25

Page 96

1. identity property of multiplication **3.** reciprocal property of multiplication **5.** reciprocal property of multiplication
7. zero property of multiplication **9.** zero property of multiplication **11.** 0; zero property of multiplication **13.** 70; associative property of multiplication **15.** 0; zero divided by a nonzero number equals 0 **17.** $12bc$; commutative and associative properties of multiplication **19.** $\frac{r}{5}$; commutative, associative, and reciprocal properties of multiplication
21. $k = 0$ **23.** $m = 3$ **25.** $b = 9$ **27.** $z = 2.1$ **29.** $r = 2$

Pages 100–102

1. $6.25; 6.3; 6; 10$ **3.** $326.00; 326.0; 326; 330$ **5.** 440 **7.** \$9
9. 0.59 **11.** \$26.40 **13.** C **15.** B **17.** B **19.** not reasonable
21. not reasonable **23.** not reasonable **25.** reasonable
27. about 64 cubic inches **29.** about \$800 **31.** about 180 votes

Page 106

1. $r = -2$ **3.** $b = 5$ **5.** $m = -12$ **7.** $x = \frac{15}{2}$ **9.** $g = -2.1$
11. $j = -14$ **13.** $b = 24$ **15.** $x = 9$ **17.** $y = -30$ **19.** $z = -8$
21. $b = 8$ **23.** $k = -12.8$ **25.** $w = -5$ **27.** $p = -\frac{13}{12}$
29. A. $24 = 1.2x$ **B.** $x = 20$ **C.** Mrs. Williams had 20 students in her class last year.

Pages 110–111

1. 49 square inches **3.** 5.76 square centimeters **5.** 48 m
7. 5 square centimeters **9.** 8.06 square meters **11.** 150.5
meters **13.** 20 kilometers **15.** 14% increase **17.** $\frac{d}{t} = r$
19. $\frac{2A}{h} = b$ **21.** $\frac{F}{m} = a$ **23.** $IR = V$ **25.** 9 inches
27. 56 miles per hour **29.** $w = 4$

Unit 4   Fractions

Page 118

1. $\frac{2}{5}$ **3.** $\frac{1}{4}$ **5.** $\frac{13}{18}$ **7.** $\frac{9}{-10}$ **9.** $\frac{27}{32}$ **11.** $\frac{12}{13}$ **13.** Yes **15.** No
17. No **19.** No **21.** $\frac{x}{8}$ **23.** $\frac{7w}{15}$ **25.** $x = 3$ **27.** $y = 35$
29. $x = 5$ **31.** $b = 4$ **33.** $x = 6$ **35.** $\frac{7}{8}$ inch **37.** $\frac{5}{12}$
39. Yes, the fraction of voters that would vote for Mrs. Mitchell is the same.

Pages 121–122

1. $\frac{1}{16}$ **3.** $-\frac{9}{20}$ **5.** $\frac{21}{32}$ **7.** $\frac{3}{10}$ **9.** $\frac{6}{35}$ **11.** $\frac{2x}{3y}$ **13.** $\frac{1}{5}$

15. $\frac{3}{10}$ **17.** $\frac{3}{8}$ **19.** $\frac{3}{5}$ **21.** 1 **23.** $\frac{2}{3}$ **25.** $\frac{3}{5}$ **27.** 1 **29.** $\frac{e}{3f}$

31. A. $\frac{3}{5}$ **B.** $\frac{2}{5}$ **33.** Dianne walked $\frac{7}{32}$ mile so far.

35. Catalina drank $\frac{1}{10}$ gallon of the juice. **37. A.** $\frac{15}{16}$ **B.** $\frac{5}{32}$

Pages 125–126

1. $\frac{1}{6}$ **3.** $-\frac{3}{2}$ **5.** $\frac{9}{8}$ **7.** $\frac{y}{x}$ **9.** $\frac{2}{5}$ **11.** 9 **13.** $\frac{5}{64}$ **15.** $\frac{1}{6}$

17. -30 **19.** 2 **21.** $\frac{20}{27}$ **23.** $\frac{1}{4}$ **25.** $-\frac{4}{15}$ **27.** $\frac{2}{m}$ **29.** $\frac{7}{9}$

31. $\frac{3}{4}$ **33.** 12 **35.** $\frac{1}{8}$ of the banana **37.** $\frac{1}{16}$ foot long **39.** 9

Page 131

1. 6 **3.** 36 **5.** 56 **7.** 40 **9.** 42 **11.** Answers will vary. Sample answer: $\frac{2}{4}$ and $\frac{3}{4}$ **13.** Answers will vary. Sample answer: $-\frac{10}{15}$ and $\frac{9}{15}$ **15.** Answers will vary. Sample answer: $\frac{20}{35}$ and $\frac{21}{35}$ **17.** Answers will vary. Sample answer: $\frac{2}{16}$ and $\frac{3}{16}$ **19.** Answers will vary. Sample answer: $\frac{6}{12}, \frac{4}{12}$, and $\frac{3}{12}$

21. $\frac{3}{5} > \frac{4}{7}$ **23.** $\frac{5}{12} < \frac{3}{5}$ **25.** $-\frac{6}{7} > -\frac{11}{12}$ **27.** $-\frac{5}{18} > -\frac{3}{10}$

29. Maria finished a greater fraction of math problems.
31. The blue jay was heavier.

Pages 135–136

1. $\frac{7}{9}$ **3.** $\frac{3}{5}$ **5.** $-\frac{1}{5}$ **7.** $\frac{3}{4}$ **9.** $\frac{5}{8}$ **11.** $\frac{1}{8}$ **13.** $\frac{41}{60}$ **15.** $-\frac{29}{150}$

17. $\frac{55}{63}$ **19.** $\frac{4}{9}$ **21.** $2\frac{1}{4}$ **23.** $1\frac{1}{3}$ **25.** $1\frac{1}{6}$ **27.** 5 **29.** $-3\frac{1}{5}$

31. $4\frac{1}{5}$ **33.** $-6\frac{3}{4}$ **35.** $3\frac{3}{4}$ **37.** D **39.** $-1\frac{7}{60}$ **41.** $-1\frac{11}{40}$

43. Ebenezer spent $\frac{23}{40}$ of his allowance. **45.** Roscoe drank $\frac{3}{8}$ quart more water than he drank milk and juice combined.

Pages 140–141

1. $7\frac{1}{2}$ **3.** $-4\frac{1}{3}$ **5.** $5\frac{2}{3}$ **7.** $2\frac{1}{2}$ **9.** $1\frac{13}{16}$ **11.** $3\frac{2}{15}$ **13.** $6\frac{1}{2}$

15. $9\frac{4}{5}$ **17.** $\frac{5}{4}$ **19.** $\frac{21}{5}$ **21.** $-\frac{11}{6}$ **23.** $-\frac{13}{5}$ **25.** $\frac{79}{8}$

27. $\frac{53}{9}$ **29.** $\frac{129}{13}$ **31.** $\frac{3b+a}{b}$ **33. A.** $5\frac{1}{4} + 2\frac{5}{8} + 4\frac{1}{2} = 12\frac{3}{8}$

B. The total amount of meat served was $12\frac{3}{8}$ pounds.

35. A. $\left(2\frac{7}{10} + 3\frac{1}{2}\right) - 4\frac{3}{4} = 1\frac{9}{20}$ **B.** The group hiked $1\frac{9}{20}$ miles farther before lunch. **37. A.** $5\frac{1}{2} + 6\frac{3}{4} + 5\frac{4}{5}$ **B.** The total was $18\frac{1}{20}$ hours. **39. A.** $3 + \frac{3}{2} + \frac{3}{4} + \frac{3}{8} + \frac{3}{16}$ **B.** The fifth term is $\frac{3}{16}$ and the sum is $5\frac{13}{16}$.

Page 145

1. 12 **3.** $32\frac{1}{2}$ **5.** $7\frac{2}{9}$ **7.** $-21\frac{1}{4}$ **9.** -200 **11.** $-12\frac{15}{16}$ **13.** $1\frac{2}{5}x$

15. 3 **17.** 7 **19.** $3\frac{3}{10}$ **21.** 16 **23.** $3\frac{1}{8}$ **25.** $\frac{x}{10}$ **27.** $1\frac{47}{55}$

29. $1\frac{5}{12}$ feet **31.** 4 cups of sugar **33.** books: $106\frac{1}{2}$ pounds; crate with books: $109\frac{3}{4}$ pounds

Page 149

1. $x = 2\frac{1}{6}$ **3.** $c = 72$ **5.** $k = 5\frac{2}{5}$ **7.** $m = -4\frac{13}{14}$ **9.** $a = \frac{8}{15}$

11. $y = \frac{2}{9}$ **13.** $d = -7\frac{8}{15}$ **15.** $q = -32$ **17.** $b = -4\frac{2}{7}$

19. $m = 4$ **21.** $g = 28$ **23.** $b = -6\frac{1}{16}$ **25. A.** $f + 2\frac{3}{4} = 5\frac{1}{2}$

B. $f = 2\frac{3}{4}$ **C.** Finn ran $2\frac{3}{4}$ miles. **27. A.** $7\frac{1}{2}x = 45$ **B.** $x = 6$

C. There were 6 runners on the team.

29. A. $\dfrac{6\frac{1}{2} + 2\frac{1}{4} + x + 4\frac{3}{4}}{4} = 4\frac{1}{8}$ **B.** $x = 3$ **C.** The value of x is 3.

Unit 5   Combined Operations

Pages 156–157

1. $18 = 18$ **3.** $1 = 1$ **5.** $-2 = -2$ **7.** $5 \cdot 5 + 5 \cdot 1$ **9.** $4v + 4 \cdot 7$

11. $-9 \cdot 1 + (-9)y$ **13.** $3(6 + 9)$ **15.** $4(2 - 11)$ **17.** $5(8 - s)$

19. $-2(x + y)$ **21.** 130 **23.** 594 **25.** 816 **27.** 800 **29.** 472.68

31. $x = 3$ **33.** $n = 7$ **35.** $s = -1$ **37.** 40 cm **39.** 4600 m^2

41. A. \$23.99 **B.** \$4.82

Pages 160–161

1. $4x, 5x; 4y, 3y$ **3.** $3c, 6c$ **5.** $4ab, -5ab; 7, -5$ **7.** $9v, 2v;$ $6uv, -uv$ **9.** $3, 1, -9; 3rs, 8rs$ **11.** $4w, 4w; 2wxy, -wxy$

13. $1.5s, 2s; 1.5w, 2w$ **15.** $7a$ **17.** $2c$ **19.** $-6.2x$ **21.** 0

23. $\frac{1}{2}a$ **25.** $6a + 5b$ **27.** $6t + 5$ **29.** 6 **31.** $12z + 7w$

33. $3r - 9rs - 6$ **35.** $3x + 15$ **37.** $-8.5x - 2.5$

39. $11b - 5ab$ **41. A.** $1.06d$ dollars **B.** $1.18m$ dollars

C. $1.045r$ dollars **43. A.** $(11x + 35)$ dollars **B.** \$167 **C.** The cost of 19 shirts is \$244 because $11 \cdot 19 + 35 = 244$. The cost of 20 shirts is \$223.10 because the cost per shirt is $11 - 0.10 \cdot 11 = 9.90$ and $9.90 \cdot 19 + 35 = 223.10$.

Pages 165–166

1. 9 **3.** -18 **5.** 12 **7.** -18 **9.** $20\frac{2}{3}$ **11.** 51 **13.** 2 **15.** -3

17. -83 **19.** -5 **21.** -26 **23.** -54 **25.** 45 **27.** $\frac{1}{2}$ **29.** $\frac{-12}{5}$

31. 11.68 **33.** 12.6 **35.** 0.0125 **37.** 4.45 **39.** -5 **41. A.** 41°F

B. -15°C **C.** -40°C

Pages 171–172

1. $x = 13$ **3.** $x = 2.5$ **5.** $x = 2.5$ **7.** $x = 4$ **9.** $x = -15$

11. $x = 9$ **13.** $x = 72$ **15.** $x = -8$ **17.** $x = 4$ **19.** $x = -4$

21. $-\frac{4}{3}$ or $-1\frac{1}{3}$ **23.** $x = 11$ **25.** $a = 22.1$ **27.** $b = 3$

29. $x = -23$ **31.** $s = -8.2$ **33. A.** Let $n =$ the number. $3n + 5 = 38$; The number is 11. **B.** Let $n =$ the number. $\frac{1}{3}n - 7 = 5$; The number is 36. **C.** Let $n =$ the number. $5n = 2n + 18$; The number is 6. **35.** Let $x =$ the price of the sweater. $x + 0.4x = 46.28$; The price was \$44.50. **37.** Let $x =$ the amount earned by each laborer. $x + (x + 0.50x) + (x + 0.50x) + (x + 0.80x) = 4205$; The laborer earned \$725, each carpenter earned \$1087.50, and the supervisor earned \$1305.

Pages 178–181

1. The student's error is subtracting 10 from 14 on the right side; $x = 6$. **3.** The student's error is subtracting 6 from -48 on the right side; $x = -7$. **5.** The student's error is multiplying by 2 on the left side; $-\dfrac{5}{2} = a$. **7.** The student's error is multiplying by 5 on the right side; $a = -3$. **9.** The student made a sign error when multiplying -4 by -7; $x = 28$. **11.** The student made a sign error when multiplying -5 by -9; $x = 41$. **13.** The student made a sign error when dividing -48 by -12; $a = 4$. **15.** The student's error is combining like terms that are on different sides of the equation (or adding $5d$ to the left side instead of subtracting $5d$ from both sides); $d = 12$. **17.** The student's error is forgetting to distribute 6 on the left side; $r = \dfrac{21}{10}$. **19.** The student's error is using the expression for perimeter instead of the expression for area; The width of the rectangle is $2\dfrac{1}{2}$ feet. **21.** The student's error is using the solution to the equation as the answer to the question; The greatest of the three integers is 31.

Pages 186–187

1. $\{-4.8, 0, 4\}$ **3.** $\{4, 4.2, 5\}$ **5.** $\left\{-\dfrac{3}{5}, 0, \dfrac{1}{10}\right\}$
7. $x < 8$;

9. $x > -6$;

11. $v \le 12$;

13. $x \ge 7$;

15. $x < 16$;

17. $d > 5$;

19. $k > -\dfrac{1}{4}$;

21. $x < -4$;

23. $a < -\dfrac{32}{7}$;

25. $x > -\dfrac{19}{2}$;

27. A. Let $x =$ the number of pounds to be sent. $2.75 + 1.05x < 4.15 + 0.85x$; It will cost less to use Ship Fast for any weight less than 7 pounds. **B.** Let $x =$ the number of pounds to be sent. $2.75 + 1.05x = 4.15 + 0.85x$; The two companies charge the same amount when the weight is 7 pounds. That amount is $10.10. **29. A.** Let $m =$ the number of miles. $2.15 + 1.95m < 2.90 + 1.80m$; It costs less to ride a Green taxicab for any distance less than 5 miles. **B.** Let $m =$ the number of miles. $2.15 + 1.95m = 2.90 + 1.80m$; The cost is the same for a ride of 5 miles. That cost is $11.90.

Unit 6 Number Properties

Pages 194–195

1. 8 **3.** 1 **5.** $\dfrac{4}{9}$ **7.** 3125 **9.** 36 **11.** 7.85 **13.** 16 **15.** -3 **17.** 4 **19.** 64 **21.** -36 **23.** 103 **25.** $\left(\dfrac{1}{2}\right)^4$ **27.** -216 **29.** 248 **31.** $-7\dfrac{3}{4}$ **33.** $3^6 = 729$ people

Page 199

1. 1, 2, 3, 4, 6, 12 **3.** 1, 2, 4, 8, 16, 32 **5.** 1, 2, 3, 4, 5, 6, 10, 12, 15, 20, 30, 60 **7.** 1, 3, 9, 11, 33, 99 **9.** composite; 7×7 **11.** composite; 5×6 **13.** composite; 3×9 **15.** $2^2 \cdot 3$ **17.** $1 \cdot 31$ **19.** $2^3 \times 3 \times 5$ **21.** $2^4 \cdot 3 \cdot 7$ **23.** $2^2 \cdot 3 \cdot 5 \cdot 11$ **25.** yes; no; yes; yes **27.** yes; no; no; no **29.** 16 rows of 8 band members or 32 rows of 4 band members

Page 202

1. 1, 2 **3.** 1, 7 **5.** 1, 2, 5, 10 **7.** 5 **9.** 16 **11.** 6 **13.** 18 **15.** 4 **17.** 11 **19.** 18 **21.** 4 **23.** not relatively prime **25.** relatively prime **27.** relatively prime **29.** The principal can arrange the chairs in rows of 14. There will be 8 rows of sixth graders, 6 rows of seventh graders, and 7 rows of eighth graders.

Pages 205–206

1. $\dfrac{1}{9}$ **3.** $\dfrac{1}{2}$ **5.** $\dfrac{1}{216}$ **7.** 25 **9.** 1 **11.** 54 **13.** $\dfrac{8}{81}$ **15.** 9 **17.** $\dfrac{1}{200}$ **19.** $-\dfrac{1}{225}$ **21.** $\dfrac{1}{4}$ **23.** $b = 2$ **25.** $k = -4$ **27.** $x = 4$ **29.** $w = 2$ **31.** $y = 2$ **33.** The nonzero real number x^{-3} is positive or negative depending on whether x is positive or negative because it can be rewritten as $\dfrac{1}{x^3}$ and the cube of any nonzero positive real number is always positive. And the cube of any nonzero negative real number is always negative.

Page 211

1. 1000 **3.** 0.0001 **5.** 0.00001 **7.** 10^6 **9.** 10^{10} **11.** 10^{-10} **13.** 3650 **15.** 2,875,000 **17.** 205,000,000 **19.** 304.5 **21.** 2.4 **23.** 640,000 **25.** 18 **27.** 314,821.5 **29.** The population of the earth is 3 orders of magnitude greater than the population of Virginia. **31.** The mass of Jupiter is 4 orders of magnitude greater than the mass of Mars.

Page 215

1. 5000   **3.** 3,000,000   **5.** 2,360,000   **7.** 125,000,000
9. 102,000   **11.** 514,800,000   **13.** 5.6×10^{-3} **15.** 6×10^{-3}
17. 7.2×10^3 **19.** 9×10^{-5} **21.** 6.8×10^{-5} **23.** 9.304×10^9
25. 9×10^5 **27.** 6×10^1 **29.** 7.92×10^2 **31.** The area of
Wyoming is about 1×10^5 square miles.   **33.** The distance
between the earth and the moon is about 3.84×10^8 meters.

Unit 7   Geometry Basics

Pages 222–223

1. $\overleftrightarrow{SD}$ or $\overleftrightarrow{DS}$ **3.** $\overleftrightarrow{PC}$ or $\overleftrightarrow{CP}$ **5.** line a and line b **7.** Answers
will vary. Sample answer: plane TUV, plane UVT, plane VTU
9. Answers will vary. Sample answer: plane y, plane WFB,
plane ABW **11. A.** point T, point M, point R **B.** Answers
will vary. Sample answer: $\overrightarrow{TM}$, $\overrightarrow{MR}$ **13. A.** point A, point B,
point P **B.** line c **C.** plane $\mathcal{K}$ **15.** B

17. 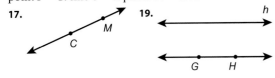   **19.**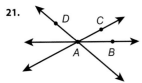

21.

23. Lori is correct because if three points form a triangle, then
those three points are not all on the same line.   **25.** A point
can be formed by the intersection of three planes, such as
two walls and a ceiling intersecting in a corner. A line can
be formed by the intersection of three planes, such as three
pages of a book intersecting at the binding.

Pages 227–229

1. $\overrightarrow{WN}$ **3.** $\overrightarrow{ED}$ or $\overrightarrow{EM}$ **5.** $\angle O$, $\angle NOP$, or $\angle PON$ **7.** $\angle S$ or
$\angle 2$ **9.** obtuse   **11.** right   **13.** acute   **15. A.** $\angle 1$ and $\angle 3$
B. $\angle 2$ **C.** none   **D.** none   **17. A.** $\angle 2$ **B.** $\angle 1$ and $\angle 3$
C. $\angle 4$ **D.** none   **19.** obtuse angle   **21.** $\overrightarrow{DA}$ and $\overrightarrow{DB}$ **23.** All 8
angles are obtuse.   **25.** acute

Pages 232–233

1. alternate interior   **3.** adjacent   **5.** alternate exterior
7. alternate exterior   **9.** corresponding   **11.** 72°   **13.** 72°
15. 82°   **17.** 98°   **19.** 38°   **21.** 142°   **23.** 127°   **25.** 53°
27. Answers will vary. Sample answer: Angle 2 is adjacent
to the angle labeled 65°, and the sum of those two angles is
180°, and $180 - 65 = 115$, so $m\angle 2 = 115°$. Angle 1 forms
a pair of corresponding angles with $\angle 2$, and $m\angle 2 = 115°$,
so $m\angle 1 = 115°$. or Angle 3 forms a pair of corresponding
angles with the angle labeled 65°, so $m\angle 3 = 65°$. Angle 1 is
adjacent to $\angle 3$, and the sum of those two angles is 180°, and
$180 - 65 = 115$, so $m\angle 1 = 115°$.   **29. A.** alternate exterior:
transversal b **B.** alternate interior: transversal c
C. corresponding: transversal a **D.** corresponding: transversal d **31.** Answers will vary. Sample answer:

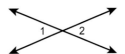

Pages 237–239

1. obtuse   **3.** right   **5.** obtuse   **7.** $x = 17$ **9.** $x = 45$
11. $x = 58$ **13.** $x = 27$ **15.** $x = 47$ **17.** $a = 38$ **19.** $c = 47$
21. $\triangle CYM$ **23.** $\triangle KAP$ **25.** $\triangle CLT$ **27.** If a triangle had
more than one obtuse angle or more than one right angle,
then the sum of its angle measures would be greater than
180°.
29. 16 inches   **31.** $3\frac{1}{3}$ inches   **33.** scalene and acute, scalene
and right, scalene and obtuse, isosceles and acute, isosceles
and right, isosceles and obtuse, equilateral and acute

Pages 243–244

1. polygon   **3.** polygon   **5.** polygon   **7.** polygon   **9.** yes
11. no   **13.** no   **15.** yes   **17.** hexagon, not regular
19. pentagon, not regular   **21.** triangle, not regular
23. decagon, regular   **25.** 600°   **27.** 35.2 feet   **29.** 13 centimeters   **31.** The two shorter sides are each 5 inches long and
the four longer sides are each 7 inches long.

Pages 248–249

1. A. $\overline{QK}, \overline{QT}$, and $\overline{QR}$ **B.** $\overline{MR}$ and $\overline{KR}$ **C.** $\overline{KR}$ **3. A.** $\overline{RP}$ and
$\overline{RF}$ **B.** $\overline{PF}$ **C.** none   **5. A.** $\overline{FL}, \overline{FR}, \overline{FD}$, and $\overline{FA}$ **B.** $\overline{LR}, \overline{LA}$,
$\overline{DR}$, and $\overline{DA}$ **C.** $\overline{LA}$ and $\overline{DR}$ **7.** True   **9.** False   **11.** True
13. $6\frac{1}{2}$ ft   **15.** 69 cm   **17.** The name of the circle is the center
point of the circle. Because $\overline{KR}$ is a chord that passes through
the center, it must be a diameter.   **19.** The boat made 15
one-way trips.   **21. A.** $\overline{AB}, \overline{CD}, \overline{EF}, \overline{AD}, \overline{AF}$ **B.** $m\angle 1 = 22°$,
$m\angle 2 = 126°$, $m\angle 3 = 32°$; Answers will vary. Sample answer:
Angle 1 forms a pair of alternate interior angles with the
angle labeled 22°, and those angles are formed by a transversal and two parallel lines. So $m\angle 1 = 22°$. Angle BAF forms
a pair of alternate interior angles with the angle labeled 54°,
and those angles are formed by a transversal and two parallel
lines. So $m\angle BAF = 54°$. And $54° - 22° = 32°$, so $m\angle 3 = 32°$. Angles 1, 2, and 3 are angles of a triangle, so the sum
of their measures is 180°. And $180° - 22° - 32° = 126°$, so
$m\angle 2 = 126°$.

Pages 254–256

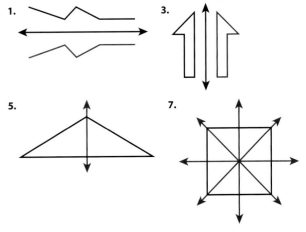

9. 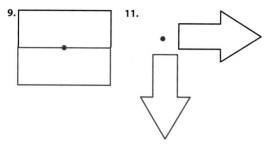 **11.**

13. 90° counterclockwise or 270° clockwise

15. **17.** **19.**

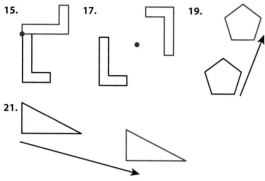

21.

23. rotation **25.** reflection **27.** none of these **29.** Vertical line of symmetry: A, H, I, M, O, T, U, V, W, X, Y; Horizontal line of symmetry: B, C, D, E, H, I, O, X

Pages 260–261

1. $\angle G$ **3.** $\angle A$ **5.** $\overline{LT}$ **7.** $\angle G \cong \angle K$, $\angle R \cong \angle L$, $\angle N \cong \angle P$, $\angle Y \cong \angle S$, $\overline{GR} \cong \overline{KL}$, $\overline{RN} \cong \overline{LP}$, $\overline{NY} \cong \overline{PS}$, $\overline{YG} \cong \overline{SK}$ **9.** $\triangle CVF$ **11.** $\triangle VFC$ **13.** $EMTJ$ **15.** $MTJE$ **17.** Answers will vary. Sample answer: $\triangle DIM \cong \triangle TIM$ **19.** Answers will vary. Sample answer: $RHLDS \cong VTOYM$ or $RHLDS \cong VMYOT$ **21.** Yes **23.** Polygons A and B appear to be congruent, and polygons C and E appear to be congruent.
25. $x = 5$ and $y = 8\frac{1}{3}$ **27.** No; For example, one quadrilateral could be a square and the other quadrilateral could be a rectangle that is not a square.

Unit 8   Ratio, Proportion, and Percent

Page 268

1. $\frac{5}{6}$, 5 to 6, 5:6 **3.** $\frac{2}{3}$, 2 to 3, 2:3 **5.** $\frac{2}{7}$, 2 to 7, 2:7 **7.** $\frac{1}{3}$, 1 to 3, 1:3 **9.** $\frac{5}{7}$, 5 to 7, 5:7 **11.** $\frac{5}{1}$, 5 to 1, 5:1 **13.** $\frac{8}{3}$, 8 to 3, 8:3 **15.** $\frac{5}{3}$, 5 to 3, 5:3 **17.** $\frac{3.96}{4}$; $0.99 per song **19.** $\frac{20}{2}$; 10 minutes per mile **21.** $\frac{37.50}{5}$; $7.50 per movie ticket **23.** $\frac{9}{10}$, 9 to 10, 9:10 **25.** $\frac{1}{6}$, 1 to 6, 1:6
27. A. $\frac{6}{1}$ **B.** The bamboo grows 6 cm in 1 hour. **29. A.** It did not rain 4 days. **B.** The ratio of rainy days to not rainy days is 3 to 4. **31. A.** $0.90 per burger **B.** $0.75 per burger **C.** Bargain Burger has the better deal.

Pages 272–273

1. Answers will vary. Sample answer: $\frac{1}{2}$; $\frac{16}{32}$ **3.** Answers will vary. Sample answer: $\frac{14}{6}$; $\frac{70}{30}$ **5.** Answers will vary.

Sample answer: $\frac{1}{3}$; $\frac{16}{48}$ **7.** Answers will vary. Sample answer: $\frac{2}{10}$; $\frac{4}{20}$ **9.** Answers will vary. Sample answer: $\frac{3}{1}$; $\frac{6}{2}$
11. yes **13.** yes **15.** yes **17.** yes **19.** $m = 1$ **21.** $b = 4$
23. $y = 6.4$ **25.** $x = 13$ **27.** $b = 22$ **29.** $n = 0.9375$
31. $a = 10$ **33. A.** $\frac{93 \text{ miles}}{1.5 \text{ hours}} = \frac{x}{3.5 \text{ hours}}$ **B.** $217 = x$
C. The car will travel 217 miles in $3\frac{1}{2}$ hours. **35. A.** $\frac{\$27.00}{3 \text{ hours}} = \frac{x}{8 \text{ hours}}$ **B.** $72 = x$ **C.** The employee will make $72 in 8 hours. **37. A.** $\frac{40 \text{ pages}}{60 \text{ minutes}} = \frac{220 \text{ pages}}{x}$ **B.** $x = 330$
C. It will take the student 330 minutes to read 220 pages.
39. A. $\frac{40 \text{ gallons}}{2 \text{ minutes}} = \frac{x}{180 \text{ minutes}}$; $3600 = x$. After 3 hours there will be 3600 gallons of water in the pool.
B. $\frac{3600 \text{ gallons}}{3 \text{ hours}} = \frac{88,000 \text{ gallons}}{x}$; $x = 73\frac{1}{3}$. It will take $73\frac{1}{3}$ hours to fill the pool.

Page 278

1. 0.7 **3.** 0.6 **5.** 0.76 **7.** $\frac{3}{4}$ **9.** $1\frac{1}{2}$ **11.** $\frac{17}{50}$ **13.** 721%
15. 3% **17.** 100.4% **19.** 0.078 **21.** 0.005 **23.** 0.1085
25. 16% **27.** 560% **29.** 42% **31.** $\frac{3}{5}$ **33.** $\frac{1}{20}$ **35.** $\frac{21}{25}$
37. Eighty percent surveyed think tickets are too expensive.
39. 0.034 **41.** Doug had finished reading 44% of the book.
43. A. $\frac{1}{4}$, 28%, and 0.32 **B.** 0.5%, 0.05, and $\frac{1}{5}$

Pages 282–283

1. No **3.** $x = 4$ **5.** $x = 10.5$ **7.** $1\frac{2}{3}$; enlargement **9.** 1.5; enlargement **11.** 7.5 cm **13.** 44 cm

Page 286

1. $\frac{x}{30} = \frac{76}{100}$; $x = 22.8$ **3.** $\frac{13}{15} = \frac{x}{100}$; $x \approx 86.7$ **5.** $\frac{20}{x} = \frac{10}{100}$; $x = 200$ **7.** $\frac{17}{x} = \frac{20}{100}$; $x = 85$ **9.** $\frac{15}{30} = \frac{x}{100}$; $x = 50$
11. $\frac{133}{x} = \frac{35}{100}$; $x = 380$ **13.** $\frac{99}{150} = \frac{x}{100}$; $x = 66$ **15.** $\frac{17}{85} = \frac{x}{100}$; $x = 20$ **17.** $\frac{x}{50} = \frac{34}{100}$; $x = 17$ **19.** $\frac{21}{28} = \frac{x}{100}$; $x = 75$
21. $\frac{7}{x} = \frac{14}{100}$; $x = 50$ **23.** $\frac{147}{210} = \frac{x}{100}$; $x = 70$ **25.** $\frac{x}{65} = \frac{150}{100}$; $x = 97.5$ **27.** $\frac{x}{3.5} = \frac{6}{100}$; $x = 0.21$ **29.** $\frac{5.07}{65} = \frac{x}{100}$; $x = 7.8$
31. $11.90 **33.** 650 students **35.** 24.4% **37.** 33.3%

Pages 290–291

1. 40% decrease **3.** 36.8% decrease **5.** 53.3% increase
7. 60% decrease **9.** 406.4% increase **11.** 16.3% increase
13. 42.9% increase **15.** 69.8% increase **17.** 125% increase
19. 21.2% increase **21.** 5% increase **23.** November to December **25.** 1250 minutes **27.** 46.2% **29.** 6.8% **31.** 6.7%

Pages 294–295

1. $75 **3.** $1600 **5.** 3500 **7.** 2.9% **9.** 3.5 **11.** $202.50
13. 9 years **15.** $883.33 **17.** 4% **19.** $713.33 **21.** 6.5 years
23. $4000 **25.** $220.80 **27.** $11,200 **29. A.** $5150; $5300; $5450 **B.** 34 years

Page 299

1. $3150; $3150; $3307.50; $3307.50; $3472.86; $3472.86; $3646.50 **3.** $3183.62 **5.** $1543.76 **7.** $434.72 **9.** $416.24 **11.** $1206.01 **13.** $8563.91 **15.** $28,210.53 **17.** $2795.67 **19.** $3045.23

Unit 9   Analytic Geometry

Page 307

1. A. Quadrant II   **B.** $(-3, 3)$ **3. A.** *x*-axis   **B.** $(2, 0)$
5. A. Quadrant III   **B.** $(-2, -2)$ **7. A.** Quadrant I   **B.** $(4, 4)$
9. A. Quadrant I   **B.** $(3, 3)$

11.

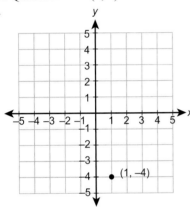

13.

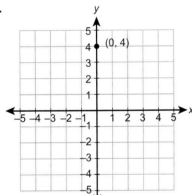

15.

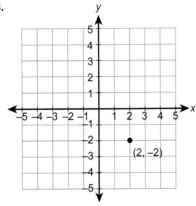

17.

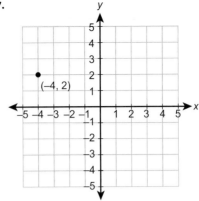

19.

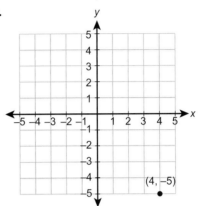

21. Quadrant I

Pages 311–312

1. Yes   **3.** No   **5.** Yes   **7.** Yes   **9.** Yes   **11.** Yes
13. Answers will vary. Sample answer: $(0, 0)$, $(2, 8)$, $(-3, -12)$ **15.** Answers will vary. Sample answer: $(0, -5)$, $(10, 0)$, $(-8, -9)$ **17.** Answers will vary. Sample answer: $(0, 5)$, $(3, 2)$, $(-4, 9)$ **19.** Answers will vary. Sample answer: $(0, 4)$, $(7, 25)$, $(-1, 1)$
21.

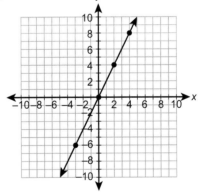

23.

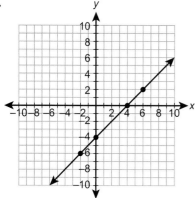

25.

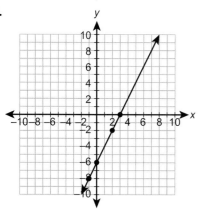

27.

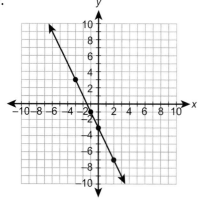

13.

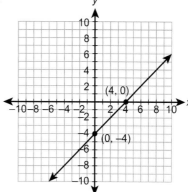

15.

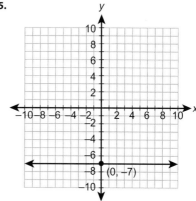

17.

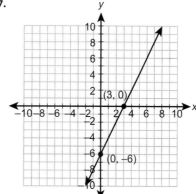

19.

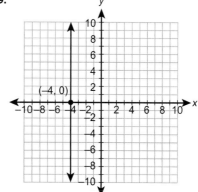

29. Because the total amount paid *t* depends on the number of climbing sessions *n*, the dependent variable is *t* and the independent variable is *n*. **31.** Because the remaining balance *r* depends on the minutes talked *t*, the dependent variable is *r* and the independent variable is *t*.

Pages 317–318

1. The *x*-intercept is 4. The *y*-intercept is −3. **3.** The *x*-intercept is −5. The line has no *y*-intercept. **5.** The *x*-intercept is −3. The *y*-intercept is 5. **7.** The *y*-intercept is 2. The *x*-intercept is 4. **9.** The *y*-intercept is 3. The *x*-intercept is 9. **11.** The *y*-intercept is 4.5. The *x*-intercept is 2.

21.

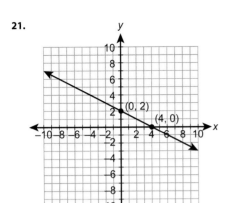

23.

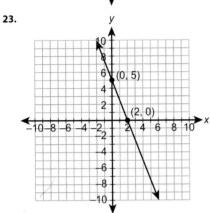

25.

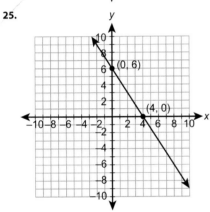

27. $x = 2$ **29.** $5x + 5y = 25$ **31.** $y = -2$

Pages 324–325

1. -2 **3.** $-\dfrac{3}{4}$ **5.** -1 **7.** 1 **9.** $-\dfrac{2}{5}$ **11.** 8 **13.** $\dfrac{17}{3}$ **15.** $-\dfrac{1}{2}$
17. 0 **19.** undefined   **21.** 4 **23.** positive   **25.** negative
27. negative   **29.** 8 **31.** $-\dfrac{2}{3}$

Pages 329–330

1. 120 feet   **3.** 60 feet   **5.** The prediction is reasonable because it is reasonable for the water level to decrease by a steady amount each week. The decrease in water level could continue until the lake is dry.   **7.** 550   **9.** Year 13
11. $16,000   **13.** less than $0   **15.** The prediction may not be reasonable. Although the car will have lost much of its value by Year 8, it is unlikely that the car is worth nothing.
17. 140 pounds   **19.** 290 pounds

Pages 334–336

1. Domain: $\{-3, 0, 2, 3\}$, Range: $\{0, 1, 2, 4\}$ **3.** Domain: $\{1\}$, Range: $\{-5, -3, -2, 4, 5\}$ **5.** Domain: $\{-1, 3, 5\}$, Range: $\{-2, 1, 5, 6\}$ **7.** No   **9.** Yes   **11.** Yes   **13.** No
15. No   **17.** $f(3) = 7$ **19.** $h(-3) = 6$ **21.** $f(5) = 2$
23. $g(9) = -3$ **25.** $g(x) = -7$ **27.** $h(x) = 5$

Pages 341–343

1. one   **3.** infinite   **5.** one   **7.** $(2, 5)$ **9.** $(-1, -2)$
11. $(0, -2)$ **13.** $(5, -2)$ **15.** $(2, 3)$ **17.** $(2, -4)$ **19.** $(2, 4)$
21. $(3, -1)$ **23.** $(0, -6)$ **25.** $(-5, -1)$ **27.** 12 piano students   **29.** 6 ounces of peanuts and 18 ounces of raisins

Unit 10   Perimeter and Area

Pages 350–351

1. pentagon   **3.** quadrilateral   **5.** nonagon   **7.** hexagon
9. regular   **11.** none of these   **13.** none of these   **15.** equiangular   **17.** regular   **19.** none of these   **21.** A circle is not a polygon because it is not made up of line segments.
23. A polygon with n sides has n vertices.   **25.** The measure of each angle is $135°$.   **27.** The measure of each angle is $150°$.   **29.** There are 4 triangles formed by connecting one vertex to the other non-adjacent vertices of a regular hexagon, 6 triangles formed with the regular octagon, and $n - 2$ triangles formed with the regular n-gon.

Pages 355–357

1. 150 centimeters   **3.** 28 meters   **5.** 42 kilometers
7. 68 centimeters   **9.** 30 units   **11.** 36 units   **13.** 4 feet
15. 5 units   **17.** $x = 14$ **19.** $l = 7$ **21.** 108 units
23. 52 units   **25.** 364 meters   **27.** 153 meters
29. 84 centimeters

Pages 361–363

1. 144 square meters   **3.** 10.8 square meters   **5.** 414 square centimeters   **7.** $1\dfrac{11}{16}$ square meters   **9.** 13 square inches
11. 6 units   **13.** 24 inches   **15.** 24 feet   **17.** 7 meters
19. 522 square yards   **21.** 154 square millimeters
23. 84 square inches   **25.** 32 square centimeters   **27.** $75.60
29. If the formula for the area of a rectangle is written as $A = bh$, where b is the length and h is the width, then the formula for the area of a triangle is one-half of it, because any rectangle can be divided into two congruent triangles by connecting opposite vertices.

Pages 368–369

1. parallelogram   **3.** parallelogram, rectangle
5. parallelogram, rhombus   **7.** parallelogram   **9.** always
11. sometimes   **13.** sometimes   **15.** always
17.

19.

21. trapezoid   **23.** parallelogram   **25.** rhombus   **27.** $x = 15$, $y = 14$ **29.** $x = 15$, $y = 6$

Pages 373–375

1. 396 square kilometers   **3.** 900 square units   **5.** 59.5 square units   **7.** 330 square inches   **9.** $37\frac{1}{8}$ square meters
11. xy square millimeters   **13.** 6 units   **15.** 16 yards
17. 8.5 meters   **19.** $3\frac{1}{2}$ feet   **21.** 2490 square units
23. 95 square units   **25.** 12 square units   **27.** $78   **29.** 5.25 square feet

Pages 380–381

1. 4π centimeters, about 12.6 centimeters   **3.** 10π units, about 31.4 units   **5.** π inches, about 3.14 inches   **7.** π meters, about 3.14 meters   **9.** 9.5 inches   **11.** about 66 meters
13. about 56.5 inches   **15.** about 28 units   **17.** about 50.1 yards   **19.** 8.5π centimeters or 26.7 centimeters   **21.** about 5.02 centimeters   **23.** about 11.1 millimeters   **25.** about 56.5 feet   **27.** about 47.1 inches   **29.** about 4.19 meters

Pages 386–387

1. 36π square centimeters, about 113 square centimeters
3. 81π square units, about 254 square units   **5.** π square units, about 3.14 square units   **7.** 121π square units, about 380 square units   **9.** 9π square units, about 28.3 square units   **11.** 4 meters   **13.** about 4 centimeters   **15.** about 190 square inches   **17.** about 75.2 square units   **19.** about 145 square centimeters   **21.** about 55 square feet   **23.** about 84.3 square yards   **25.** about 113 square feet   **27.** 18-inch pizza   **29.** square   **31.** Draw segments at the top and bottom of the figure to form a rectangle. Then subtract the area of the two semicircles in the rectangle.

Unit 11   Square Roots and Right Triangles

Pages 393–394

1. ± 7 **3.** ± 10 **5.** ± 4 **7.** $\pm\frac{4}{9}$ **9.** $\pm\frac{7}{10}$ **11.** 2   **13.** -10
15. -4 **17.** $-\frac{1}{3}$ **19.** 0.5   **21.** $x = \pm 9$ **23.** $a = \pm 12$
25. $v = \pm\frac{7}{9}$ **27.** $x = \pm 3$ **29.** $t = \pm\frac{1}{7}$ **31.** $x = \pm 10$
33. $g = \pm 7$ **35.** $c = \pm 2$ **37.** $x = \pm\frac{4}{5}$ **39.** 8 squares
41. 30 feet   **43. A.** 900 square centimeters   **B.** 30 centimeters
C. 120 centimeters

Pages 398–399

1. irrational   **3.** rational   **5.** irrational   **7.** rational   **9.** rational
11. 5 and 6   **13.** 9 and 10   **15.** 7 and 8   **17.** 4 and 5   **19.** 13 and 14   **21.** 2.8   **23.** 4.2   **25.** 9.2   **27.** 6.2   **29.** 11.8
31. $2\sqrt{2}$ **33.** $3\sqrt{5}$ **35.** $2\sqrt{5}$ **37.** $5\sqrt{3}$ **39.** $3\sqrt{3}$ **41.** about 9.8 centimeters   **43.** about 2.8 meters   **45.** about 10.2 feet
47. If the area of the square is 50 cm², then one side measures about 7.07. So the length measures 21.21 centimeters and the width measures 7.07 centimeters. The perimeter is about 56.56 centimeters.

Pages 404–405

1. hypotenuse: $\overline{DF}$, legs: $\overline{DE}$, $\overline{EF}$ **3.** hypotenuse: $\overline{TV}$, legs: $\overline{UV}$, $\overline{TU}$ **5.** $c \approx 9.4$ **7.** $c \approx 11.7$ **9.** $b \approx 7.9$ **11.** $b \approx 10.2$
13. $c \approx 11.7$ **15.** $a \approx 13.7$ **17.** $b \approx 14.7$ **19.** 5, 12, 13 and 9, 40, 41   **21.** about 22.8 meters   **23. A.** 182 meters
B. Answers will vary. Sample answer: To find the perimeter, I added all the sides. I used the Pythagorean theorem to find the length of the missing side.

Pages 408–409

1. $d \approx 7.3$ **3.** $d \approx 6.4$ **5.** $d \approx 4.1$ **7.** $d \approx 6.1$ **9.** $d \approx 17.7$
11. $d \approx 10.3$ **13.** $d \approx 9.2$ **15.** $d \approx 15.7$ **17.** $P \approx 16.6$
19. $P \approx 8.8$ **21.** $d = 4$ **23.** $d \approx 7.1$ **25.** $d \approx 9.8$ **27.** $d \approx 12.0$ **29.** The distance is the greatest between the bakery and the park.

Pages 415–416

1. $x = 2$ **3.** $x = 5$ **5.** $x = 7$ **7.** $y = 9\sqrt{2}$ **9.** $x = 5$
11. $x = 12$ **13.** 45°-45°-90°   **15.** about 11.3 centimeters
17. 45   **19.** about 113 feet   **21.** hypotenuse: 14 meters, short leg: 7 meters   **23.** 16 centimeters

Pages 420–421

1. $\frac{40}{41}$ **3.** $\frac{40}{9}$ **5.** $\frac{40}{41}$ **7.** $\frac{3}{5}$ **9.** $\frac{3}{4}$ **11.** $\frac{3}{5}$ **13.** $\frac{5}{13}$ **15.** $\frac{5}{12}$
17. $\frac{5}{13}$ **19.** $\frac{1}{\sqrt{2}}$ **21.** 1   **23.** $\frac{1}{\sqrt{2}}$ **25.** 3   **27.** $\sqrt{41}$
29. A. The length of x is about 16.97 feet   **B.** The roof forms a 45°-45°-90° triangle. If the legs are 12 feet, then the hypotenuse is 16.97.   **31.** $\sin 45° \approx 0.7071$; $\cos 45° \approx 0.7071$; $\tan 45° = 1$

Unit 12   Solid Figures

Pages 428–429

1. 64 in³   **3.** 1331 ft³   **5.** 125 in³   **7.** 216 ft³   **9.** 29.791 m³
11. 421,875 cm³   **13.** 12,824 in³   **15.** 1 mL   **17.** 4 mL
19. 2 L   **21. A.** 64,000 mL   **B.** 64 L   **23. A.** 27,000 mL
B. 27 L   **25.** >   **27.** =   **29.** about 0.499 liters

Pages 434–435

1. 36 in³   **3.** 12,000 ft³   **5.** 360 in³   **7.** 54 m³   **9.** 112 m³
11. 2992.98 cm³   **13. A.** 196π in³   **B.** about 615 in³
15. A. 225π cm³   **B.** about 707 cm³   **17. A.** 137.78π cm³
B. about 432 cm³   **19. A.** 500π cm³   **B.** 1570 cm³
21. A. 1200π cm³   **B.** 3770 cm³   **23. A.** 4312π cm³   **B.** about 13,500 cm³   **25.** about 5209 cm³   **27.** about 12 inches
29. 6 L

Pages 440–441

1. $106\frac{2}{3}$ ft³   **3.** 4.8 mm³   **5.** 32 cm³   **7.** 2000 mm³
9. 20 cm³   **11.** 0.64 m³   **13.** 48 in³   **15.** 12.32 m³
17. 480 cm³   **19.** 264 cm³   **21. A.** 81π in³   **B.** about 254 in³
23. A. 196π cm³   **B.** about 615 cm³   **25. A.** 75π ft³   **B.** about 236 ft³   **27. A.** 720π mm³   **B.** about 2260 mm³   **29.** 344 cups

Pages 446–448

1. 24 m²   **3.** 73.5 mm²   **5.** 2904 in²   **7.** 170 m²   **9.** 96 m²
11. 400 mm²   **13.** 1694 cm²   **15.** 152 m²   **17.** 3552 mm²

19. 304 in² **21.** 108 cm² **23.** 152 m² **25.** 256 ft²
27. 670 cm² **29.** 3 cans

Pages 452–453

1. 52 m² **3.** 360 cm² **5.** 1288 m² **7.** 443.2 in² **9.** 756
cm² **11. A.** 150π in² **B.** about 471 in² **13. A.** 368π m²
B. about 1160 m² **15. A.** 110.4π m² **B.** about 347 m²
17. A. 332.5π in² **B.** about 1040 in² **19. A.** 34.32π in²
B. about 108 in² **21. A.** 468.18π cm² **B.** about 1470 cm²
23. $\frac{6}{1}$ **25.** $\frac{0.6}{1}$ **27.** $\frac{2.6}{1}$ **29.** first can

Unit 13 Counting and Probability

Pages 460–461

1. 15 days **3.** 7 different tops **5.** 7 choices **7.** 24 combinations **9.** 60 ways **11.** 6 ways **13.** about 16 possible
outcomes **15.** 20 ways **17.** 6 ways **19. A.** 36 possible
outcomes **B.** 260 possible outcomes **21.** juice, burger,
apple; juice, burger, raisins; juice, pizza, apple; juice, pizza,
raisins; juice, turkey sandwich, apple; juice, turkey sandwich, raisins; milk, burger, apple; milk, burger, raisins; milk,
pizza, apple; milk, pizza, raisins; milk, turkey sandwich,
apple; milk, turkey sandwich, raisins **23.** H11, H12, H13,
H14, H15, H16, H21, H22, H23, H24, H25, H26, H31, H32,
H33, H34, H35, H36, H41, H42, H43, H44, H45, H46, H51,
H52, H53, H54, H55, H56, H61, H62, H63, H64, H65, H66,
T11, T12, T13, T14, T15, T16, T21, T22, T23, T24, T25,
T26, T31, T32, T33, T34, T35, T36, T41, T42, T43, T44,
T45, T46, T51, T52, T53, T54, T55, T56, T61, T62, T63,
T64, T65, T66

Pages 466–467

1. 1 **3.** 24 **5.** 40,320 **7.** 6 **9.** 144 **11.** 718 **13.** 9 **15.** 120
17. 40,320 **19.** 5040 ways **21.** 151,200 ways **23.** 360 ways
25. A. 5040 ways **B.** 2520 ways **C.** 210 ways **27.** 5040
passwords **29. A.** 239,500,800 **B.** 39,916,800 **31.** cat,
cta, act, atc, tac, tca **33.** There are more permutations of the
letters in *dear* than of the letters in *deer*. Two of the letters
in *deer* are the same. When the two E's are switched, a new
permutation is not formed.

Pages 471–472

1. 6 **3.** 1 **5.** 70 **7.** 5 **9.** 10 **11. A.** combinations **B.** $_{12}C_6$
13. A. combinations **B.** $_{20}C_{12}$ **15. A.** combinations **B.** $_{30}C_5$
17. 45 sets **19.** 10 ways **21.** 495 ways **23.** 15 ways
25. ma, mt, mh, at, ah, th **27.** It makes more sense to call
a combination lock a permutation lock because the order of
the numbers matters. For example, 12-4-36 and 4-12-36 are
the same combination, but they are different permutations.
If 12-4-36 is required to open the lock, then 4-12-36 will not
work. **29.** Yes, $_nC_r = {}_nC_{n-r}$; $_nC_r = \dfrac{n!}{(n-r)!\,r!}$;

$$_nC_{n-r} = \frac{n!}{[n-(n-r)]!\,(n-r)!} = \frac{n!}{[n-n+r]!\,(n-r)!}$$
$$= \frac{n!}{r!\,(n-r)!}$$

Pages 477–478

1. HT **3.** HHH, HHT, HTH, HTT, THT, TTH, TTT
5. H1, H2, H3, H4, H5, H6, T1, T2, T3, T4, T5, T6
7. AA, AB, AC, AD, BA, BB, BC, BD, CA, CB, CC, CD,
DA, DB, DC, DD **9. A.** 25 **B.** $\frac{7}{25}$ **C.** $\frac{3}{5}$ **D.** 0 **E.** $\frac{2}{5}$
11. A. 12 **B.** $\frac{1}{12}$ **C.** $\frac{1}{4}$ **D.** $\frac{1}{3}$ **13. A.** 13 **B.** $\frac{3}{13}$ **C.** $\frac{10}{13}$ **15.** $\frac{3}{5}$
17. $\frac{1}{120}$

Pages 482–483

1. A. mutually exclusive **B.** not mutually exclusive
C. mutually exclusive **D.** not mutually exclusive
3. A. mutually exclusive **B.** mutually exclusive **C.** not
mutually exclusive **D.** not mutually exclusive **5. A.** No
B. Yes **C.** 50% **D.** 87.5% **7. A.** Yes **B.** 69% **C.** 50%
9. A. No **B.** Yes **C.** 55% **D.** 39.7% **E.** 69.8%

Pages 486–487

1. Yes, many people who ski might not be home to answer
the call—they might be out skiing. **3.** No **5.** No **7.** No
9. Yes, people who go to school or work are not likely to be
in the supermarket at that time. There is likely to be a greater
percentage of stay at home moms or dads and retired citizens
in the sample than in the population. **11.** No **13. A.** about
5132 people **B.** about 157,338 people **15. A.** about 267
people **B.** about 1333 people **17. A.** People who order
entrees with the sauce probably already like hot and spicy
dishes. Possible change: Ask every 5th customer to sample
the sauce, regardless of the entrée they order. **B.** Odd-
numbered houses tend to be on one side of the street and
even-numbered houses tend to be on the other. One side of
a street might get more sunlight, allowing those residents to
use less energy. Possible change: Choose the same number of
even-numbered and odd-numbered houses. **C.** Due to wind,
more debris might be at one end of the lake than the other.
Due to the effects of sunlight and air temperature, water near
the surface will be different than near the bottom. Possible
change: Collect samples from random locations in the lake
and from random depths.

Unit 14 Statistics

Pages 495–497

1. Wintergreen **3.** 11 **5.** 23 **7.** 30% **9. A.** The lowest
math score was 6. **B.** The person that got the lowest math
score had a reading score of 6. **11.** Positive **13.** 5%
15. January and December **17.** 7 cm **19.** May to June;
July to August to September

21.

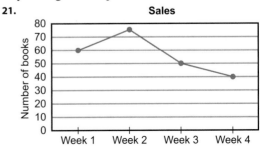

23. Because the test grades increase as the study hours increase, the correlation is positive.

Pages 501–502

1. mean: 93.6; median: 96; mode: 96   **3.** mean: $5\frac{1}{3}$; median: 5.5; mode: 2   **5.** mean: about 99.3; median: 100; modes: 92 and 106   **7.** mean: 45; median: 45; no mode **9.** mean: 100; median: 102; mode: 102   **11.** mean: about 0.83; median: 1; mode: 1   **13.** mean: 0; median: −0.5; mode: none   **15.** mean: $\frac{21}{40}$; median: $\frac{1}{2}$; mode: $\frac{1}{21}$ **17.** Because 32 is a potential outlier, the best measure of center is the median. There is no mode.   **19.** Because there are no potential outliers, the best measure of center is the mean or median. There is no mode.   **21.** Because there are so many values of 1, the best measure of center is the median or the mode.   **23.** Because there are no potential outliers, the best measure of center is the mean or median. The mode is 0, but there are several values above that so mode may not be the best measure of center.   **25.** Because the mode is much smaller than the other values in the set, the best measure of center is the mean or median.   **27.** Because there are no potential outliers, the best measure of center is the mean or median. There is no mode.   **29.** Class A has the highest mean.   **31.** Class B has the highest mode   **33.** The median weight of the beetles is 1.85 ounces.   **35. A.** Mean with outlier: $69.80; Median with outlier: $28.00; Mean without outlier: $27.25; Median without outlier: $27.50   **B.** The mean and median are closer together without the outlier and far apart with the outlier.   **C.** If the mean and median of a data set are far apart then it is possible there is an outlier. **37.** Answers will vary. Sample answer: 1, 1, 3, 5, 5

Pages 507–508

1.
0	4	8		
1	7			
2	3	7	7	9
3	1	5		

Key: 3|1 means 31

3.
3	0	1	2	5	5
4	0	1	2	3	7
5	3	3	9		
6	3				

Key: 5|3 means 5.3

5.
0	0	6	7	8	
1	0	3	3	8	8
2	3	3			

Key: 2|3 means 2.3

7.
2	1	2	7	
3	5	6	9	9
4	1	4	4	
5	0	7		
6	5	5		

Key: 4|1 means 41

9. Mean: 99; Median: 97; Mode: 80   **11.** Mean: about 30.9; Median: 31; Mode: 20   **13.** Median: 4, Q_1: 2, Q_3: 9, Range: 9   **15.** Median: 88, Q_1: 85.5, Q_3: 91, Range: 8   **17.** Median: 145.5, Q_1: 137.5, Q_3: 154, Range: 35   **19.** Median: 82; Q_1: 77; Q_3: 98; range: 35   **21.** Median: 55; Q_1: 42.5; Q_3: 70; range: 48   **23. A.** Mean: 47; Median: 45; Mode: none **B.** Q_1: 33; Q_3: 56; Range: 52

25. A.
0	5	7	8		
1	6				
2	1	2	7	9	
3	0	1	2	2	8
4	1	5	9	9	
5	4	4	8		

Key: 3|2 means 3.2

B. Mean: 3.24; Median: 31.5; Modes: 3.2, 4.9, 5.4

27. Answers will vary. Sample answer: 0, 5, 7, 9, 10, 15, 20

Pages 511–512

1. min: 2; Q_1: 3.5; med: 7; Q_3: 9.5; max: 10;

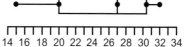

3. min: 15; Q_1: 20; med: 27; Q_3: 30.5; max: 32;

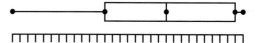

5. min: 0; Q_1: 12; med: 20; Q_3: 29; max: 30;

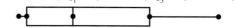

7. min: 41; Q_1: 42; med: 48; Q_3: 58; max: 67;

9. 25%   **11.** 16   **13.** Twenty-five percent of the data points are between 20 and 28. If there are 52 data points, then $52 \cdot 0.25 = 13$, the number of the points that lie between 20 and 28.   **15.** Range is 100. IQR is 20. So 100% of the data lie within a 100 point range and 50% lie within a 20 point range.   **17.** 75%   **19.** Range is 20. IQR is 6. So, 100% of the data lie within a 20 point range and 50% lie within a 6 point range.   **21.** Fifty-four students have heights between 138 cm and 148 cm.   **23.** City A has the greater IQR.   **25.** Answers will vary. Sample answer: Although City B has the lowest price of $8, City A has the lower median. Half of the prices in City A are below $22 and half of the prices in City B are below $26. I would choose City A.

Pages 517–519

1.

	Tally	Frequency
10	||||	4
11	|||||	5
12	||||	4
13	|	1
14	||||	4
15	|||	3

3.

	Tally	Frequency
80	||||	4
81	卌 |	6
82	||||	4
83	卌 卌	10
84	||||	4
85	||	2

5.

	Tally	Frequency
100	|||	3
101	卌	5
102	|||	3
103	卌 ||	7
104	||||	4
105	||	2
106	卌 |	6

7. mean: about 14.2, median: 14, mode: 14   **9.** mean: about 1.2, median: 1.3, mode: 1.3   **11.** 16   **13.** There are 30 visitors so the median is between the 15th and 16th value. The 15th and 16th value occur in interval 20–25 so the median is in interval 20–25.   **15.** 27   **17.** mean: about 1.8, median: 2, modes: 0 and 3

19. A.

Distance (miles) From School	Tally	Frequency
0.0–0.9	卌 ||	7
1.0–1.9	卌 卌 ||||	14
2.0–2.9	卌 卌	10
3.0–3.9	卌 ||	7
4.0–4.9	||	2

B.

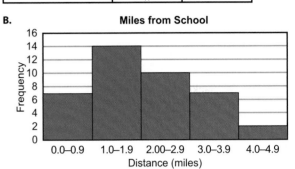

Illustrations Credits

Cover: Guggenheim museum © Art Kowalsky/Alamy; Bicycle racing © Shariffc/Dreamstime.com; Stock trading board © Joseph Sohm/Visions of America/Corbis; Antique navigational map © Comstock Images/Jupiterimages.

Unit 1: © Juergen Sack/iStockphoto.com

Unit 2: © iStockphoto.com

Unit 3: © CuboImages srl/Alamy

Unit 4: © Marc Romanelli/Alamy

Unit 5: © Miklav/Dreamstime.com

Unit 6: NASA

Unit 7: © Art Kowalsky/Alamy

Unit 8: © Mark E. Gibson/Corbis

Unit 9: © David Spurdens/Corbis

Unit 10: © Jon McIntosh/iStockphoto.com

Unit 11: © Irina Shoyhet/BigStockPhoto.com

Unit 12: © Povl Eskild/age fotostock

Unit 13: © Thinkstock Images/Jupiterimages

Unit 14: © Eric Feferberg/AFP/Getty Images

Index

Grouping. *see also* Regrouping
  order of operations, 6
  placing symbols to get a specified
    value, 7
  simplifying numerical expressions, 162
  simplifying with symbols, 6
  simplifying without symbols, 5–6
  using the Distributive Property to
    rewrite expressions, 154

H

Height. *see also* Quadrilaterals, special
  defined, 370
  of a pyramid, 437
Heptagon
  classifying a polygon by its number of
    sides, 242
Hexagon
  classifying a polygon by its number of
    sides, 242
  finding the perimeter of a regular
    n-gon, 352
Hexagonal prism
  identifying parts of, 430
Histograms. *see also* Frequency tables
  applications, 517
  creating, 516
  defined, 515
  finding the median in, 517
  interpreting, 516
Horizontal change
  defined, 319
Horizontal line. *see* Lines
Hypotenuse
  angles of an equilateral triangle,
    412–413
  angles of an isosceles triangle, 411
  applications, 403, 414
  defined, 400
  distance formula, 406
  to identify sides in trigonometric
    ratios, 417
  identifying the sides of a right
    triangle, 400
  Pythagorean theorem, 401
  sine and cosine ratios, 417–418
  using trigonometric ratios to find
    length, 418

I

Identifying. *see also* Problem-solving
    plan
  axes and quadrants, 303
  chords and diameters, 246
  congruent parts, 257–258
  coordinates of points on a number
    line, 39–40

  domain and range, 331
  errors in equation solutions, 173–175
  errors in solutions to application
    problems, 176–177
  the intercepts of a line, 313
  like terms, 158, 159
  parts of prisms, 430
  pyramids, 436
  quadrilaterals on a coordinate grid,
    367
  radii, 245–246
  regular polygons, 241
  the sides of a right triangle, 400
  solutions of inequalities, 182
  transformations, 253
  writing equations and identifying
    solutions, 31
Identity Property of Division
  defined, 92
Identity Property of Multiplication
  defined, 92–93
  using the Division Property of
    Equality to solve equations, 103
  using the multiplicative inverse, 94–95
Image
  identifying transformations, 253
Improper fractions
  converting mixed numbers to,
    137–138
  converting to mixed numbers,
    133–134
  defined, 133
  and mixed numbers, working with,
    137–141
  writing and simplifying ratios, 265
Increase or decrease of percent. *see*
    Percents
Independent variables
  defined, 310
  determining dependent variables and,
    310–311
Indicated operations
  defined, 167
Inequalities, 182–187
  applications, 186
  defined, 182
  graphing simple, 182–183
  identifying solutions of, 182
  reversing the direction, 183–184
  solving and graphing, 183–185
  symbols, 18, 19, 182–185
  using, to approximate irrational square
    roots, 396
Inequality
  defined, 18
Inequality symbols. *see also* Comparing
  defined, 18
Inputs
  defined, 108, 331

Integers
  adding, 45–49
  applications, 42, 48, 51
  comparing expressions, 47
  defined, 39, 53
  dividing, 89–91
  evaluating expressions, 46, 51
  graphing, 40
  identifying coordinates of points,
    39–40
  multiplying, 85–88
  negative, 45
  number line, 39–44, 45–46, 53
  positive, 45
  rules to add, 45–46
  simplifying expressions with decimals
    and fractions, 164
  subtracting, 50–52
Intercepts
  linear equations and, 313–318
Interest
  compound, 296–299
  simple, 292–295
Interpolation
  defined, 326
  linear graph applications, 326
Interquartile range
  defined, 510
  using, 510–511
Inverse operations. *see also* Reciprocal;
    Related equations
  division, 27
  multiplication, 27
  multiplicative inverse, 94–95
  using related equations, 63
Irrational side lengths
  finding with trigonometric ratios, 418
Irrational square roots, 395–399
  applications, 397
  approximating on a number line, 396
  defined, 395
  simplifying radicals, 396
  using a calculator to approximate
    square roots, 397
  using inequalities to approximate,
    396
  using the product property of radical
    to simplify, 397
Isosceles triangle
  angles of, 411
  defined, 236, 410

L

Lateral area
  finding, of a prism, 442–444
Lateral faces
  identifying pyramids, 436
  parts of prisms, 430

Money
    borrowing, 292
    saving, 293
Multiplication
    applications, 107–111
    borrowing money, 292
    calculating factorials, 463
    decimals, 85–88
    Distributive Property, 153–157
    equations involving, 103–106
    evaluating algebraic expressions,
        163
    evaluating expressions, 11
    evaluating expressions with variables
        and exponents, 193
    finding equivalent ratios, 269
    finding missing lengths, 371–372
    finding percent increase and decrease,
        287–288
    finding perimeters of partial and
        combination figures, 378–379
    finding the area of a circle, 382–383
    finding the area of a parallelogram,
        370
    finding the area of a rectangle, 358
    finding the area of a trapezoid, 371
    finding the area of a triangle, 359
    finding the circumference of a circle,
        376–377
    finding the perimeter of a rectangle,
        353
    finding the perimeter of a regular
        n-gon, 352, 353
    finding the surface area of a complex
        figure, 445
    finding the surface area of a cube, 442
    finding the surface area of a cylinder,
        450
    finding the surface area of a prism,
        444, 449
    finding the volume of a cone, 439
    finding the volume of a prism,
        431–432
    finding the volume of a pyramid, 437
    fractions, 119–122
    integers, 85–88
    lateral area of a prism, 443
    matching words and phrases, 14
    mixed numbers, 142–145
    Multiplication and Division Properties
        of Order, 183–184
    by powers of ten, 209
    properties, 92–96
    repeated, 203
    saving money, 293
    simplifying and evaluating integer
        expressions, 87
    simplifying expressions, exponents 0
        and 1, 192

simplifying expressions with decimals
    and fractions, 164
simplifying expressions with grouping
    symbols, 6
simplifying expressions with negative
    exponents, 204
simplifying expressions without
    grouping symbols, 5–6
by simplifying first, 120
simplifying numerical expressions,
    162–163
simplifying powers, 191
solving and graphing inequalities,
    183–185
solving proportions, 271
trigonometric ratios, 418, 419
undo, 167–170
using, and division to solve equations
    with fractions, 147–148
using formulas to compare
    expressions, 20
using properties to solve equations, 95
using scientific notation, 213–214
using the percent proportion, 284–285
using the simple interest formula to
    calculate other values, 293–294
writing related equations, 27
Multiplication Property of Equality
    using to solve equations, 104
    using to solve equations with
        fractions, 147–148
Multiplicative inverse. *see also*
        Reciprocal
    defined, 123
Mutually exclusive events, 479–483
    applications, 481
    defined, 479
    determining if events are, 479
    finding probabilities of, 480–481
    probabilities of two events, 479

N
n-gon
    classifying a polygon by its number of
        sides, 242
    finding the perimeter of a regular,
        352–353
    naming polygons, 347
Natural numbers
    defined, 197
Negative correlation, 494–495
Negative exponents, 203–206
    simplifying, 203
    simplifying expressions with, 204
    simplifying powers, 208
    solving equations with, 205
Negative integers
    defined, 45

Negative numbers
    defined, 39
Negative One Property of Division
    defined, 92
Negative One Property of Multiplication
    defined, 92
Negative square roots. *see* Rational
        square roots
Notation
    approximation, 396
    closed dots, 182
    domain and range, 331
    fraction as a way to show division, 90
    function, 333
    graphing inequalities, 182
    multiplication, 5
    negative, 41
    null (empty) set, 23
    opposite, 41
    principal square root, 392
    relations, 331
    subtraction, 41
    trigonometric ratio abbreviations, 417
    x bar, 498
Null (empty) set
    defined, 23
Number line
    absolute value, 41
    applications, 42, 56
    approximating square roots on a, 396
    comparing on a, 40, 55
    decimals on a, 53–57, 58
    defined, 39
    density on a, 53–54
    graphing, 40, 54
    identifying coordinates of points on,
        39–40
    identifying decimal coordinates of
        points on a, 53–54
    identifying integer solutions of
        absolute value open sentences, 42
    inequalities, 182–185
    integers on a, 39–44
    opposite numbers, 41
    ordering decimals, 55–56
    using to add integers, 45–46
Number properties
    factors, 196–199
    greatest common factor, 200–202
    negative exponents, 203–206
    positive exponents, 191–195
    powers of ten, 207–211
    primes, 196–199
    relative primes, 200–202
    scientific notation, 212–215
Numbers. *see also* Primes
    comparing, 40
    composite, 197
    natural, 197

opposite, 41
  writing, as a power, 193
Numerators. *see also* Fractions
  converting a fraction to a decimal, 274
  defined, 115
  evaluating algebraic expressions, 163
  evaluating expressions, 11
  finding equivalent ratios, 269
  finding unit rates, 266
  simplifying expressions with a
    fraction bar, 7
  simplifying expressions with decimals
    and fractions, 164
  simplifying numerical expressions, 163
  writing and simplifying ratios, 265
Numerical expressions. *see* Expressions
Numerical terms
  defined, 158

O

Obtuse angle
  defined, 225
  measuring and classifying, 225–226
Obtuse triangle
  classifying by angle measures,
    234–235
  defined, 234
Octagon
  classifying a polygon by its number of
    sides, 242
  naming polygons, 347
One
  as exponent, 192
  properties involving, 92–93
Open dots, 182–183
Open sentences and solutions. *see also*
    Sentences
  absolute value, 42
  defined, 19
  finding solutions of, from a
    replacement set, 22–23
Operations. *see also* Order of
    Operations; specific operation
  defined, 5
Opposite. *see also* Trigonometric ratios
  defined, 417
Opposite numbers
  additive inverses, 47
  defined, 39
  integers on a number line, 41
  subtracting decimals, 62–63
  subtracting integers, 50
Opposite of a Sum Property
  defined, 66
  equivalent equations, 73
  identifying addition properties, 67
  solving equations by recognizing
    properties of addition, 68

Order
  determining importance in
    combinations, 468
Order of magnitude
  defined, 208
  powers of ten, 208
Order of operations
  applications, 8
  defined, 5, 162
  evaluating expressions when
    simplifying, 10
  expressions with mixed operations, 162
  placing grouping symbols to get a
    specified value, 7
  simplifying expressions with a
    fraction bar, 7
  simplifying expressions with grouping
    symbols, 6
  simplifying expressions without
    grouping symbols, 5–6
  simplifying expressions, exponents 0
    and 1, 192
  simplifying expressions with negative
    exponents, 204
  verifying the Distributive Property, 153
Ordered pair
  defined, 304
  determining whether an, is a solution,
    308
  graphing, 305–306, 310
  using an, to describe a location,
    304–305
Ordering
  decimals on a number line, 55–56
Origin
  defined, 39, 303
Outcome. *see also* Probability
  defined, 473
Output
  defined, 108, 331

P

Parallel lines, 229–233
  defined, 229
  finding angle measures, 231
  properties, 231
Parallelograms
  classifying quadrilaterals, 365–366
  defined, 220, 364
  finding the area of, 370
  properties of, 367
  using properties of, 367
  using quadrilateral classifications, 366
Parentheses
  addition and subtraction properties, 66
  calculating factorials, 463
  combining like terms to solve
    equations, 169

determining if order matters, 468
Distributive Property, 153–154
finding permutations, 464
finding the area of a trapezoid, 371
finding the distance between two
  points, 407
negatives not inside, 192
performing operations in, 407
placing grouping symbols to get a
  specified value, 7
simplifying expressions, exponents 0
  and 1, 192
simplifying expressions with a
  fraction bar, 7
simplifying expressions with grouping
  symbols, 6
simplifying expressions with negative
  exponents, 204
simplifying inside, 159
simplifying numerical expressions,
  163
using a formula to calculate a number
  of combinations, 469–470
Parts
  comparing, and wholes, 267
Parts of prisms, 430
Pentagon
  classifying a polygon by its number of
    sides, 242
  determining scale factor, 281
  naming polygons, 347
Pentagonal prism
  identifying parts of, 430
Pentagonal pyramid
  identifying, 436
Percents
  applications, 100, 277, 285, 289–290
  converting decimals to, 275–276
  converting fractions to, 277
  converting to decimals, 276
  converting to fractions, 277
  defined, 274
  fractions, and decimals, 274–278
  of increase or decrease, 287–291
  percent change, 108
  using percent proportion, 284–285
  using to estimate, 100
  working with, 284–286
Perfect square
  defined, 395
Perimeter, 352–357
  applications, 355
  areas of circles, 382–387
  areas of rectangles and triangles,
    358–363
  areas of special quadrilaterals,
    370–375
  circumference, 376–381
  defined, 12, 352

of parallelograms, 367
product counting principle, 459
product property of radicals, 397
Property of Inverses for Addition, 47
Reciprocal Property of Multiplication, 94–95
Square Root, 392–393
Substitution Property of Equality, 71, 146
subtraction, 66–70
Subtraction Property of Equality, 71, 146
sum counting principle, 458
Triangle Angle Sum, 235
using, of parallelograms, 367
using to solve equations, 95
Zero Property of Multiplication, 92–93
Proportion, 269–273
    applications, 272
    cross-multiplying, 270
    determining whether ratios are proportional, 269–271
    extremes, 269–271
    finding equivalent ratios, 269
    means, 269–271
    means-extremes product property, 270
    solving, 271
    using percent, 284–285
Pyramids, 436–441. *see also* Cones
    defined, 436
    identifying, 436
    volume of, 437
Pythagorean theorem, 400–405
    30°-60°-90° triangle, 412
    45°-45°-90° triangle, 411
    angles of equilateral triangles, 412–413
    angles of isosceles triangles, 411
    applications, 403
    defined, 401
    finding the distance between two points, 406–407
    finding the missing leg length in a right triangle, 402
    identifying the sides of a right triangle, 400
    triples, 402–403

Q

Quadrants
    defined, 303
    identifying points on a plane, 303
Quadrilaterals
    classifying a polygon by its number of sides, 242
    naming polygons, 347
Quadrilaterals, special
    applications, 372

areas of special, 370–375
classifying, 365–366
defined, 364–365
finding missing lengths, 371–372
finding the area of a trapezoid, 371
finding the area of, 370
identifying, on a coordinate grid, 367
special, 364–369
using, classifications, 366
using properties of parallelograms, 367
Quartiles
    defined, 505
    finding, 505
    finding in a stem-and-leaf plot, 506

R

Radicals
    product property of radicals, 397
    simplifying, 396
    using the product property to simplify, 397
Radius/radii
    applications, 247
    calculating a, or diameter, 246–247
    defined, 245
    finding the surface area of a cylinder, 450
    identifying radii, 245–246
    property, 246
Range
    defined, 331, 505
    identifying, 331
Rate. *see also* Unit rate
    defined, 266
    error analysis, 177
    writing to represent situations, 266
Ratio, 265–268
    applications, 267
    calculating slope, 319
    comparing parts and wholes, 267
    cross multiplying, 270
    defined, 265
    determining whether ratios are proportional, 269–271
    finding equivalent, 269
    finding unit rates, 266
    means-extremes product property, 270
    surface area to volume, 451
    trigonometric ratios, 417–421
    writing and simplifying, 265
    writing rates to represent situations, 266
Ratio, proportion, and percent
    compound interest, 296–299
    percent of increase or decrease, 287–291
    percents, fractions, and decimals, 274–278

proportion, 269–273
ratio, 265–268
similarity and scale, 279–283
simple interest, 292–295
working with percent, 284–286
Rational square roots, 391–394
    applications, 393
    defined, 391
    finding positive and negative, 391
    perfect square, 395
    principal square root, 392
    solving equations with, 392–393
Rays, 224–228
    defined, 224
    naming, 224
Real-world applications
    age, 15–16
    amusement park, 79
    animals, 60
    astronomy, 214
    automotive engineering, 428
    ballooning, 77–78
    banking, 48
    beverage packaging, 433
    biology, 78, 285, 517
    boating, 247
    business, 8
    carpentry, 134, 139–140
    catering, 144
    climatology, 64
    comparing membership fees, 186
    competition, 130
    construction, 397
    consumer economics, 511
    consumer finance, 298
    cooking, 121
    distance, 177
    education, 506
    electronics, 413–414
    elevation, 76–77
    entertainment, 117, 481
    estimating capacity, 99–100
    food, 384–385
    fuel economy, 267
    genealogy, 194
    geography, 51
    geometry, 34
    graphic design, 254
    growth, 148
    health, 326
    home improvement, 237
    interior design, 393
    inventory, 69
    land usage, 355
    landscape design, 74
    management, 501
    marketing, 277
    number problem, 170, 176–177
    nutrition, 76
    packaging, 201

Real-world applications (continued)
  painting, 372
  perimeter, 155, 176, 242–243
  personal banking, 78–79
  personal finance, 327
  photography, 282
  product packaging, 451
  public safety, 439
  rate, 177
  real estate, 289
  sales tax, 159–160
  science, 56, 105
  security, 465
  sewing, 125
  simple interest, 170
  sports, 12, 77, 236, 290, 328, 349,
    379, 403, 465
  surveying, 420
  surveys, 476
  temperature, 11, 24, 77, 164
  ticket sales, 341
  time, 177, 227
  tourism, 407
  traffic signs, 414
  transportation, 33
  travel, 272
  using percent to estimate, 100
  weather, 42, 475
  win-loss ratio, 267
  writing formulas, 31
  zoology, 289
Reasonable estimates, 99
Reasonableness
  determining whether an answer is
    reasonable, 98–99
Reciprocal
  defined, 94, 123
  dividing fractions, 124
  dividing mixed numbers, 143
  finding, of fractions, 123
  Reciprocal Property of Multiplication,
    94–95
  solving simple equations in one
    variable, 168
  using the, to solve an equation, 105
  using the multiplicative inverse,
    94–95
Rectangles
  classifying quadrilaterals, 365–366
  defined, 364
  finding the area of, 358
  finding the perimeter of, 353
  formula for perimeter, 443
  using quadrilateral classifications, 366
  using the Distributive Property to find
    the perimeter of, 155
Rectangular prism
  identifying parts of, 430
  lateral area, 443
  surface area of, 444
Reflections
  defined, 250

line of, 250
line of symmetry, 250
Regrouping. *see also* Grouping
  adding decimals vertically, 59
  using scientific notation to multiply
    numbers, 213–214
Regular polygon
  defined, 241, 348
  describing polygons, 348
Related equations. *see also* Equations
  defined, 26
  using multiplication and division
    properties to solve equations, 95
  using to solve a subtraction equation,
    60
  using to solve an addition equation, 63
  using to solve an equation, 28
  writing, for addition and subtraction, 26
  writing, for multiplication and
    division, 27
Relations and functions, 331–336
  applying the vertical line test, 332–333
  determining whether a relation is a
    function, 331–332
  evaluating functions, 333–334
  identifying domain and range, 331
Relative primes. *see also* Primes
  defined, 201
  and greatest common factor, 200–202
Remember sidebars
  absolute value, 46
  adding decimals, 60
  approximating square roots, 396
  area of a rectangle, 34
  bases of a prism, 449
  biased sample, 485
  box-and-whisker plots, 509
  calculating simple interest, 296
  changing a percent to a decimal, 298
  checking solutions, 72
  combination lock, 471
  combining like terms, 159
  comparing numbers, 40
  congruent angles, 279
  congruent polygons, 259
  denominators, 115, 321
  dividend and divisors, 123
  divisibility rules, 198
  equations express relationships, 30
  equations with all the same solutions,
    315
  equiangular polygons, 352
  equilateral polygons, 352
  equivalent equations, 103
  equivalent fractions, 128
  exponents, 87
  expressions show relationships, 15
  finding the radius, 384
  fraction bar, 163
  graphing an ordered pair, 305
  graphing $x = a$, 316
  greater than or equal to symbol, 97

lateral faces of a prism, 449
mean, 504
means and extremes, 280
median, 504
mL equivalent, 427
multiplication, 10
multiplicative inverse, 123
multiplying a constant by a variable, 94
numerators, 115, 321
"of" indicates multiplication, 121
open dots, 185
open sentence, 42
operations in parentheses, 407
opposite of a negative number, 68
opposites, 93
opposites to subtract, 132
order of operations, 18, 162, 204
perimeter of a rectangle, 443
permutation lock, 471
permutations, 468
pi (π), 438
properties of equality, 146, 147
rational numbers, 391
ratios are not usually numbers or
  decimals, 267
reading decimals, 54
reciprocals, 123
relationships among quantities, 24
scale, 58
signs for directions, 305
signs when multiplying fractions,
  120
solutions to an equation, 205
solving and graphing inequalities to
  multiply numbers, 185
solving simple equations, 168
stem-and-leaf plots, 504
substituting, 31
surface area of a cube, 442
tick marks, 58
using the reciprocal equality to solve
  an equation, 105
whole numbers, 16
writing a percent as a decimal, 292
writing an improper fraction as a
  mixed number, 164
zero as denominator, 321
zero as numerator, 321
Renaming
  comparing fractions, 129–130
  expressing fractions with the same
    denominator, 128–129
Repeated division. *see* Division;
  Exponents
Repeated multiplication. *see* Exponents;
  Multiplication
Replacement sets, 22–25
  applications, 24
  defined, 22
  finding solutions of an equation with
    the variable on both sides, 23